OPERATOR METHODS IN LIGAND FIELD THEORY

PRENTICE-HALL INTERNATIONAL SERIES IN CHEMISTRY

PRENTICE-HALL, INC.
PRENTICE-HALL INTERNATIONAL, INC., UNITED KINGDOM AND EIRE
PRENTICE-HALL OF CANADA, LTD., CANADA

J. S. Griffith:

THE IRREDUCIBLE TENSOR METHOD FOR
MOLECULAR SYMMETRY GROUPS

J. H. Hildebrand and R. L. Scott:

REGULAR SOLUTIONS

E. K. Hyde, I. Perlman, and G. T. Seaborg:

THE NUCLEAR PROPERTIES OF THE HEAVY ELEMENTS
Volume I: Systematics of Nuclear Structure and Radioactivity

E. K. Hyde, I. Perlman, and G. T. Seaborg:

THE NUCLEAR PROPERTIES OF THE HEAVY ELEMENTS
Volume II: Detailed Radioactivity Properties

E. K. Hyde:

THE NUCLEAR PROPERTIES OF THE HEAVY ELEMENTS
Volume III: Fission Phenomena

M. M. Jones:

ELEMENTARY COORDINATION CHEMISTRY

R. W. Kiser:

INTRODUCTION TO MASS SPECTROMETRY
AND ITS APPLICATIONS

W. T. Simpson:

THEORIES OF ELECTRONS IN MOLECULES

H. Watanabe:

OPERATOR METHODS
IN LIGAND FIELD THEORY

OPERATOR METHODS IN LIGAND FIELD THEORY

Hiroshi Watanabe

Professor of Physics
Hokkaido University, Japan

Prentice-Hall, Inc.

Englewood Cliffs, New Jersey

PRENTICE-HALL INTERNATIONAL, INC., *London*
PRENTICE-HALL OF AUSTRALIA, PTY. LTD., *Sydney*
PRENTICE-HALL OF CANADA, LTD., *Toronto*
PRENTICE-HALL OF INDIA (PRIVATE) LTD., *New Delhi*
PRENTICE-HALL OF JAPAN, INC., *Tokyo*

Current printing (last digit):
10 9 8 7 6 5 4 3 2 1

Library of Congress Catalog Card Number 66-20259
Printed in the United States of America
C63790

PREFACE

This book offers an introduction to operator techniques of spectral analysis for the iron-group ions in crystal lattices and in complexes. Special attention is given to varied types of symmetries, chiefly the point group symmetry, time inversion, and the concept of seniority and complementarity. A brief account is presented of the theory of angular momentum and the theory of finite groups. Seniority theory is developed to give matrix relations in many-electron systems.

The reader is assumed to be acquainted with elementary quantum mechanics for spectral analysis, e.g., Condon and Shortley's "theory of atomic spectra," and elementary matrix theory, e.g., properties of unitary matrices. The reader may start with Chapter 4, "Ligand Field Theory", referring back when necessary to materials discussed in the preceding chapters.

The book is based upon lecture notes delivered for graduate students at the Department of Nuclear Engineering, University of Michigan, and at the Department of Physics, Hokkaido University, Japan.

It is my pleasure to thank Professor Thomas M. Dunn, University of Michigan, for his careful reading of the manuscript and his valuable suggestions. I am grateful to Professor S. Sugano, Tokyo University, for permission to reproduce Figure 4.10–1.

HIROSHI WATANABE

CONTENTS

OPERATOR METHODS IN LIGAND FIELD THEORY

INTRODUCTION

Since Bethe's milestone work in 1929,† electronic properties of transition-metal ions in crystalline solids have been extensively studied experimentally and theoretically. In recent years there have been remarkable applications of these properties; maser and laser actions are typical examples. One would expect more applications of practical importance in the future. An understanding of the quantum mechanical properties of transition-metal ions is increasingly required to make the applications possible. Accumulated experimental observations have also stimulated theorists to handle the problems from first principles. Varied aspects of transition-metal ions are studied with optical and infrared spectroscopy, electron paramagnetic resonance, nuclear magnetic and quadrupole resonance, magnetic susceptibility measurement, and so forth. These experimental results are favorably interpreted in terms of parameters based on phenomenological theories—that is, theories that do not necessarily claim interpretation from first principles, but that provide sensible parameters for the analysis of experimental data. Calculations from first principles are also being put forward with increasing success, but much still remains to be done. Difficulties in the calculations are due to the many-body nature of the systems. Electron nuclear double resonance experiments on CdTe doped with Cr^+ reveal that the unpaired electrons around the chromium ion have considerable probability, several per cent, of being on the next nearest Cd ions.‡ This observation appears to be a challenge to theorists

†H. A. Bethe, *Ann. Physik* **3**, 133 (1929).
‡G. W. Ludwig and M. R. Lorenz, *Phys. Rev.* **131**, 601 (1963).

trying first-principle calculations, but we should still appreciate phenomenological theories, with which first-principle calculations would be put forward. In this book, the author claims only phenomenological theories.

Transition-metal ions incorporated into ionic crystalline lattices may be assumed to preserve some qualitative features of their free ionic states. For example, the principal and azimuthal quantum numbers n and l may approximately describe the electronic states in the lattice, even though the electrons in the outermost shells are rather disturbed by the surrounding ions. Single-electron wavefunctions based on the $nlm_l m_s$ scheme may be used as approximate wavefunctions, if appropriate modifications are made. The interaction between the transition-metal electron and the surrounding ions may be treated using the Russell-Saunders schemes $LSM_L M_S$ in some cases. These schemes are best interpreted by the theory of angular momentum. The elementary theory of angular momentum is studied in Chapter 1 and the applications are treated in the later chapters. It would not be an exaggeration to say that the Wigner-Eckart theorem should be the most basic and useful theorem in quantum mechanical calculations. The theorem is proved in terms of the theory of angular momentum and in terms of the theory of finite groups.

Transition-metal ions incorporated into a crystalline lattice are subject to a potential with the particular point symmetry of the surroundings, and this symmetry property is best tackled by the theory of point groups. Chapter 2 is devoted to the theory of finite groups.

Transition-metal ions have an incomplete shell that is to be filled with electrons. If there is more than a single electron in the shell, the method of filling throws useful light on the matrix relations between many-electron states. Chapter 3 deals with the method of filling, using the *seniority* concept originally introduced by Racah.† Racah's interpretation of seniority is terse from the physical point of view. The author hopes that the interpretation in Chapter 3 leads the reader to a physical understanding of seniority. Seniority itself is not a physical observable, but may be regarded as an important quantum number. Another concept, that of *complementary states*, is also useful in calculating matrix elements of many-electron systems. Condon and Shortley were the first to point out many similarities in two complementary states.‡ Griffith also makes use of this concept to find matrix relations in the strong field scheme.§ The complementary concept is formulated in the seniority theory in Chapter 3.

Chapter 4 is devoted to the ligand field problems. The single-ion model

†G. Racah, *Phys. Rev.* **63**, 367 (1943).

‡E. U. Condon and G. H. Shortley, *The Theory of Atomic Spectra* (London: Cambridge University Press, 1953), Chaps. 12 and 13.

§J. S. Griffith, *The Theory of Transition-Metal Ions* (London: Cambridge University Press, 1961), pp. 245–256.

is discussed in some detail since it reveals the fundamental features of the problems; however, the cluster model is shown to be more satisfactory for interpretation of the experimental results. Examples will help the reader learn the techniques of spectral analysis for the first transition-metal ions in crystalline lattices and complexes.

1

ELEMENTS OF ANGULAR MOMENTUM

1.1 INTRODUCTION

In this chapter, the angular momentum operator is defined through commutation relations (1.2–1). We choose a matrix representation of the angular momentum operator such that the y-component matrix is imaginary, and the x-and z-component matrices are real. This choice leads to the phase of eigenfunctions of orbital angular momentum [see (1.6–6) and (1.6–7)]. The reader is reminded that there are two definitions of Eulerian angles commonly used in the literature; the relation between the two is presented in Appendix 1.1. A three-dimensional rotation is related to the angular momentum operator through (1.3–10). The Wigner-Eckart theorem is proved in Sec. 1.9. The concept of time reversal leads to Kramers' theorem and to the Kramers pair concept. The replacement theorem is the justification of equivalent operators as used in Chapter 4. The accompanying block diagram indicates the logical relationships; the numbers in parentheses refer to sections.

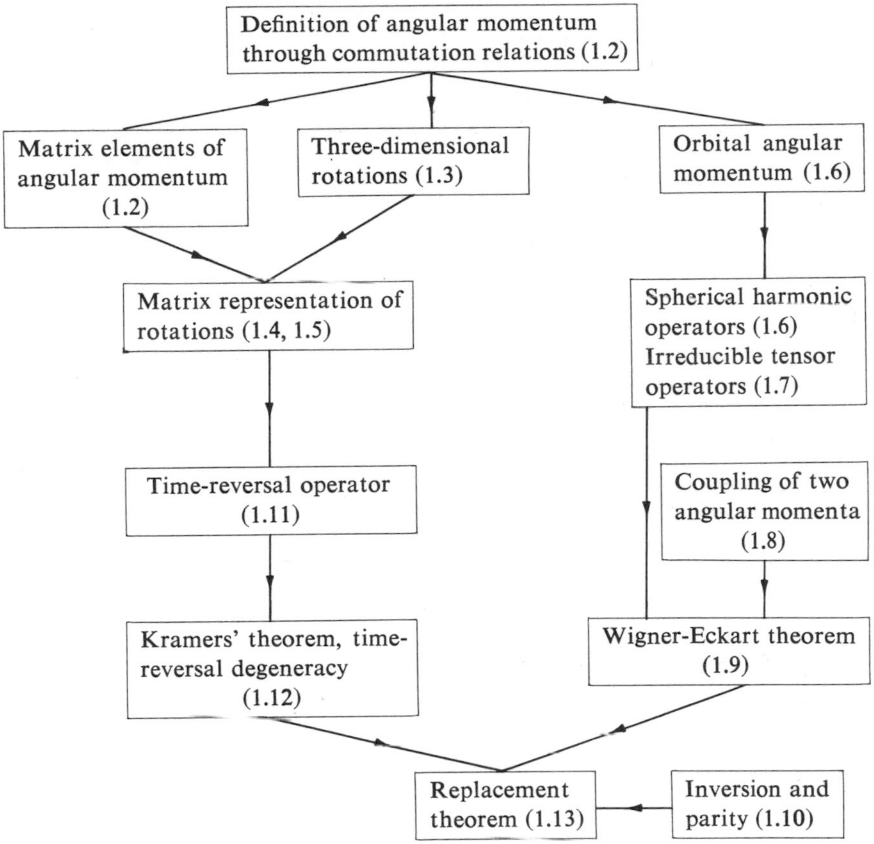

1.2 DEFINITION OF ANGULAR MOMENTUM

The angular momentum operator $\boldsymbol{j}$ may be defined through the commutation relations among the components

$$[j_x, j_y] = ij_z, \quad [j_y, i_z] = ij_x, \quad [j_z, j_x] = ij_y. \tag{1.2–1}$$

If *shift operators* j_+ and j_- are defined as

$$j_+ = j_x + ij_y \qquad \text{and} \qquad j_- = j_x - ij_y, \tag{1.2–2}$$

the following commutation relations are derived from (1.2–1):

$$[j_z, j_+] = j_+, \quad [j_z, j_-] = -j_-, \quad [j_+, j_-] = 2j_z. \tag{1.2–3}$$

Throughout these relations, the natural unit $\hbar = h/2\pi$ is used. One may easily verify that components of orbital angular momentum satisfy the commutation relations (1.2–1), and the components are written in terms of Cartesian coordinates

$$l_x = -i\left(y\frac{\partial}{\partial z} - z\frac{\partial}{\partial y}\right),$$
$$l_y = -i\left(z\frac{\partial}{\partial x} - x\frac{\partial}{\partial z}\right), \qquad (1.2\text{–}4)$$
$$l_z = -i\left(x\frac{\partial}{\partial y} - y\frac{\partial}{\partial x}\right),$$

The commutation relations (1.2–1) and (1.2–3) serve to derive the matrix elements†

$$\langle jm|j_{\mp}j_{\pm}|jm\rangle = \langle jm|\boldsymbol{j}^2 - j_z^2 + j_z|jm\rangle = [(j \mp m)(j \pm m + 1)]^{1/2} \quad (1.2\text{–}5)$$

for a value of m within the range $j \geqslant m \geqslant -j$. The statevectors $|jm\rangle$ are eigenvectors of $\boldsymbol{j}^2$ and j_z with eigenvalues $j(j+1)$ and m; i. e.,

$$\boldsymbol{j}^2|jm\rangle = j(j+1)|jm\rangle \quad \text{and} \quad j_z|jm\rangle = m|jm\rangle. \qquad (1.2\text{–}6)$$

Since j_+ is adjoint to j_-, and since $j_z j_\pm = j_+(j_z \mp 1)$, the statevector $j_+|jm\rangle$ is proportional to $[(j \mp m)(j \pm m + 1)]^{1/2}|jm \pm 1\rangle$ with an arbitrary phase factor of absolute value unity. If the phase factor is chosen as unity, we have‡

$$j_\pm|jm\rangle = [(j \mp m)(j \pm m + 1)]^{1/2}|jm + 1\rangle. \qquad (1.2\text{–}7)$$

The spin operator $\boldsymbol{s}$ with $s = 1/2$ is another example of an angular momentum operator. The matrix representation of the components is

$$s_x = \tfrac{1}{2}\begin{bmatrix} 0 & 1 \\ 1 & 0 \end{bmatrix}, \quad s_y = \tfrac{1}{2}\begin{bmatrix} 0 & -i \\ i & 0 \end{bmatrix}, \quad s_z = \tfrac{1}{2}\begin{bmatrix} 1 & 0 \\ 0 & -1 \end{bmatrix}, \qquad (1.2\text{–}8)$$

where the phase choice is in accordance with the above convention. The eigenvector is chosen as column vectors given by

$$|\tfrac{1}{2}\tfrac{1}{2}\rangle = \begin{bmatrix} 1 \\ 0 \end{bmatrix} \quad \text{and} \quad |\tfrac{1}{2}-\tfrac{1}{2}\rangle = \begin{bmatrix} 0 \\ 1 \end{bmatrix}. \qquad (1.2\text{–}9)$$

The squared $\boldsymbol{s}^2$ is simply $s(s+1) = \frac{3}{4}$.

1.3 THREE-DIMENSIONAL ROTATIONS

If an electronic system consists of n electrons, the jth of which is characterized by $\boldsymbol{l}_j$ and $\boldsymbol{s}_j$, the total angular momentum $\boldsymbol{J}$ of the system is given by the sum

†For detailed discussion refer, for instance, to P. A. M. Dirac, *The Principles of Quantum Mechanics* (London: Oxford University Press, 1947).

‡The choice in (1.2–7) is the same as that of E. U. Condon and G. H. Shortley, *The Theory of Atomic Spectra* (London: Cambridge University Press, 1953), Chap. 3.

$$J = \sum_{j=1}^{n} (l_j + s_j).$$

The Cartesian coordinates x, y, and z of an electron in the system satisfy the commutation relations with J:

$$[x \pm iy, J_z] = \mp(x \pm iy), \tag{1.3–1}$$

and

$$[z, J_z] = 0. \tag{1.3–2}$$

We find by induction the relations

$$(x \pm iy)\cdot J_z^n = (J_z \mp 1)^n (x \pm iy), \tag{1.3–3}$$

and

$$z\cdot J_z^n = J_z^n \cdot z, \tag{1.3–4}$$

where n is a positive integer.

Let us observe properties of a unitary operator $e^{-i\alpha J_z}$, with α a real number. Expanding the operator in a Taylor series and using (1.3–3), we find

$$e^{-i\alpha J_z}\cdot(x \pm iy)\cdot e^{i\alpha J_z} = e^{\mp i\alpha}(x \pm iy). \tag{1.3–5}$$

In a similar way, we find

$$e^{-i\alpha J_z}\cdot z\cdot e^{i\alpha J_z} = z. \tag{1.3–6}$$

If we write $x \pm iy$ as $re^{\pm i\phi} \sin\theta$ and $z = r \cos\theta$, we easily notice that the unitary operator $e^{-i\alpha J_z}$ is an operator for a counterclockwise rotation of the coordinate axes by an angle α around the z-axis. Figure 1.3–1 shows the rotation. We may also interpret that the operator $e^{-i\alpha J_z}$ rotates the *point* clockwise by α around the z-axis. One may easily verify relations, similar to (1.3–3) and (1.3–4), between $y \pm iz$, and x and J_x, and between $z \pm ix$, and y and J_y:

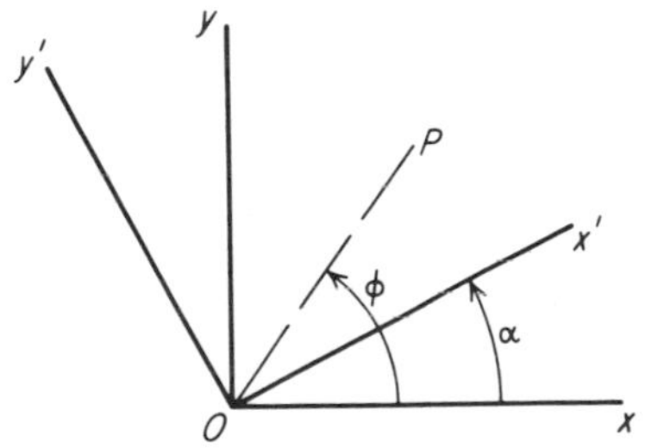

Fig. 1.3-1 Counterclockwise rotation of coordinate axes by α around z-axis.

$$e^{-i\delta J_x}(y \pm iz)e^{i\delta J_x} = e^{\mp i\delta}(y \pm iz), \tag{1.3–7}$$

and

$$e^{-i\beta J_y}(z \pm ix)e^{i\beta J_y} = e^{\mp i\beta}(z \pm ix). \tag{1.3–8}$$

The operator $e^{-i\delta J_x}$ is a counterclockwise rotation of the coordinate axes by an angle δ around the x-axis; the operator $e^{-i\beta J_y}$ is understood in a similar way. A unitary operator $e^{-i\varphi(\boldsymbol{n}\cdot\boldsymbol{J})}$ is a counterclockwise rotation by an angle φ around the axis whose direction is specified by the unit vector

$\boldsymbol{n}$. Note that a unitary operator $e^{-i\varphi(\boldsymbol{n}\cdot\boldsymbol{l})}$ is a rotation of coordinate space, but does not operate upon the spin space.

Instead of φ and $\boldsymbol{n}$, Eulerian angles α, β, and γ are commonly used to specify a coordinate rotation. A rotation operator $R(\alpha\beta\gamma)$ is now written in the form

$$R(\alpha\beta\gamma) = e^{-i\gamma J_{z''}} e^{-i\beta J_{y'}} e^{-i\alpha J_z}, \tag{1.3–9}$$

where y' is the new y-axis after the first rotation $e^{-i\alpha J_z}$ is performed; the z'' is the new z-axis after the second rotation $e^{-i\beta J_{y'}}$. The operator (1.3–9) is in turn written in terms of J_z and J_y referred to the original coordinate axes in the form†

$$R(\alpha\beta\gamma) = e^{-i\alpha J_z} e^{-i\beta J_y} e^{-i\gamma J_z}, \tag{1.3–10}$$

where we use, for instance, the relation

$$e^{-i\beta J_{y'}} = e^{-i\alpha J_z} e^{-i\beta J_y} e^{+i\alpha J_z}. \tag{1.3–11}$$

1.4 MATRIX REPRESENTATION OF ROTATIONS

The $(2j+1)$ angular momentum eigenvectors $|jm\rangle$ are transformed among themselves under a rotation (1.3–10) as

$$R(\alpha\beta\gamma)|jm\rangle = \sum_{m'=-j}^{j} |jm'\rangle \cdot D^j_{m'm}(\alpha\beta\gamma), \tag{1.4–1}$$

where

$$\begin{aligned} D^j_{m'm}(\alpha\beta\gamma) &= \langle jm'|e^{-i\alpha J_z} e^{-i\beta J_y} e^{-i\gamma J_z}|jm\rangle \\ &= e^{-i(\alpha m' + \gamma m)} \langle jm'|e^{-i\beta J_y}|jm\rangle \\ &= e^{-i(\alpha m' + \gamma m)} d^j_{m'm}(\beta), \end{aligned} \tag{1.4–2}$$

where the matrix $d^j(\beta)$ is given by‡

$$\begin{aligned} d^j_{m'm}(\beta) = {} & [(j+m)!\,(j-m)!\,(j+m')!\,(j-m')!]^{1/2} \\ & \times \sum_{\nu} (-1)^{\nu} \frac{(\cos \frac{1}{2}\beta)^{2j+m-m'-2\nu}(-\sin \frac{1}{2}\beta)^{2\nu-m+m'}}{(j+m-\nu)!\,(j-m'-\nu)!\,\nu!\,(\nu-m+m')!}, \end{aligned} \tag{1.4–3}$$

where the sum is taken over all values of ν which lead to nonnegative factorials.

The rotation matrix for $e^{-i\beta J_y}$ is particularly simple for $j = \frac{1}{2}$ since

†We follow Whittaker's definition of Eulerian angles. See another definition in Appendix 1.1.

‡For the proof refer, for instance, to M. E. Rose, *Elementary Theory of Angular Momentum* (New York: John Wiley & Sons, Inc., 1957), App. II.

$$J_y = \tfrac{1}{2}\begin{bmatrix} 0 & -i \\ i & 0 \end{bmatrix} \quad \text{and} \quad J_y^2 = \tfrac{1}{4}\begin{bmatrix} 1 & 0 \\ 0 & 1 \end{bmatrix}.$$

Introducing $\sigma_y = \begin{bmatrix} 0 & -i \\ i & 0 \end{bmatrix}$, we find

$$\begin{aligned} e^{-i\beta J_y} &= \sum_{n=0}^{\infty}\left(-i\frac{\beta}{2}\right)^n \frac{\sigma_y^n}{n!} = \mathbf{1}\cdot\cos\tfrac{1}{2}\beta - i\sigma_y \sin\tfrac{1}{2}\beta \\ &= \begin{bmatrix} \cos\tfrac{1}{2}\beta & -\sin\tfrac{1}{2}\beta \\ \sin\tfrac{1}{2}\beta & \cos\tfrac{1}{2}\beta \end{bmatrix}, \end{aligned} \tag{1.4–4}$$

where $\mathbf{1}$ is the two-dimensional unit matrix.

The matrix d^j has the symmetry relation:

$$\begin{aligned} d^j_{m'm}(\beta) &= d^j_{-m-m'}(\beta) = (-1)^{m-m'} d^j_{mm'}(\beta) \\ &= (-1)^{j-m'} d^j_{m'-m}(\pi - \beta) = d^j_{mm'}(-\beta) \\ &= (-1)^{j+m} d_{m'-m}(\pi + \beta). \end{aligned}$$

Formulas for $d^j_{m'm}(\beta)$ for $j = 1$ and $\frac{3}{2}$ are listed in Table 1.4–1.

TABLE 1.4–1

FORMULAS FOR $d^j_{m'm}(\beta)$ FOR $j = 1$ AND $\frac{3}{2}$

j	$d^j_{m'm}(\beta)$
1	$d_{11} = d_{-1-1} = (1 + \cos\beta)/2$
	$d_{1-1} = d_{-11} = (1 - \cos\beta)/2$
	$d_{01} = d_{-10} = -d_{0-1} = -d_{10} = \sin\beta/\sqrt{2}$
	$d_{00} = \cos\beta$
$\frac{3}{2}$	$d_{(3/2)(3/2)} = d_{(-3/2)(-3/2)} = \cos^3(\frac{1}{2}\beta)$
	$d_{(3/2)(1/2)} = d_{(-1/2)(-3/2)} = -d_{(1/2)(3/2)} = -d_{(-3/2)(-1/2)}$ $= -3\cos^2(\frac{1}{2}\beta)\sin(\frac{1}{2}\beta)$
	$d_{(3/2)(-1/2)} = d_{(-1/2)(3/2)} = d_{(1/2)(-3/2)} = d_{(-3/2)(1/2)}$ $= \sqrt{3}\cos(\frac{1}{2}\beta)\sin^2(\frac{1}{2}\beta)$
	$d_{(3/2)(-3/2)} = -d_{(-3/2)(3/2)} = -\sin^3(\frac{1}{2}\beta)$
	$d_{(1/2)(1/2)} = d_{(-1/2)(-1/2)} = \cos(\frac{1}{2}\beta)[3\cos^2(\frac{1}{2}\beta) - 2]$
	$d_{(1/2)(-1/2)} = -d_{(-1/2)(1/2)} = \sin(\frac{1}{2}\beta)[3\sin^2(\frac{1}{2}\beta) - 2]$

The set of three-dimensional rotations forms the three-dimensional rotation group $\mathbf{R}_3$. The set of matrices $D^j(\alpha\beta\gamma)$ within a constant j is called the $(2j + 1)$-dimensional irreducible representation of $\mathbf{R}_3$.† The matrix $D^j(\alpha\beta\gamma)$ is unitary:

$$D^j_{m'm}(\alpha\beta\gamma)^* = D^j_{mm'}(-\gamma - \beta - \alpha), \tag{1.4–5}$$

†For a brief summary of the representation of the three-dimensional rotation group, see Sec. 2.16.

$$\sum_{m'} D^j_{m'n}(\alpha\beta\gamma)^* D^j_{m'm}(\alpha\beta\gamma) = \delta_{nm}, \tag{1.4-6}$$

and

$$\sum_{m'} D^j_{mm'}(\alpha\beta\gamma) D^j_{nm'}(\alpha\beta\gamma)^* = \delta_{nm} \tag{1.4-7}$$

The trace of a matrix $D^j(\alpha\beta\gamma)$ of a representation is called a *character*, which is written as $\chi^j(\alpha\beta\gamma)$. A rotation $R(\alpha\beta\gamma)$ is shown to be equivalent to a single rotation $R(\boldsymbol{n}, \varphi)$. It is also known that equivalent rotations have the same character. If the axis along $\boldsymbol{n}$ is chosen as the z-axis, the character for $R(\boldsymbol{n}, \varphi)$ is

$$\chi^j(\varphi) = \sum_{m=-j}^{j} e^{-im\varphi} = \frac{\sin(j+\frac{1}{2})\varphi}{\sin\frac{1}{2}\varphi}. \tag{1.4-8}$$

For $j = 1$, the character is simply

$$\chi^1(\varphi) = 1 + 2\cos\varphi. \tag{1.4-9}$$

1.5 DOUBLE ROTATION GROUP

If j is a half integer, the character $\chi^j(\varphi)$, (1.4-8), takes two distinct values for φ and $\varphi + 2\pi$; these values are related by

$$\chi^j(\varphi + 2\pi) = -\chi^j(\varphi). \tag{1.5-1}$$

Actually $\chi^j(\varphi)$ is a periodic function of φ with the period of 4π since

$$\chi^j(\varphi) = \sin j\varphi \cot\tfrac{1}{2}\varphi + \cos j\varphi.^\dagger$$

On the other hand, these two rotations must be regarded as one and the same rotation of the three-dimensional xyz space. We have, therefore, a

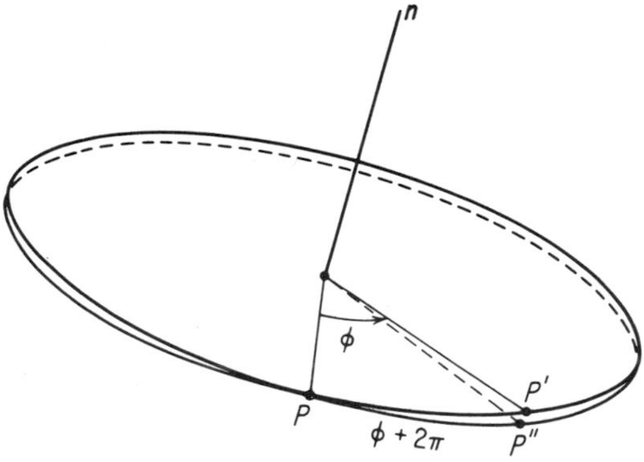

Fig. 1.5-1 Artificial rotation QR by $\phi + 2\pi$ around an axis directed along $\boldsymbol{n}$.

†If $\varphi = \pi$, one obtains $\chi^{\frac{1}{2}}(3\pi) = \chi^{\frac{1}{2}}(\pi) = 0$. This does not affect the period of 4π.

two-to-one correspondence between characters, or matrices, for half-integral j and rotations of the xyz space.

One-to-one correspondence may be set up by introducing an artificial operator Q visualized as follows. By analogy with the Riemann surface in the theory of complex functions, let us introduce two sheets of surfaces perpendicular to the rotation axis. The new operator Q transforms a point P' on one surface to its corresponding point P'' on the other. Figure 1.5-1 schematically shows the artificial transformation QR, where R is a rotation by an angle φ around an axis directed along $\boldsymbol{n}$. The operator Q commutes with every rotation operator:

$$QR = RQ. \tag{1.5–2}$$

If Q is applied twice, the resultant operator is the identity E, which corresponds to a rotation through an angle zero:

$$Q^2 = E. \tag{1.5–3}$$

The new rotation group augmented with Q has double the number of operators as the original group and is called the *double rotation group.*

1.6 ORBITAL ANGULAR MOMENTUM

The orbital angular momentum operator (1.2–4) can be rewritten in terms of polar coordinates:

$$\begin{aligned} l_x &= i\left(\sin\phi\frac{\partial}{\partial\theta} + \cot\theta\cos\phi\frac{\partial}{\partial\phi}\right), \\ l_y &= i\left(-\cos\phi\frac{\partial}{\partial\theta} + \cot\theta\sin\phi\frac{\partial}{\partial\phi}\right), \\ l_z &= -i\frac{\partial}{\partial\phi}, \end{aligned} \tag{1.6–1}$$

and the shift operators are

$$l_\pm = l_x \pm il_y = e^{\pm i\phi}\left(\pm\frac{\partial}{\partial\theta} + i\cot\theta\frac{\partial}{\partial\phi}\right). \tag{1.6–2}$$

The squared operator $\boldsymbol{l}^2$ is written in the form

$$\boldsymbol{l}^2 = -\left[\frac{1}{\sin^2\theta}\frac{\partial^2}{\partial\phi^2} + \frac{1}{\sin\theta}\frac{\partial}{\partial\theta}\left(\sin\theta\frac{\partial}{\partial\theta}\right)\right]. \tag{1.6–3}$$

The eigenvectors $|lm\rangle$ satisfy the equations

$$\boldsymbol{l}^2|lm\rangle = l(l+1)|lm\rangle$$

and

$$l_z|lm\rangle = m|lm\rangle.$$

These equations become a pair of differential equations for the eigenfunctions $\psi_{lm}(\theta\phi)$:

$$-\left[\frac{1}{\sin^2\theta}\frac{\partial^2}{\partial\phi^2}+\frac{1}{\sin\theta}\left(\frac{\partial}{\partial\theta}\sin\theta\frac{\partial}{\partial\theta}\right)\right]\psi_{lm}=l(l+1)\psi_{lm} \tag{1.6–4}$$

and

$$-i\frac{\partial}{\partial\phi}\psi_{lm}=m\psi_{lm}. \tag{1.6–5}$$

The variables θ and ϕ can be separated in the form

$$\psi_{lm}(\theta\phi)=P_{lm}(\cos\theta)e^{im\phi}.$$

Equation (1.6–4) becomes

$$\left[\frac{1}{\sin\theta}\frac{d}{d\theta}\left(\sin\theta\frac{d}{d\theta}\right)-\frac{m^2}{\sin^2\theta}+l(l+1)\right]P_{lm}=0,$$

which is the differential equation for the associated Legendre function of order l. The bounded, normalized solutions of (1.6–4) are the spherical harmonics $Y_{lm}(\theta\phi)$:

$$Y_{lm}(\theta\phi)=(-1)^m\left[\frac{(2l+1)}{4\pi}\right]^{1/2}\left[\frac{(l-m)!}{(l+m)!}\right]^{1/2}P_{lm}(\cos\theta)e^{im\phi} \tag{1.6–6}$$

$$Y_{l-m}(\theta\phi)=\left[\frac{(2l+1)}{4\pi}\right]^{1/2}\left[\frac{(l-m)!}{(l+m)!}\right]^{1/2}P_{lm}(\cos\theta)e^{-im\phi} \tag{1.6–7}$$

for positive integer m, where $P_{lm}(\cos\theta)$ is the unnormalized associated Legendre function:

$$P_{lm}(x)=(1-x^2)^{m/2}\left(\frac{d}{dx}\right)^m P_l(x),$$

and

$$P_l(x)=\left(\frac{1}{2^l l!}\right)\left(\frac{d}{dx}\right)^l(x^2-1)^l.$$

The phase factor $(-1)^m$ is introduced so that the previous phase convention of (1.2–6) is satisfied.

If the spherical harmonics $Y_{lm}(\theta\phi)$ are regarded as operators, the commutation relations hold; that is,

$$[l_z, Y_{lm}]=mY_{lm}, \tag{1.6–8}$$

and

$$[l_\pm, Y_{lm}]=[(l\mp m)(l\pm m+1)]^{1/2}\,Y_{lm\pm1}. \tag{1.6–9}$$

Spherical harmonics are listed to sixth order in Appendix 1.2.

1.7 IRREDUCIBLE TENSOR OPERATOR

In analogy to (1.6–8) and (1.6–9), an irreducible tensor operator $\boldsymbol{T}_k$ of rank k is defined through the commutation relations:

$$[j_z, T_{kq}] = qT_{kq}, \tag{1.7-1}$$

and

$$[j_\pm, T_{kq}] = [(k \mp q](k \pm q + 1)]^{1/2}\, T_{kq\pm 1}, \tag{1.7-2}$$

where q is in the range $k \geqslant q \geqslant -k$. One can easily show that

$$e^{-i\alpha j_z} T_{kq} e^{i\alpha j_z} = e^{-i\alpha q} T_{kq}, \tag{1.7-3}$$

where one needs the relation

$$T_{kq} j_z^n = (j_z - q)^n T_{kq}. \tag{1.7-4}$$

This relation may be proved by induction. The relation (1.7–3) is simply a generalization of Eqs. (1.3–5) and (1.3–6), although (1.3–5) must be replaced by

$$e^{-i\alpha j_z} \left\{\mp \frac{x \pm iy}{\sqrt{2}}\right\} e^{i\alpha j_z} = e^{\mp i\alpha} \left\{\mp \frac{x \pm iy}{\sqrt{2}}\right\}.$$

If the irreducible tensor operators T_{kq} are regarded as functions, they satisfy Eqs. (1.2–6) and (1.2–7) as do the eigenvectors $|kq\rangle$. The transformation property of $|kq\rangle$ under three-dimensional rotations is entirely determined by (1.2–6) and (1.2–7); therefore, the $(2k + 1)$ components T_{kq} transform among themselves in the same manner as $|kq\rangle$:

$$R(\alpha\beta\gamma) T_{kq} (R(\alpha\beta\gamma))^{-1} = \sum_{q'=-k}^{k} T_{kq'} D^k_{q'q}(\alpha\beta\gamma). \tag{1.7-5}$$

An example of an irreducible tensor operator of rank one is

$$T_{11} = -\frac{x + iy}{\sqrt{2}}, \quad T_{10} = z, \quad T_{1-1} = \frac{x - iy}{\sqrt{2}}. \tag{1.7-6}$$

Using the relations (1.7–1) and (1.7–2), one can find irreducible tensor operators in terms of the angular momentum operators j_z, j_+ and j_-, apart from an arbitrary factor. One may start with the component given by

$$T_{kk} = \left(\frac{-1}{\sqrt{2}}\right)^k j_+^k. \tag{1.7-7}$$

The Equations (1.7–1) and (1.7–2) defining irreducible tensor operators do not fix the absolute magnitudes but only the relative magnitudes of the tensor components. The factor $(-1/\sqrt{2}\,)^k$ on the right-hand side of (1.7–7) is introduced simply for convenience. The expression (1.7–7) satisfies Eq. (1.7–1). To find components T_{kq} with $q < k$, one successively uses Eq. (1.7–2),

$$[j_-, T_{kq}] = [(k + q)(k - q + 1)]^{1/2} T_{kq-1},$$

and the commutation relations such as

$$[j_-, j_+^n] = -j_+^{n-1}\{2nj_z + n(n-1)\},$$

$$[j_-, j_+^n j_z] = -j_+^{n-1}\{(2n+1)j_z^2 + (n^2 - n - 1)j_z - j(j+1)\},$$

and

$$[j_-, j_+^n j_z^m] = [j_-, j_+^n j_z^{m-1}]j_z + j_+^{n-1}\{-j_z^2 + j_z + j(j+1)\} \times (j_z - 1)^{m-1}.$$

In Appendix 1.3, irreducible tensors in terms of j_z, j_+, and j_- are listed up to rank six.

Note that an operator j_z^n is reduced to a polynomial of j_z of order less than $2j + 1$ if n is an integer larger than $2j$. This is proved by noting the identical relation:

$$(j_z - j)\{j_z - (j-1)\} \cdots \{j_z + (j-1)\}(j_z + j) = 0.$$

The left-hand side is rearranged in the form

$$(j_z^2 - j^2)\{j_z^2 - (j-1)^2\} \cdots \{j_z^2 - (\tfrac{1}{2})^2\} = 0 \qquad \text{for half-integral } j.$$

or

$$(j_z^2 - j^2)\{j_z^2 - (j-1)^2\} \cdots j_z = 0 \qquad \text{for integral } j.$$

Expanding and rearranging these equations, one obtains

$$j_z^{2j+1} = \{\sum_{m=0 \text{ or } 1/2}^{j} m^2\} \cdot j_z^{2j-1} + \text{lower order in } j_z. \tag{1.7–8}$$

Rotating the coordinates so that j_z is transformed into j_x or j_y, one can show the same relation for j_x and j_y as (1.7–8). The shift operators j_+^n and j_-^n reduce to a null operator if n is larger than $2j$.

1.8 COUPLING OF TWO ANGULAR MOMENTA

We shall often work on a system of two or more components; for instance, one component may be an orbital angular momentum, and the other a spin momentum of an electron, or else one may be the total angular momentum of one electron, and the other the total angular momentum of the other electron. In this section, let us consider a two-component system, which is of fundamental importance for other many-component systems. The state of the one component is to be specified by j_1 and m_1; that of the other by j_2 and m_2. There are $2j_1 + 1$ states for the former, and $2j_2 + 1$ for the latter. The total number of product statevectors $|j_1m_1, j_2m_2\rangle = |j_1m_1\rangle \cdot |j_2m_2\rangle$ is simply $(2j_1 + 1)(2j_2 + 1)$. The angular momentum $\boldsymbol{j}$ of the whole system is the sum $\boldsymbol{j}_1 + \boldsymbol{j}_2$, and the z-component j_z is $j_{1z} + j_{2z}$. The statevector for the whole system will be designated by $|j_1 j_2 jm\rangle$, where j and m refer to $\boldsymbol{j}$ and j_z.

It is obvious that $m = m_1 + m_2$ since $j_z = j_{1z} + j_{2z}$, and that the maximum value of m is $j_1 + j_2$. Two sets of statevectors $|j_1 m_1, j_2 m_2\rangle$ and $|j_1 j_2 jm\rangle$ are related through unitary transformation by

$$|j_1 j_2 jm\rangle = \sum_{m_1 m_2} \delta(m, m_1 + m_2) |j_1 m_1, j_2 m_2\rangle \langle j_1 m_1, j_2 m_2 | j_1 j_2 jm\rangle. \tag{1.8–1}$$

The coefficient $\langle j_1 m_1, j_2 m_2 | j_1 j_2 jm\rangle$ is called the *Clebsch-Gordan coefficient*. A general expression for the Clebsch-Gordan coefficient is†

$$\langle j_1 m_1, j_2 m_2 | j_1 j_2 jm\rangle = \delta(m, m_1 + m_2)$$
$$\times \left[\frac{(2j+1)(j_1+j_2-j)!(j_1-m_1)!(j_2-m_2)!(j+m)!(j-m)!}{(j_1+j_2+j+1)!(j+j_1-j_2)!(j+j_2-j_1)!(j_1+m_1)!(j_2+m_2)!}\right]^{1/2}$$
$$\times \sum_\nu (-1)^{j_1-m_1-\nu} \frac{(j_1+m_1-\nu)!(j_2+j-m_1-\nu)!}{\nu!(j-m-\nu)!(j_1-m_1-\nu)!(j_2-j+m_1+\nu)!} \tag{1.8-2}$$

for $j_1 + j_2 \geqslant j \geqslant |j_1 - j_2|$, where ν is summed over nonnegative factorials.

When the total angular momentum $\boldsymbol{j}$ is the addition of the orbital angular momentum $\boldsymbol{l}$ and the spin $\boldsymbol{s}$, i. e., $\boldsymbol{j} = \boldsymbol{l} + \boldsymbol{s}$, the total angular momentum operator $\boldsymbol{j}$ satisfies the relations

$$[\boldsymbol{j}^2, \boldsymbol{l}^2] = [\boldsymbol{j}^2, \boldsymbol{s}^2] = [j_z, \boldsymbol{l}^2] = [j_z, \boldsymbol{s}^2] = 0, \tag{1.8-3}$$

while we have

$$[\boldsymbol{j}^2, l_z] \neq 0 \quad \text{and} \quad [\boldsymbol{j}^2, s_z] \neq 0, \tag{1.8-4}$$

where we use the relation

$$\boldsymbol{l}\cdot\boldsymbol{s} = \tfrac{1}{2}\{j(j+1) - l(l+1) - s(s+1)\}.$$

We conclude that in a state of well-defined $\boldsymbol{j}^2$ and j_z, two operators l_z and s_z cannot have eigenvalues simultaneously, and that $\boldsymbol{l}^2$ and $\boldsymbol{s}^2$ are well defined. Using (1.8-2), we find the Clebsch-Gordan coefficients $\langle lm_l, \tfrac{1}{2}m_s | l\tfrac{1}{2}jm\rangle$ listed in Table 1.8-1.

TABLE 1.8-1

CLEBSCH-GORDAN COEFFICIENTS $\langle lm_l, \tfrac{1}{2}m_s | l\tfrac{1}{2}jm\rangle$

j \ m_s	$\frac{1}{2}$	$-\frac{1}{2}$
$l+\frac{1}{2}$	$[(l+\frac{1}{2}+m)/(2l+1)]^{1/2}$	$[(l+\frac{1}{2}-m)/(2l+1)]^{1/2}$
$l-\frac{1}{2}$	$[(l+\frac{1}{2}-m)/(2l+1)]^{1/2}$	$-[(l+\frac{1}{2}+m)/(2l+1)]^{1/2}$

1.9 WIGNER-ECKART THEOREM

We will now prove a very important theorem on matrix elements of irreducible tensor operators. Equations (1.7-1) and (1.7-2), with kq replaced by $j_2 m_2$, are rearranged in the form:

$$j_z T_{j_2 m_2} - T_{j_2 m_2} j_z = m_2 T_{j_2 m_2}, \tag{1.9-1}$$

and

†For the derivation refer, for instance, to B. R. Judd, *Operator Techniques in Atomic Spectroscopy* (New York: McGraw-Hill Book Company, 1963), pp. 10–12.

$$j_{\pm}T_{j_2m_2} - T_{j_2m_2}j_{\pm} = [(j_2 \mp m_2)(j_2 \pm m_2 + 1)]^{1/2}T_{j_2m_2\pm 1}, \qquad (1.9\text{–}2)$$

where j is to be $j_1 + j_2$. Taking a matrix element $\langle jm| \quad |j_1m_1\rangle$ of (1.9–2), we find

$$\begin{aligned}&[(j \pm m)(j \mp m + 1)]^{1/2}\langle jm \mp 1|T_{j_2m_2}|j_1m_1\rangle \\ &\quad - [(j_1 \mp m_1)(j_1 \pm m_1 + 1)]^{1/2}\langle jm|T_{j_2m_2}|j_1m_1 \pm 1\rangle \\ &\quad = [(j_2 \mp m_2)(j_2 \pm m_2 + 1)]^{1/2}\langle jm|T_{j_2m_2\pm 1}|j_1m_1\rangle. \end{aligned} \qquad (1.9\text{–}3)$$

On the other hand, taking a matrix element $\langle j_1j_2jm| \quad |j_1m_1, j_2m_2\rangle$ of

$$j_{\pm} - j_{1\pm} = j_{2\pm}, \qquad (1.9\text{–}4)$$

we have

$$\begin{aligned}&[(j \pm m)(j \mp m + 1)]^{1/2}\langle j_1j_2jm \mp 1|j_1m_1, j_2m_2\rangle \\ &\quad - [(j_1 \mp m_1)(j_1 \pm m_1 + 1)]^{1/2}\langle j_1j_2jm|j_1m_1 \pm 1, j_2m_2\rangle \\ &\quad = [(j_2 \mp m_2)(j_2 \pm m_2 + 1)]^{1/2}\langle j_1j_2jm|j_1m_1, j_2m_2 \pm 1\rangle, \end{aligned} \qquad (1.9\text{–}5)$$

where we use Eq. (1.8–1). Comparing (1.9–3) and (1.9–5), we note that matrix elements $\langle jm|T_{j_2m_2}|j_1m_1\rangle$ satisfy the same set of linear homogeneous equations as the Clebsch-Gordan coefficients $\langle j_1j_2jm|j_1m_1, j_2m_2\rangle$ satisfy. We conclude that the matrix elements $\langle jm|T_{j_2m_2}|j_1m_1\rangle$ are proportional to the Clebsch-Gordan coefficients $\langle j_1j_2jm|j_1m_1, j_2m_2\rangle$ unless the matrix elements vanish, i. e.,

$$\langle jm|T_{j_2m_2}|j_1m_1\rangle = \langle j\|T_{j_2}\|j_1\rangle\langle j_1j_2, jm|j_1m_1, j_2m_2\rangle. \qquad (1.9\text{–}6)$$

This relation is known as *Wigner-Eckart theorem*. The proportionality factor $\langle j\|T_{j_2}\|j_1\rangle$ does not depend on the values of m, m_1, and m_2, since the transformation property of $\langle jm|T_{j_2m_2}|j_1m_1\rangle$ under three-dimensional rotations is entirely the same as that of $\langle j_1j_2jm|j_1m_1, j_2m_2\rangle$. The proportionality factor is usually calculated with reference to a set of particular values of m, m_1, and m_2—for instance, $m = j_1 + j_2$, $m_1 = j_1$, and $m_2 = j_2$. We may often leave the proportionality factor as a parameter to be determined from experiment.

With reference to the properties of Clebsch-Gordan coefficients, we find selection rules:

$$\langle jm|T_{j_2m_2}|j_1m_1\rangle = 0, \qquad (1.9\text{–}7)$$

unless $m = m_1 + m_2$, or unless $j_1 + j_2 \geqslant j \geqslant |j_1 - j_2|$.

1.10 INVERSION AND PARITY

Inversion is a transformation that transforms Cartesian coordinates x, y, and z into $-x$, $-y$, and $-z$. In polar coordinates, the inversion transforms r, θ, and ϕ into r, $\pi - \theta$, and $\pi + \phi$. The orbital angular momentum is invariant under inversion; more explicitly, one sees that $l_z = -i(x\,\partial/\partial y - y\,\partial/\partial x)$ is unaltered under the coordinate transformation (x, y, z) to $(-x, -y, -z)$. We may assume† that angular momentum operator $\boldsymbol{j}$ is unchanged under inversion, or in other words, that $\boldsymbol{j}$ commutes with the inversion operator I:

$$I\boldsymbol{j}I^{-1} = \boldsymbol{j} \qquad \text{or} \qquad I\boldsymbol{j} = \boldsymbol{j}I. \tag{1.10–1}$$

Using (1.10–1), we can partially determine the transformation property of eigenvectors $|jm\rangle$ under inversion, with the additional requirement that the operation I^2 be equivalent to the identity:

$$I^2 = E. \tag{1.10–2}$$

The result is as follows:

$$I|jm\rangle = \pm|jm\rangle, \tag{1.10–3}$$

where the plus or minus sign must be determined by specifying more details of $|jm\rangle$. Functions and operators are said to be of *even* or *odd parity* according to whether the sign is unaltered or reversed under the inversion.

Orbital angular momentum eigenfunctions $\psi_{lm}(\theta\phi)$ are multiplied by $(-1)^l$ under the inversion, since the polynomial $P_{lm}(\cos\theta)$ is multiplied by $(-1)^{l-m}$, and the exponent $e^{im\phi}$ by $(-1)^m$. We may write, therefore,

$$I|lm\rangle = (-1)^l|lm\rangle. \tag{1.10–4}$$

Spin eigenvectors are invariant under the inversion, i. e.,

$$I|\tfrac{1}{2}m_s\rangle = |\tfrac{1}{2}m_s\rangle. \tag{1.10–5}$$

By coupling two angular momenta $l = 1$ and $s = \frac{1}{2}$, we have two eigenvectors $|j = \frac{1}{2}, m\rangle$ and $|j = \frac{3}{2}, m\rangle$. The corresponding wavefunctions are both odd. From this observation, one may note that the parity of $|jm\rangle$ is not determined unless the detail of $|jm\rangle$ is specified.

Reflection σ, with respect to a plane passing through the origin of the coordinate, is represented by the operator relation

$$\sigma = I\cdot R(\pi), \tag{1.10–6}$$

where $R(\pi)$ is a rotation by π around the axis which is perpendicular to the reflection plane and passes through the origin.

The character for inversion with respect to $|jm\rangle$ is

$$\chi^j(I) = \pm(2j + 1); \tag{1.10–7}$$

while the character for reflection is

$$\chi^j(\sigma) = \begin{cases} 0 & \text{for half-integral } j, \\ \pm 1 & \text{for integral } j. \end{cases} \tag{1.10–8}$$

†For a more rigorous treatment the reader may refer, for instance, to V. Heine, *Group Theory in Quantum Mechanics* (New York: Pergamon Press, 1960), Sec. 11.

The character for reflection with respect to ψ_{lm} is always unity:

$$\chi^l(\sigma) = 1. \tag{1.10–9}$$

1.11 TIME REVERSAL

Time reversal is a transformation that reverses the sense of time; that is, $t \longrightarrow -t$. One may assume that angular momentum operators reverse the sign under time reversal. Following Wigner's procedure,† the time-reversal operator K is represented by the product of the unitary operator U and the complex conjugate operator K_0:

$$K = UK_0. \tag{1.11–1}$$

The phase convention in (1.2–6) leads to a matrix representation such that matrices are real for j_x and j_z, and imaginary for j_y. The unitary operator, U, may be shown to be equivalent to a rotation by π around the y-axis, i. e., $e^{-i\pi j_y}$, since

$$U(j_x, j_y, j_z)U^{-1} = (-j_x, +j_y, -j_z), \tag{1.11–2}$$

where $KjK^{-1} = -j$ is used. The operator U may be chosen as

$$U = ie^{-i\pi j_y}, \tag{1.11–3}$$

where the factor i is introduced for phase convenience. For a particular case $j = s = \frac{1}{2}$, the operator U is expressed, according to (1.4–4), in the matrix form

$$U = \begin{bmatrix} 0 & -i \\ i & 0 \end{bmatrix}. \tag{1.11–4}$$

The time-reversal operator thus transforms spin eigenvectors (1.2–9) as

$$K|\tfrac{1}{2}m_s\rangle = (-1)^{m_s}|\tfrac{1}{2} -m_s\rangle. \tag{1.11–5}$$

The time-reversal operator K transforms the orbital angular momentum eigenvector $|lm_l\rangle$ as

$$K|lm_l\rangle = (-1)^{m_l}|l -m_l\rangle, \tag{1.11–6}$$

where we refer to (1.6–6) and (1.6–7). One may notice that the factor i in (1.11–3) is introduced so that the phase factor $(-1)^{m_s}$ for the spin eigenvector conforms with $(-1)^{m_l}$ for the orbital eigenvector. In order to preserve this type of phase factor for $|l\frac{1}{2}, jm\rangle$ under time reversal, the following phase should be chosen:

$$|l\tfrac{1}{2}, jm\rangle = (i)^{j-l-(1/2)} \sum_{m_l} |lm_l, \tfrac{1}{2}m_s\rangle\langle lm_l, \tfrac{1}{2}m_s|l\tfrac{1}{2}, jm\rangle. \tag{1.11–7}$$

†See, for instance, E. P. Wigner, *Göttingen Nachrichten,* no. 32, 1932; E. P. Wigner, *Group Theory* (New York: Academic Press Inc., 1959).

Operating with K on (1.11–7), we have

$$K|l\tfrac{1}{2}, jm\rangle = (-i)^{j-l-(1/2)} \sum_{m_l} (-1)^{m_l+m_s}|l -m_l, \tfrac{1}{2} -m_s\rangle$$
$$\times \langle lm_l, \tfrac{1}{2}m_s|l\tfrac{1}{2}, jm\rangle$$
$$= (-1)^m(i)^{j-l-(1/2)} \sum_{m_l} |l -m_l, \tfrac{1}{2} -m_s\rangle\langle l -m_s, \tfrac{1}{2} -m_s|l\tfrac{1}{2}, j -m\rangle, \quad (1.11\text{–}8)$$

where we use $\langle lm_l, \tfrac{1}{2}m_s|l\tfrac{1}{2}, jm\rangle = (-1)^{j-l-(1/2)}\langle l -m_l, \tfrac{1}{2} -m_s|l\tfrac{1}{2}, jm\rangle$.†

For a system consisting of n electrons, the time-reversal operator K is simply given by the product:

$$K = \prod_{\nu=1}^{n} (\sigma_y)_\nu \cdot K_0, \quad (1.11\text{–}9)$$

where σ_y is the so-called Pauli matrix (1.11–4), and the subscript ν refers to the νth electron.

1.12 KRAMERS' THEOREM AND TIME-REVERSAL DEGENERACY

Kramers' theorem states that when a system consisting of an odd number of electrons is subject to a time reversal invariant Hamiltonian H, the energy eigenstates are necessarily doubly degenerate.

Proof: The squared operator, K^2, of (1.11–9), is easily shown to be

$$K^2 = (-1)^n. \quad (1.12\text{–}1)$$

The eigenvalue equation

$$H|E, \gamma\rangle = E|E, \gamma\rangle$$

is also satisfied with $K|E, \gamma\rangle$, where E is the energy eigenvalue, and γ is a set of other quantum numbers. The statevector $K|E, \gamma\rangle$ is, therefore, either

$$\text{(i)} \quad K|E, \gamma\rangle = e^{i\delta}|E, \gamma\rangle,$$

or

$$\text{(ii)} \quad K|E, \gamma\rangle \neq e^{i\delta}|E, \gamma\rangle,$$

where δ is a real number. Suppose that $K|E, \gamma\rangle$ were the case (i) for an odd number of electrons. This is in contradiction with

$$K^2|E, \gamma\rangle = -|E, \gamma\rangle,$$

since

$$K^2|E, \gamma\rangle = Ke^{i\delta}|E, \gamma\rangle = e^{-i\delta}(e^{i\delta})|E, \gamma\rangle = |E, \gamma\rangle.$$

†See, for instance, R. G. Sachs, *Nuclear Theory* (Reading, Mass.: Addison-Wesley Publishing Co., Inc., 1953), App. 3; A. R. Edmonds, *Angular Momentum in Quantum Mechanics* (Princeton, N. J.: Princeton University Press, 1957), p. 42.

The statevector $K|E, \gamma\rangle$ is, therefore, different from $|E, \gamma\rangle$, apart from the phase factor. The two states $|E, \gamma\rangle$ and $K|E, \gamma\rangle$ are degenerate in the energy E of the Hamiltonian H.

Note that Kramers' theorem does not exclude the possibility that a system consisting of an even number of electrons can have a double degeneracy due to time reversal. Regardless of whether the number of electrons is odd or even, if $K|E, \gamma\rangle$ is a state different from $|E, \gamma\rangle$, the pair of states $|E, \gamma\rangle$ and $K|E, \gamma\rangle$ are degenerate. This degeneracy may be called a *time-reversal degeneracy*. The state $K|E, \gamma\rangle$ is paired through time reversal to $|E, \gamma\rangle$, and vice versa. For practical calculations, if the wavefunction ψ for $|E, \gamma\rangle$ is known, the wavefunction for $K|E, \gamma\rangle$ is obtained by applying K upon ψ, apart from a phase factor. Examples of time-reversal pair states are

$$|jm\rangle \text{ and } |j\ -m\rangle; \qquad |lm_l\rangle \text{ and } |l\ -m_l\rangle.$$

1.13 REPLACEMENT THEOREM

In this section, arguments are limited to within a manifold of constant j. Spherical harmonic operators Y_{nm} satisfy (1.7–1) and (1.7–2) as irreducible tensor operators T_{nm}. The Wigner-Eckart theorem leads to the matrix relation between Y_{nm} and T_{nm} in the form:

$$\langle jm_1|Y_{nm}|jm_2\rangle = c(jn)\langle jm_1|T_{nm}|jm_2\rangle, \tag{1.13–1}$$

where

$$c(jn) = \langle j\|Y_n\|j\rangle/\langle j\|T_n\|j\rangle. \tag{1.13–2}$$

If the irreducible tensor operators T_{nm} are expressed in terms of j_z, j_+, and j_-, the matrix elements $\langle jm_1|T_{nm}|jm_2\rangle$ are easily calculated in terms of n, j, m_1, and m_2. The rest of the matrix calculation of Y_{nm} reduces to the calculation of the ratio $c(jn)$, which may be left as a parameter to be determined by experiment. We can formulate this as a theorem: *Replacement theorem*: Within a manifold of constant j, spherical harmonic operators Y_{nm} can be replaced with corresponding irreducible tensor operators T_{nm} in the form

$$Y_{nm} = c(jn)T_{nm}. \tag{1.13–3}$$

Note that if the irreducible tensor operator T_{nm} differs in parity from the spherical harmonic operator Y_{nm}, the replacement is no longer valid. The spherical harmonic operators Y_{nm} of odd order are null operators within the multiplets of constant j. One may verify this statement, using the inversion, or time-reversal, operator.

We shall use the replacement theorem in Sec. 4.4.

2

ELEMENTS OF FINITE GROUPS

2.1 INTRODUCTION

In this chapter we study the theory of finite groups, particularly the theory of representations, and the applications to quantum mechanics. The results will be fully used in Chapters 3 and 4. The four sections to follow are devoted to some fundamental aspects of finite group. We will give examples, particularly referring to the point group $\mathbf{D}_3$, so as to help the reader understand the abstract aspects more completely. Secs.2.20, 2.21, and 2.22 will show how the theory of representations, presented in Secs. 2.6 to 2.15, is applied to calculations in quantum mechanics. The point groups are studied in some detail since they are essential for an understanding of the ligand field theory.

The arrows in the accompanying block diagram show the logical relationships among equations and theorems.

2.2 GROUP POSTULATES

Any set of distinct elements $P, Q, R, S, \ldots$, among which the product is defined, is said to form a *group* if the following conditions are satisfied:

1. The product of any two elements in the set is also an element of the set.
2. The associative law of multiplication holds:

| Equation (2.5–2): |
| Class multiplication formula |
| $$C_i C_j = \sum_k c_{ijk} C_k$$ |

| Theorem 2.9–4: |
| Orthogonality of irreducible representations |

| Theorem 2.11–3: |
| $$g_i \chi_i^\alpha g_j \chi_j^\alpha = d_\alpha \sum_k c_{ijk} g_k \chi_k^\alpha$$ |

| Theorem 2.11–1: |
| Orthogonality of characters between irreducible representations |
| $$\sum_P \chi^\alpha(P)^* \chi^\beta(P) = g\delta_{\alpha\beta}$$ |

| Equation (2.13–3): |
| $$\sum_\alpha \chi_i^\alpha \chi_k^\alpha = g\delta_{1k}$$ |

| Theorem 2.11–2: |
| The number of classes q is not less than the number of irreducible representations r, i. e., |
| $$q \geqslant r.$$ |

| Theorem 2.14–1: |
| Orthogonality of characters between classes |
| $$g_i \sum_\alpha \chi_i^{\alpha*} \chi_j^\alpha = g\delta_{ij}$$ |

| Theorem 2.14–2: |
| The number of classes q is not more than the number of irreducible representations r, i.e., |
| $$q \leqslant r.$$ |

| Theorem 2.14–3: |
| The number of classes q equals the number of irreducible representations r, i. e., |
| $$q = r.$$ |

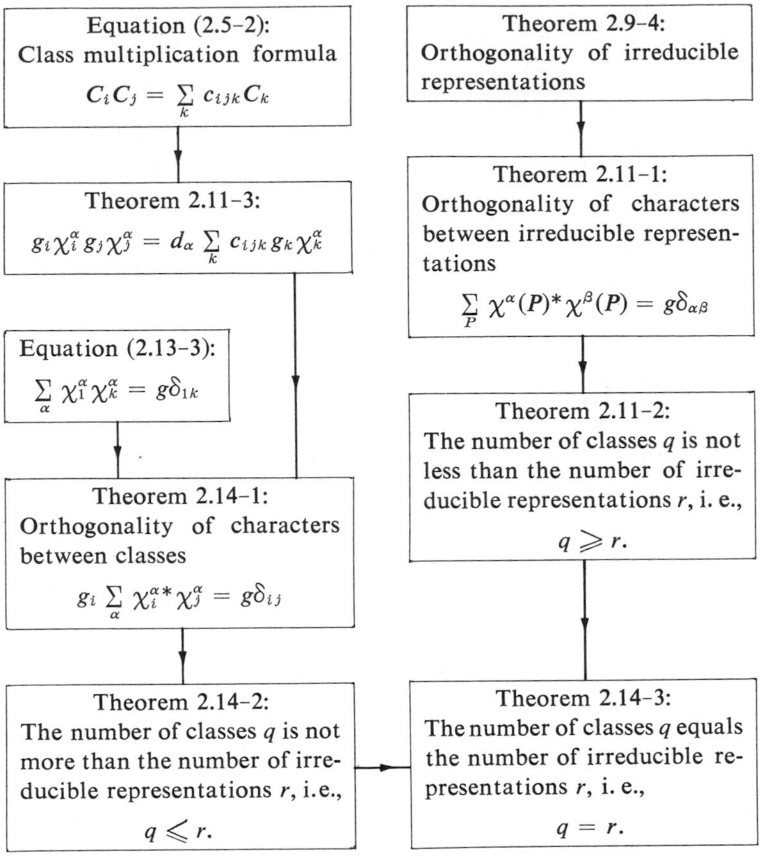

$$P(QR) = (PQ)R;$$

that is, P times the product (QR) must be equal to the product (PQ) times R.

3. The set must contain the identity element E, which satisfies the relation

$$ER = RE = R \qquad \text{for every } R.$$

4. Every element S must have its reciprocal (or inverse) S^{-1} such that

$$SS^{-1} = S^{-1}S = E.$$

A group G, which consists of elements $P, Q, R, S, \ldots$, is the same as the product of an element S and the group G; that is, $G = SG$. The number of elements in both sets is obviously the same. If two elements in SG were the same, e. g., $ST = SQ$, then two elements T and Q ought to be the same, in disagreement with the postulate that all elements of G are distinct. The set SG is, therefore, simply a rearrangement of the set G.

Examples of groups are a set of coordinate transformations, a set of permutations of a certain number of objects, a set of matrices (nonsingular), a set of abstract symbols, and so forth. Multiplication must be defined among the elements in the set.

EXAMPLE: The point group $\mathbf{D}_3$

The point group $\mathbf{D}_3$ is a set of rotations which rotate an equilateral triangle into the same configuration. The equilateral triangle is shown in Fig. 2.2–1. The group $\mathbf{D}_3$ consists of six rotations:

E: the identity (zero rotation),
A: a rotation by π around OA,
B: a rotation by π around OB,
C: a rotation by π around OC,
D: a rotation by $2\pi/3$ around the z-axis,
F: a rotation by $4\pi/3$ around the z-axis.

One may easily verify that these six rotations satisfy the four group postulates. The product AD stands for two successive rotations; that is, the rotation D is followed by the rotation A. The product AD is the same as the rotation B. The three rotations A, B and C are reciprocals of themselves; the rotation F is the reciprocal of D, and vice versa.

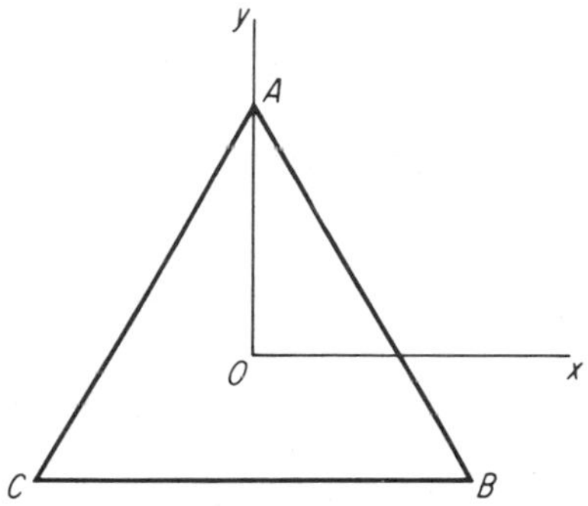

Fig. 2.2-1 Equilateral triangle ABC remains in the same configuration under the point group $\mathbf{D}_3$.

EXAMPLE: The permutation group $\mathbf{S}_3$

The permutation group $\mathbf{S}_3$ on three letters consists of six permutations:

$$E = (a)(b)(c), \qquad A = (a)(bc), \qquad B = (ac)(b),$$
$$C = (ab)(c), \qquad D = (acb), \qquad F = (abc).$$

The element A, for instance, permutes b and c, leaving a in the original position. The element F permutes a, b, and c in a cyclic manner; that is, a is replaced with b, b with c, and c with a.

2.3 GROUP MULTIPLICATION TABLE

A group multiplication table is of considerable importance for the following discussions. Let us explain a group multiplication table by an example. The multiplication table for the point group $\mathbf{D}_3$ is presented in Table 2.3–1. An entity D in row B of column C means that the product BC is equivalent to D. The Table 2.3–1 itself may also represent an abstract

TABLE 2.3–1

MULTIPLICATION TABLE FOR $\mathbf{D}_3$

E	A	B	C	D	F
A	E	D	F	B	C
B	F	E	D	C	A
C	D	F	E	A	B
D	C	A	B	F	E
F	B	C	A	E	D

group that is defined through the multiplication table for six objects: A, B, C, D, E, and F. One may also note that the multiplication table for S_3 is exactly the same as for $\mathbf{D}_3$. The Table 2.3–1 for the group $\mathbf{D}_3$ will be used in various ways, e.g., in classifying all the elements in distinct classes of conjugate elements (Sec. 2.4), in determining coefficients of class multiplications c_{ijk} (Sec. 2.5), and in constructing the regular representation (Sec. 2.13). These new concepts will be interpreted in the respective sections and are important in actual applications of group theory. The usefulness of such multiplication tables should not be underestimated.

2.4 CLASSES OF CONJUGATE ELEMENTS

An element Q of a group G is called the *conjugate element of P with respect to T*, when Q and P are related through $Q = TPT^{-1}$ for an element T in the group G. Since $P = T^{-1}QT$, the element P is also conjugate to Q. This is also stated as: *P is transformed into Q with T*. The number, g, of all elements in the group G is termed the *order of the group G*. One may form g possible conjugate elements of P; however, some of them are the same. For example, $EPE^{-1} = PPP^{-1} = P^{-1}PP = P$. A set of all distinct elements that are conjugate to P is called the *class of conjugate elements of P*, or simply the *class of P*. Let $P_1, P_2, \ldots, P_{g_i}$ be elements of a class C_i; the number g_i of elements is termed the *order of the class C_i*. If $P_1, P_2, \ldots, P_{g_i}$ are transformed into TP_1T^{-1}, $TP_2T^{-1}, \ldots, TP_{g_i}T^{-1}$, with an arbitrary element T, the latter set belongs to the same class as C_i, since only the order of elements is changed, but the entities remain the same. Conversely, if a set of elements remains the same under transformation with an arbitrary element, the set is a class or sum of classes. The identity element is a class by itself, since it commutes with every element of the group. A group can be exhausted by classes, since no class has any element in common with another class.

EXAMPLE: $\mathbf{D}_3$. The six elements are classified in three classes:

$$E = C_1, \quad (A, B, C) = C_2 \quad \text{and} \quad (D, F) = C_3.$$

A group is called *Abelian* when all the elements commute with each other. Every element of an Abelian group forms a class by itself.

2.5 CLASS MULTIPLICATION

Let us define *class multiplication* of two classes C_i and C_j as a set of elements which are products of the type $P_i P_j$ for $P_i \in C_i$ and $P_j \in C_j$. The class multiplication is written in the form

$$C_i C_j = \sum_{ij} P_i P_j, \tag{2.5–1}$$

where the summation is over the set of $P_i P_j$. The right-hand side of (2.5–1) remains the same under transformation with an arbitrary element of the group. It follows that

$$C_i C_j = \sum_{k} c_{ijk} C_k, \tag{2.5–2}$$

where c_{ijk} is the positive integer that tells how often the complete class C_k appears in the multiplication $C_i C_j$; k is summed over all classes. A particular coefficient c_{ij1}, where C_1 is to be the identity class, is nonvanishing only when C_i is made up of inverse of elements in C_j; and we find

$$c_{ij1} = \begin{cases} 0 & \text{if } C_i \neq C_j^{-1}, \\ g_i & \text{if } C_i = C_j^{-1}, \end{cases} \tag{2.5–3}$$

where C_j^{-1} stands for a set of inverse elements of C_j.

EXAMPLE: $\mathbf{D}_3$. There are three nontrivial class multiplications:

$$C_2 C_2 = 3E + 3C_3, \quad C_3 C_3 = 2E + C_3, \quad C_2 C_3 = 2C_2, \tag{2.5–4}$$

where $c_{221} = 3$, $c_{331} = 2$, and so on.

2.6 REPRESENTATION AND CHARACTER

A set of nonsingular square matrices is called a *representation* of group G if the matrices satisfy the same multiplication table as G. The representation is called *faithful* if there is one-to-one correspondence between the elements and the matrices. We will hereafter discuss faithful representations unless otherwise stated.

A matrix corresponding to an element P will be written as $D(P)$. The dimension of all the matrices in the set must be the same, since otherwise the multiplication of the matrices cannot be defined. Corresponding to the identity element E, there must be a matrix $D(E)$ which is a unit matrix. All the matrices must be nonsingular, i. e., no determinant of $D(P)$ is zero. It is the matrix $D(P)^{-1}$ that corresponds to the reciprocal P^{-1} since $D(P)^{-1} D(P) = D(P) D(P)^{-1} = D(E)$ as $P^{-1} P = PP^{-1} = E$. The representation, i. e., the set of matrices $D(P)$, is denoted by a Greek letter $\Gamma\{D(P)\}$ or simply Γ. The dimension of the representation matrices is called the *dimension of the representation.* The simplest, one-dimensional representation consists entirely of unities. This representation is called the *identity representation.* Every group has the identity representation.

An element TPT^{-1}, which is a conjugate element of P with respect to T, corresponds to the matrix $D(TPT^{-1}) = D(T)D(P)D(T)^{-1}$. The trace of $D(P)$—that is, the sum of the diagonal elements—is equal to that of $D(TPT^{-1})$ since trace of a product of matrices does not depend on the cyclic order of the factors, i. e.,

$$\begin{aligned}\text{trace } D(TPT^{-1}) &= \text{trace } D(T)D(P)D(T)^{-1} = \text{trace } D(P)D(T)^{-1}D(T)\\ &= \text{trace } D(P).\end{aligned}$$

From this, one may note that the traces of all the elements in the same class are equal. The trace of $D(P)$ will be denoted by a Greek letter $\chi(P)$. The quantities $\chi(P)$ are called the *characters* of the representation $\Gamma\{D(P)\}$.†

When a group consists of linear transformations, the representation may be chosen to be a set of coefficient matrices of the functions which are to be transformed with each other. The dimension of the representation is then the number of the functions. The functions are called *bases* or *basis functions* of the representation. The space which the functions span is called a *representation space* of the group.

EXAMPLE: $\mathbf{D}_3$. If the Cartesian coordinate frame, to which an equilateral triangle is fixed, is chosen as in Fig. 2.2–1, the six clockwise frame rotations transform Cartesian coordinates x, y, and z into new x', y', and z'. The transformation matrices are:

$$D(E) = \begin{bmatrix} 1 & 0 & 0 \\ 0 & 1 & 0 \\ 0 & 0 & 1 \end{bmatrix}, \quad D(A) = \begin{bmatrix} -1 & 0 & 0 \\ 0 & 1 & 0 \\ 0 & 0 & -1 \end{bmatrix},$$

$$D(B) = \begin{bmatrix} \frac{1}{2} & -\frac{\sqrt{3}}{2} & 0 \\ -\frac{\sqrt{3}}{2} & -\frac{1}{2} & 0 \\ 0 & 0 & -1 \end{bmatrix},$$

$$D(C) = \begin{bmatrix} \frac{1}{2} & \frac{\sqrt{3}}{2} & 0 \\ \frac{\sqrt{3}}{2} & -\frac{1}{2} & 0 \\ 0 & 0 & -1 \end{bmatrix}, \quad D(D) = \begin{bmatrix} -\frac{1}{2} & \frac{\sqrt{3}}{2} & 0 \\ -\frac{\sqrt{3}}{2} & -\frac{1}{2} & 0 \\ 0 & 0 & 1 \end{bmatrix},$$

†In some literature, the character is defined to be the set of $\chi(P)$.

$$D(F) = \begin{bmatrix} -\frac{1}{2} & -\frac{\sqrt{3}}{2} & 0 \\ \frac{\sqrt{3}}{2} & -\frac{1}{2} & 0 \\ 0 & 0 & 1 \end{bmatrix}. \tag{2.6–1}$$

The characters are

$$\chi(E) = 3, \quad \chi(A) = \chi(B) = \chi(C) = -1, \quad \chi(D) = \chi(F) = 0. \tag{2.6–2}$$

EXAMPLE: $\mathbf{S}_3$. The six permutations are represented by the matrices:

$$D(E) = \begin{bmatrix} 1 & 0 & 0 \\ 0 & 1 & 0 \\ 0 & 0 & 1 \end{bmatrix}, \quad D(A) = \begin{bmatrix} 1 & 0 & 0 \\ 0 & 0 & 1 \\ 0 & 1 & 0 \end{bmatrix}, \quad D(B) = \begin{bmatrix} 0 & 0 & 1 \\ 0 & 1 & 0 \\ 1 & 0 & 0 \end{bmatrix},$$
$$D(C) = \begin{bmatrix} 0 & 1 & 0 \\ 1 & 0 & 0 \\ 0 & 0 & 1 \end{bmatrix}, \quad D(D) = \begin{bmatrix} 0 & 0 & 1 \\ 1 & 0 & 0 \\ 0 & 1 & 0 \end{bmatrix}, \quad D(F) = \begin{bmatrix} 0 & 1 & 0 \\ 0 & 0 & 1 \\ 1 & 0 & 0 \end{bmatrix}, \tag{2.6–3}$$

The characters are

$$\chi(E) = 3, \quad \chi(A) = \chi(B) = \chi(C) = 1, \quad \chi(D) = \chi(F) = 0. \tag{2.6–4}$$

2.7 EQUIVALENT AND INEQUIVALENT REPRESENTATIONS

Two representations are called *equivalent* if all matrices of the one representation are transformed by a single matrix into the matrices of the other in one-to-one correspondence. If there is no such matrix, two representations are called *inequivalent* or *nonequivalent*. More specifically, if matrices $D(P)$ are transformed by a single matrix M into $D'(P) = MD(P)M^{-1}$, the new matrices D' evidently satisfy the same multiplication table as the original matrices. The set of basis functions is also transformed into a new set under the transformation by M.

2.8 REDUCIBLE AND IRREDUCIBLE REPRESENTATIONS

If, by some means, we find a similarity transformation which transforms every matrix $D(P)$ of n-dimension into the form

$$\begin{bmatrix} D_1(P) & 0 \\ 0 & D_2(P) \end{bmatrix}, \tag{2.8–1}$$

the representation $\Gamma\{D(P)\}$ is called *reducible*. If the dimension of square matrices $D_1(P)$ is m, the dimension of $D_2(P)$ is $n - m$. The null matrices 0 are rectangular. The set of matrices (2.6–1) is an example of a reducible representation.

If no such similarity transformation exists, the representation is called *irreducible*. Basis functions for an irreducible representation are called the *irreducible basis functions*; the space which the irreducible basis functions span is termed the *irreducible space*.

EXAMPLE: S_3. One may note that the representation (2.6–3) reducible through the matrix

$$M = \begin{bmatrix} 0 & \sqrt{\frac{1}{2}} & -\sqrt{\frac{1}{2}} \\ \sqrt{\frac{2}{3}} & -\sqrt{\frac{1}{6}} & -\sqrt{\frac{1}{6}} \\ -\sqrt{\frac{1}{6}} & -\sqrt{\frac{1}{6}} & -\sqrt{\frac{1}{6}} \end{bmatrix}.$$

2.9 THEOREMS CONCERNING IRREDUCIBLE REPRESENTATION

In this section we shall present four theorems, the first two without proof.†

Theorem 2.9–1 (EQUIVALENCE TO UNITARY REPRESENTATION)

Every representation of a finite group is equivalent to a unitary representation.

A *unitary representation* is to consist of unitary matrices. We need not assume that the representation is irreducible.

Theorem 2.9–2 (SCALAR MATRIX)

A matrix that commutes with every matrix of an irreducible representation is necessarily scalar.

Theorem 2.9–3 (SCHUR'S LEMMA)

If $\Gamma_\alpha\{D^\alpha(P)\}$ and $\Gamma_\beta\{D^\beta(P)\}$ are two irreducible representations of dimension m and n, and if there exists an $m \times n$ matrix X such that $XD^\beta(P) = D^\alpha(P)X$ for every P, then either

(a) X is a null matrix, or

(b) X is square and nonsingular; and Γ_β is equivalent to Γ_α.

Proof: For definiteness, we may assume $m \geqslant n$. According to Theorem 2.9–1, we may assume that the two representations are unitary. According to the hypothesis, we put

$$XD^\beta(P) = D^\alpha(P)X. \tag{2.9–1}$$

†See, for instance, E. P. Wigner, *Group Theory* (New York: Academic Press Inc., 1950); or L. Marriot, *Group Theory and Solid State Physics* (Englewood Cliffs, N. J.: Prentice-Hall, Inc., 1962).

Taking the adjoint of (2.9–1), we find

$$D^{\beta}(P)X^{\dagger} = X^{\dagger}D^{\alpha}(P), \tag{2.9–2}$$

where P^{-1} is rewritten as P. Multiplying (2.9–1) by $X^{\dagger}$ from the right, and (2.9–2) by X from the left, we find

$$XD^{\beta}(P)X^{\dagger} = D^{\alpha}(P)XX^{\dagger} = XX^{\dagger}\,D^{\alpha}(P).$$

The hermitian matrix $XX^{\dagger}$ is a scalar matrix cE, according to Theorem 2.9–2. If $m > n$, then the matrix X is augmented with an $m \times (m - n)$ null matrix 0 to form a square matrix $Y = [XO]$. We then have $YY^{\dagger} = XX^{\dagger} = cE$, and $\det YY^{\dagger} = 0 = c^m$. The augmented matrix Y is, therefore, an $m \times m$ null matrix; the rectangular matrix X is also a null matrix. If $m = n$ and $c = 0$, then X is a square null matrix. If $m = n$ and $c \neq 0$, then $\det XX^{\dagger} = \det X \det X^{\dagger} = c^m$. Since $\det X \neq 0$, the relation $D^{\alpha}(P)X = XD^{\beta}(P)$ can be written as

$$D^{\alpha}(P) = XD^{\beta}(P)X^{-1}.$$

The representation Γ_{β} is equivalent to Γ_{α}.

Theorem 2.9–4 (Orthogonality of Representations)

Between two irreducible representations $\Gamma_{\alpha}\{D^{\alpha}(P)\}$ and $\Gamma_{\beta}\{D^{\beta}(P)\}$, therefore, the orthogonality relation holds:

$$\sum_{P} D^{\alpha}_{nm}(P)D^{\beta}_{m'n'}(P^{-1}) = \frac{g}{d_{\alpha}}\,\delta_{\alpha\beta}\delta_{mm'}\delta_{nn'}, \tag{2.9–3}$$

where P is summed over all elements in the group $\boldsymbol{G}$; g is the order of the group $\boldsymbol{G}$; d_{α} is the dimension of Γ_{α}.

When Γ_{α} and Γ_{β} are unitary representations, the relation (2.9–3) is written as

$$\sum_{P} D^{\alpha}_{mn}(P)^{*}\, D^{\beta}_{m'n'}(P) = \frac{g}{d_{\alpha}}\,\delta_{\alpha\beta}\delta_{mm'}\delta_{nn'}. \tag{2.9–4}$$

Proof: Using an arbitrary matrix X of order $d_{\alpha} \times d_{\beta}$, let us construct a matrix Y where

$$Y = \sum_{P} D(P)^{\alpha}XD^{\beta}(P^{-1}). \tag{2.9–5}$$

Multiplying (2.9–5) by $D^{\alpha}(R)$ from the left, and $D^{\beta}(R^{-1})$ from the right, we have

$$D^{\alpha}(R)YD^{\beta}(R^{-1}) = \sum_{P} D^{\alpha}(RP)XD^{\beta}((RP)^{-1}) = Y, \tag{2.9–6}$$

and, therefore,

$$D^{\alpha}(R)Y = YD^{\beta}(R) \qquad \text{for every } R. \tag{2.9–7}$$

If Γ_{α} and Γ_{β} are inequivalent, the constructed matrix Y is a null matrix; i.e.,

$$\sum_R D^\alpha(R) X D^\beta(R^{-1}) = 0. \tag{2.9–8}$$

Taking the (nn') element of (2.9–8), we have

$$\sum_{mm'} \sum_R D^\alpha_{nm}(R) X_{mm'} D^\beta_{m'n'}(R^{-1}) = 0.$$

Since X is arbitrary, we find

$$\sum_R D^\alpha_{nm}(R) D^\beta_{m'n'}(R^{-1}) = 0. \tag{2.9–9}$$

If $\Gamma_\alpha = \Gamma_\beta$, according to (2.9–7), the matrix Y is a scalar matrix cE:

$$Y = \sum_R D^\alpha(R) X D^\alpha(R^{-1}) = cE. \tag{2.9–10}$$

Taking the trace of (2.9–10), we have

$$c = \frac{g}{d_\alpha} \sum_{m=1}^{d_\alpha} X_{mm}.$$

Substituting this expression into (2.9–10), we have

$$\sum_R D^\alpha(R) X D^\alpha(R^{-1}) = \frac{g}{d_\alpha} \left(\sum_{m=1}^{d_\alpha} X_{mm}\right) E.$$

Equating the coefficients $X_{mm'}$ on both sides, we find

$$\sum_R D^\alpha_{nm}(R) D^\alpha_{m'n'}(R^{-1}) = \frac{g}{d_\alpha} \delta_{mm'} \delta_{nn'}. \tag{2.9–11}$$

Equations (2.9–9) and (2.9–11) establish the proof of (2.9–3).

The orthogonality relation (2.9–4) is important in the application of group theory in quantum mechanics.

2.10 KRONECKER PRODUCTS AND PRODUCT REPRESENTATION

The *Kronecker product*, or *direct product*, of two square matrices A and B is defined by

$$A \times B = \begin{bmatrix} A_{11}B & A_{12}B & \cdots \\ A_{21}B & A_{22}B & \cdots \\ \cdots & \cdots & \cdots \end{bmatrix}, \tag{2.10–1}$$

where $A_{11}B$ is a matrix, being B times A_{11}.

If A is m-dimensional, and B is n-dimensional, the matrix $A \times B$ is $m \times n$-dimensional. An element in the (jp) row and (kq) column of (2.10–1) is $A_{jk}B_{pq}$. Kronecker products are:

(1) in general, noncommutative;

(2) associative:

$$A \times (B \times C) = (A \times B) \times C, \tag{2.10–2}$$

[compare the $(j_1 j_2 j_3, k_1 k_2 k_3)$ element of both sides].

(3) $$(A \times B)(C \times D) = (AC) \times (BD), \qquad (2.10\text{–}3)$$

[compare the (jp) row and (kq) column of both sides].

When matrices A and B are nonsingular, the following properties are found:

(4) inverse:

$$(A \times B)(A \times B)^{-1} = (A \times B)(A^{-1} \times B^{-1})$$
$$= (AA^{-1}) \times (BB^{-1}) = E,$$

where E is a unit matrix of $m \times n$-dimension;

(5) adjoint:

$$(A \times B)^\dagger = A^\dagger \times B^\dagger, \qquad (2.10\text{–}4)$$

[compare the (jp) row and (kq) column of both sides].

(6) If A and B are unitary, the product is also unitary:

$$(A \times B)^\dagger(A \times B) = (A^\dagger A) \times (B^\dagger B) = E.$$

Returning to representations, we define a *direct product* of two representations Γ_α and Γ_β so that the direct product is a set of Kronecker products $D(P) = D^\alpha(P) \times D^\beta(P)$. The direct product is also a representation of the group, since

$$D^\gamma(P)D^\gamma(Q) = \{D^\alpha(P) \times D^\beta(P)\}\{D^\alpha(Q) \times D^\beta(Q)\}$$
$$= \{D^\alpha(P)D^\alpha(Q)\} \times \{D^\beta(P)D^\beta(Q)\} = D^\gamma(PQ).$$

The direct-product representation is denoted as $\Gamma_\gamma = \Gamma_\alpha \times \Gamma_\beta$. The character $\chi^\gamma(P)$ of the direct-product representation is simply given by the product:

$$\chi^\gamma(P) = \chi^\alpha(P) \cdot \chi^\beta(P). \qquad (2.10\text{–}5)$$

2.11 THEOREMS CONCERNING CHARACTERS

Theorem 2.11–1 (ORTHOGONALITY OF CHARACTERS)

The characters $\chi^\alpha(P)$ and $\chi^\beta(P)$ of two irreducible representations Γ_α and Γ_β are related through the orthogonality relations

$$\sum_P \chi^\alpha(P)^* \chi^\beta(P) = g\delta_{\alpha\beta}, \qquad (2.11\text{–}1)$$

where P is summed over all elements.

Proof: One can easily prove (2.11–1) by summing (2.9–4) over m and m' for the case $m = n$, and $m' = n'$.

The relation (2.11–1) is also written in the form

$$\sum_{i=1}^{q} g_i \chi_i^{\alpha *} \chi_i^{\beta} = g\delta_{\alpha\beta}, \tag{2.11-2}$$

where i is summed over all classes; q is the number of classes; g_i is the order of the class C_i. Equation (2.11–2) is further modified as

$$\sum_{i=1}^{q} \left(\sqrt{\frac{g_i}{g}}\, \chi_i^{\alpha}\right)^* \left(\sqrt{\frac{g_i}{g}}\, \chi_i^{\beta}\right) = \delta_{\alpha\beta}. \tag{2.11-3}$$

Theorem 2.11–2: For a given finite group, the number of classes q is not less than the number of irreducible representations r;

$$r \leqslant q. \tag{2.11-4}$$

Proof: The relation (2.11–3) may be understood from the viewpoint that the numbers $\sqrt{g_i/g}\,\chi_i^{\alpha}$, $i = 1, 2, \ldots, q$, form unit vectors in a q-dimensional space. The r vectors obtained from r inequivalent representations are orthogonal because of (2.11–3). The number of vectors r must be less than or equal to the dimension q.

Referring to the class multiplication (2.5–2), we obtain a theorem.

Theorem 2.11–3:

$$g_i \chi_i^{\alpha} g_j \chi_j^{\alpha} = d_{\alpha} \sum_{k=1}^{q} c_{ijk} g_k \chi_k^{\alpha}. \tag{2.11-5}$$

Proof: Let us construct the matrix

$$M_i^{\alpha} = \sum_{P \in C_i} D^{\alpha}(P), \tag{2.11-6}$$

where P is summed over elements in the class C_i. Multiplying (2.11–6) by $D^{\alpha}(R)$ from the left, and $D^{\alpha}(R^{-1})$ from the right, we have

$$D^{\alpha}(R) M_i^{\alpha} D^{\alpha}(R^{-1}) = \sum_{P \in C_i} D^{\alpha}(R) D^{\alpha}(P) D^{\alpha}(R^{-1}) = M_i^{\alpha},$$

or

$$D^{\alpha}(R) M_i^{\alpha} = M_i^{\alpha} D^{\alpha}(R),$$

where R is an arbitrary element in the group. According to Theorem 2.9–2, the matrix M_i^{α} must be a scalar matrix, to be written as $c_i^{\alpha} E$. The trace of M_i^{α} is

$$\text{trace } M_i^{\alpha} = c_i^{\alpha} d_{\alpha} = g_i \chi_i^{\alpha}, \tag{2.11-7}$$

where d_{α} is the dimension of Γ_{α}. Referring to the class multiplication (2.5–2), we have the matrix multiplication

$$M_i^{\alpha} M_j^{\alpha} = \sum_{k=1}^{q} c_{ijk} M_k^{\alpha}.$$

Taking the trace of both sides, we have

$$d_{\alpha} c_i^{\alpha} c_j^{\alpha} = \sum_{k} c_{ijk} c_k^{\alpha} d_{\alpha}.$$

Multiplying this equation by d_{α} and using (2.11–7), we obtain

$$g_i \chi_i^\alpha g_j \chi_j^\alpha = d_\alpha \sum_k c_{ijk} g_k \chi_k^\alpha.$$

Equation (2.11–5) is also written in the form

$$g_i \chi_i^\alpha g_j \chi_j^\alpha = \chi_1^\alpha \sum_k c_{ijk} g_k \chi_k^\alpha, \tag{2.11–8}$$

since $d_\alpha = \chi_1^\alpha$.

2.12 DECOMPOSITION OF A REDUCIBLE REPRESENTATION

A reducible representation Γ of a group may be decomposed into a direct sum of the irreducible representations. The character $\chi(R)$ of the reducible representation is expressible in the form

$$\chi(R) = \sum_{\gamma=1}^{r} n_\gamma \chi^\gamma(R), \tag{2.12–1}$$

where n_γ is the number of times the γth irreducible representation. In order to find n_α, multiplying (2.12–1) by $\chi^\alpha(R)^*$ and summing it over all elements, we find

$$n_\alpha = \frac{1}{g} \sum_R \chi^\alpha(R)^* \chi(R) = \frac{1}{g} \sum_{i=1}^{q} g_i \chi_i^{\alpha *} \chi_i, \tag{2.12–2}$$

where we use (2.11–1); i is summed over all classes. If the characters of all irreducible representations are known, the decomposition of a reducible representation is easily found by (2.12–2);

$$\Gamma = \sum_\alpha n_\alpha \Gamma_\alpha, \tag{2.12–3}$$

where the summation is called *direct sum* of the irreducible representations.

Theorem 2.12–1: The direct product of two irreducible representations Γ_α and Γ_β contains the identity representation only once if the complex conjugate of Γ_α is equivalent to Γ_β.

Proof: Using (2.11–1), we find

$$n_1 = \frac{1}{g} \sum_R \chi^\alpha(R) \chi^\beta(R) = \delta_{\alpha^* \beta}, \tag{2.12–4}$$

If all $\chi^\alpha(R)$ are real, the direct product of Γ_α with itself contains the identity representation.

2.13 REGULAR REPRESENTATION

The concept of *regular representation* is introduced to prove two relations concerning characters:

$$\sum_{\alpha=1}^{r} (d_\alpha)^2 = \sum_{\alpha=1}^{r} (\chi_1^\alpha)^2 = g, \tag{2.13–1}$$

and

$$\sum_{\alpha=1}^{r} \chi_1^\alpha \chi_k^\alpha = 0 \qquad \text{for } k \neq 1. \tag{2.13–2}$$

The relation (2.13–1) is useful in determining the irreducible character for the identity class, i. e., the dimensions of the irreducible representations, in cases of finite groups of low order. The relation (2.13–2) is also useful in determining irreducible characters of other classes.

The regular representation is defined below. Let us name the g elements of a group, **G**, for instance, by numbers $1, 2, \ldots, g$. The group is expressed for convenience as a row matrix $(1, 2, \ldots, g)$. If an element, not the identity, is multiplied on $(1, 2, \ldots, g)$ from the left, the order of the label is completely altered to another order, in which there is no element remaining in its original position. The multiplication is, therefore, equivalent to a label permutation, which is represented by a g-dimensional matrix. The identity element is simply represented by the g-dimensional unit matrix. The matrices for all other elements have a single unity in every row and column and zero elsewhere, in particular zero along the diagonal. The set of these g-dimensional matrices is termed the *regular representation of the group* **G**. The character for the identity is equal to g and all other characters are zero. Using (2.12–2), we find that the number of times the αth irreducible representation in the regular representation is given by

$$n_\alpha = \frac{1}{g} \sum_R \chi^\alpha(R)^* \chi(R) = d_\alpha,$$

where d_α is the dimension of the αth irreducible representation. The αth irreducible representation occurs d_α times in the regular representation; therefore, the character g for the identity is given by (2.13–1). Characters for other elements may be given by (2.13–2). The two relations (2.13–1) and (2.13–2) can be expressed as a single relation

$$\sum_{\alpha=1}^{r} d_\alpha \chi_k^\alpha = \sum_{\alpha=1}^{r} \chi_1^\alpha \chi_k^\alpha = g\delta_{1k}. \tag{2.13–3}$$

EXAMPLE: $\mathbf{D}_3$. The regular representation of $\mathbf{D}_3$ is characterized by the nonzero matrix elements:

$$D(E)_{ii} = 1, \quad i = 1, 2, \ldots, 6,$$

$$D(A)_{21} = D(A)_{12} = D(A)_{53} = D(A)_{64} = D(A)_{35} = D(A)_{46} = 1,$$

$$D(B)_{31} = D(B)_{62} = D(B)_{13} = D(B)_{54} = D(B)_{45} = D(B)_{26} = 1,$$

$$D(C)_{41} = D(C)_{52} = D(C)_{63} = D(C)_{14} = D(C)_{25} = D(C)_{36} = 1,$$

$$D(D)_{51} = D(D)_{42} = D(D)_{23} = D(D)_{34} = D(D)_{65} = D(D)_{16} = 1,$$

$$D(F)_{61} = D(F)_{32} = D(F)_{43} = D(F)_{24} = D(F)_{15} = D(F)_{56} = 1,$$

all other elements being zero.

2.14 MORE THEOREMS CONCERNING CHARACTERS

We shall prove a few further theorems, which are used to determine irreducible characters.

Theorem 2.14–1 (ORTHOGONALITY OF CHARACTERS BETWEEN CLASSES)

$$g_i \sum_{\alpha=1}^{r} \chi_i^{\alpha *} \chi_j^{\alpha} = g\delta_{ij}, \tag{2.14–1}$$

where α is summed over all irreducible representations.

Proof: Summing Eq. (2.11–8) over all irreducible representations, we have

$$g_i g_j \sum_{\alpha=1}^{r} \chi_i^{\alpha} \chi_j^{\alpha} = \sum_{k=1}^{q} c_{ijk} g_k \sum_{\alpha=1}^{r} \chi_1^{\alpha} \chi_k^{\alpha}$$
$$= c_{ij1} g, \tag{2.14–2}$$

where we use the relation (2.13–3). According to (2.5–3), the coefficient c_{ij1} is nonvanishing only for $C_i = C_j^{-1}$ and then is g_i. Equation (2.14–2) then reduces to (2.14–1).

The relation (2.14–1) is interpreted such that the q sets of numbers $(g_i/g)^{1/2}\chi_i^{\alpha}$, $i = 1, 2, \ldots, r$, form orthogonal unit vectors in an r-dimensional space.

Theorem 2.14–2: The number of classes q must be equal to, or less than, the number of irreducible representations r.

Combination of theorems 2.11–2 and 2.14–2 proves an important theorem.

Theorem 2.14–3: The number of classes q in a group is equal to the number of inequivalent, irreducible representations r.

2.15 CHARACTER TABLE

The characters of all irreducible representations for a group are listed in the form of a square array called the *character table*:

	$E = C_1$	C_2	$\cdots$
Γ_1	χ_1^1	χ_2^1	$\cdots$
Γ_2	χ_1^2	χ_2^2	$\cdots$
$\cdots$	$\cdots$	$\cdots$	$\cdots$

(2.15–1)

The rows refer to the irreducible representation; the columns to the class.

The irreducible characters can be determined by the use of four relations—(2.11–2), (2.11–8), (2.13–1), and (2.14–1).

EXAMPLE: $\mathbf{D}_3$. The six elements are classified in three classes; i.e., there are three irreducible representations. There is a unique decomposition of the order six into a sum of three squared integers:

$$1^2 + 1^2 + 2^2 = 6.$$

The three irreducible representations, say Γ_1, Γ_2, and Γ_3, are one-, one-, and two-dimensional respectively, i. e.,

$$\chi_1^1 = \chi_1^2 = 1 \qquad \text{and} \qquad \chi_1^3 = 2.$$

Since the identity representation consists entirely of unity, the other characters χ_2^2, χ_2^3, χ_3^2, and χ_3^3 are determined through (2.11–2), (2.11–8), and (2.14–1). The characters are found to be as listed in Table 2.15–1.

TABLE 2.15–1

CHARACTER TABLE FOR $\mathbf{D}_3$

D_3	E	C_2	C_3
Γ_1	1	1	1
Γ_2	1	-1	1
Γ_3	2	0	-1

NOTE 2.15–1: If two groups have the same multiplication table, they are called *isomorphic*. Two isomorphic groups have the same character table since they have the relations (2.11–2), (2.11–8), (2.13–1) and (2.14–1) in common, although the representation matrices may be different from each other. Two groups $\mathbf{D}_3$ and $\mathbf{S}_3$ are isomorphic.

NOTE 2.15–2: If we can pick up from a group $\boldsymbol{G}$ a set of elements such that the latter set $\boldsymbol{H}$ forms a group by itself, the group $\boldsymbol{H}$ is called a *subgroup* of the group $\boldsymbol{G}$. The number of representation matrices for $\boldsymbol{H}$ is less than that for $\boldsymbol{G}$ if the same basis functions are referred to. An irreducible representation of $\boldsymbol{G}$ is generally further decomposed into a direct sum of irreducible representations of $\boldsymbol{H}$. The decomposition relation is called a *compatibility relation* between $\boldsymbol{G}$ and $\boldsymbol{H}$.

2.16 THREE-DIMENSIONAL ROTATION GROUP

We have proved theorems on representations and characters only for finite groups, but many of these theorems are also valid for the three-dimensional rotation group. Theorems 2.9–1, 2.9–2, and 2.9–3 are valid without modification. The orthogonality relation (2.9–4) is generalized to

$$\frac{\int D^j_{mn}(R)^* D^{j'}_{m'n'}(R)d\tau_R}{\int d\tau_R} = (2j+1)^{-1}\delta_{jj'}\delta_{mm'}\delta_{nn'} \tag{2.16–1}$$

where the integration replaces the previous summation. The three-dimensional rotation group consists of an infinite number of rotations, which are specified with continuously variable angles. Each irreducible representation contains a continuous series of matrices; however, the number of dimensions is finite. There are infinite series of representations, which are denumerable. When the angles are specified with the Eulerian angles, the volume element $d\tau_R$ is given by

$$d\tau_R = \sin\beta\, d\alpha\, d\beta\, d\gamma, \tag{2.16–2}$$

where

$$0 \leqslant \alpha, \quad \gamma \leqslant 2\pi, \quad 0 \leqslant \beta \leqslant \pi. \tag{2.16–3}$$

When a rotation is specified with the angle φ and the direction (θ, ϕ) of the axis, the volume element is given by

$$d\tau_R = 4\pi(1 - \cos\varphi)d\varphi = 8\pi \sin^2 \tfrac{1}{2}\varphi\, d\varphi, \tag{2.16–4}$$

where

$$0 \leqslant \varphi \leqslant 2\pi. \tag{2.16–5}$$

The volume integral of the denominator of (2.16–1) is easily shown to be $8\pi^2$.

The orthogonality for characters (2.11–1) is generalized to

$$\frac{\int \chi^j(R)^* \chi^{j'}(R)d\tau_R}{\int d\tau_R} = \delta_{jj'}. \tag{2.16–6}$$

Decomposition of product representation $\Gamma_j \times \Gamma_{j'}$ is performed along the lines of generalization of (2.12–2); i. e.,

$$n_k = \frac{\int \chi^j(\varphi)\chi^{j'}(\varphi)\chi^k(\varphi)8\pi \sin^2 \frac{1}{2}\varphi\, d\varphi}{\int d\tau_R}. \tag{2.16–7}$$

Using (1.4–8) for characters, we find

$$n_k = \begin{cases} 1 & \text{for } j + j' \geqslant k \geqslant |j - j'| \\ 0 & \text{otherwise.} \end{cases} \tag{2.16–8}$$

This result is in agreement with what we learned in Sec. 1.8.

2.17 THE OCTAHEDRAL GROUP

In Chapter 4 we shall study in detail the case where transition-metal ions are located at a center of octahedral coordination; the present section will therefore treat various aspects of the octahedral group. The octahedral group consists of twenty-four rotations that rotate a regular octahedron (or a cube) into the same configuration. The rotations are classified in five classes:

E: the identity,
C_2: three rotations by π around [001] and the two other equivalent axes,
C_2': six rotations by π around [110] and the five other equivalent axes,
C_3: eight rotations by $2\pi/3$ and $4\pi/3$ around [111] and the three other equivalent axes,
C_4: six rotations by $\pi/2$ and $3\pi/2$ around [001] and the two other equivalent axes (see Fig. 2.17–1).

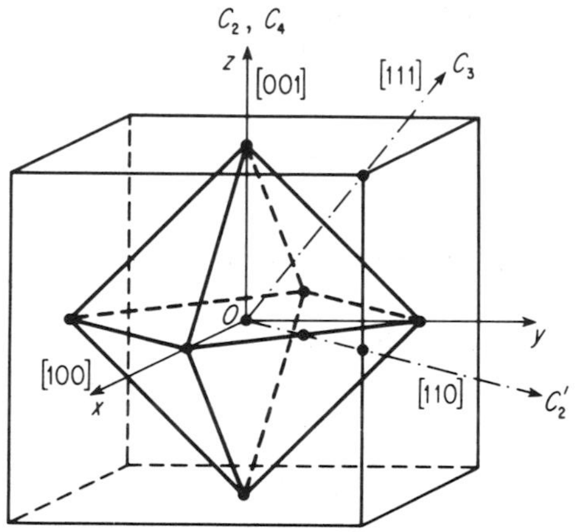

Fig. 2.17-1 Regular octahedron and cube. One rotation axis for each class is shown with the symbols C_2, C_2', C_3, and C_4.

The class multiplications are:

$$C_2C_2 = 3E + 2C_2, \qquad C_2C_3 = 3C_3,$$
$$C_3C_3 = 8E + 8C_2 + 4C_3, \qquad C_2C_2' = 2C_4 + C_2',$$
$$C_2'C_2' = 6E + 2C_2 + 4C_3, \qquad C_2C_4 = C_4 + 2C_2',$$
$$C_4C_4 = 6E + 2C_2 + 3C_3, \qquad C_3C_2' = 4C_4 + 4C_2',$$
$$C_3C_4 = 4C_4 + 4C_2', \qquad C_2'C_4 = 4C_2 + 3C_3.$$

With full use of (2.11–2), (2.11–8), (2.13–1), and (2.14–1), one may find the character table for the octahedral group (see Table 2.17–1).

TABLE 2.17–1

CHARACTER TABLE FOR **O**

O	E	$8C_3$	$3C_2$	$6C_2'$	$6C_4$
A_1	1	1	1	1	1
A_2	1	1	1	-1	-1
E	2	-1	2	0	0
T_1	3	0	-1	-1	1
T_2	3	0	-1	1	-1

The octahedral group **O** is a subgroup of the three-dimensional rotation group $\mathbf{R}_3$. The irreducible representation of the latter group with respect to ψ_{lm} is decomposed into a sum of the irreducible representations of **O**. The characters $\chi^l(\varphi) = \sin(l + \frac{1}{2})\varphi/\sin \frac{1}{2}\varphi$ are listed in Table 2.17–2 for the various classes of **O**. The decomposition of Γ_l into the direct sum of the irreducible representations of **O** is listed for $l = 0, 1, \ldots, 6$ in Table 2.17–3.

TABLE 2.17–2

CHARACTERS $\chi^l(\varphi)$ FOR **O**

	E	C_3	C_2	C_2'	C_4
Γ_l	$2l + 1$	$1(l = 3n)$‡ $0(l = 3n + 1)$ $-1(l = 3n + 2)$	$(-1)^l$	$(-1)^l$	$1(l = 4n, 4n + 1)$ $-1(l = 4n + 2, 4n + 3)$

‡n is a positive integer.

TABLE 2.17–3

COMPATIBILITY RELATION BETWEEN $\mathbf{R}_3$ AND **O**

l	Direct sum
0	A_1
1	T_1
2	$E + T_2$
3	$A_2 + T_1 + T_2$
4	$A_1 + E + T_1 + T_2$
5	$E + 2T_1 + T_2$
6	$A_1 + A_2 + E + T_1 + 2T_2$

Such a decomposition of Γ_l implies that appropriate linear combinations of ψ_{lm} with a given l form basis functions of the irreducible representations that appear in the decomposition. The five functions ψ_{2m}, $m = 2, 1, \ldots, -2$, are grouped into two: one group, consisting of two functions, is the basis for the irreducible representation E; the other, consisting of three functions, is the basis for T_2. The linear combinations will be obtained in Sec. 4.5. In Table 2.17–4, examples of real basis functions are listed for the five irreducible representations of **O**.

TABLE 2.17–4

REAL BASIS FUNCTIONS FOR **O**

Name	Example
a_1	$1, x^2 + y^2 + z^2$
a_2	xyz
eu	$3z^2 - r^2$
ev	$(3)^{1/2}(x^2 - y^2)$
$t_1\, x$	x
$t_1\, y$	y
$t_1\, z$	z
$t_2\, \xi$	yz
$t_2\, \eta$	zx
$t_2\, \zeta$	xy

Transformation properties of these real bases are presented with respect to a transformation of each class in Table 2.17–5. In Appendix 2.1, basis functions for octahedral group **O** are given in terms of spherical harmonics up to order six.

TABLE 2.17–5

TRANSFORMATION PROPERTIES OF REAL BASIS FUNCTIONS FOR THE GROUP **O**

	$C_3^{[111]}$	$C_2^{[001]}$	$C_2^{[110]}$	$C_4^{[001]}$
a_1	a_1	a_1	a_1	a_1
a_2	a_2	a_2	$-a_2$	$-a_2$
eu	$-\frac{1}{2}u + \frac{\sqrt{3}}{2}v$	u	u	u
ev	$-\frac{\sqrt{3}}{2}u - \frac{1}{2}v$	v	$-v$	$-v$
$t_1\, x$	y	$-x$	y	y
$t_1\, y$	z	$-y$	x	$-x$
$t_1\, z$	x	z	$-z$	z
$t_2\, \xi$	η	$-\xi$	$-\eta$	$-\eta$
$t_2\, \eta$	ζ	$-\eta$	$-\xi$	ξ
$t_2\, \zeta$	ξ	ζ	ζ	$-\zeta$

The products of two irreducible representations of **O** are decomposed into a direct sum, as listed in Table 2.17–6.

TABLE 2.17–6

DECOMPOSITION OF PRODUCT REPRESENTATION FOR **O**

	A_2	E	T_1	T_2
A_2	A_1	E	T_2	T_1
E	E	$A_1 + A_2 + E$	$T_1 + T_2$	$T_1 + T_2$
T_1	T_2	$T_1 + T_2$	$A_1 + E + T_1 + T_2$	$A_2 + E + T_1 + T_2$
T_2	T_1	$T_1 + T_2$	$A_2 + E + T_1 + T_2$	$A_1 + E + T_1 + T_2$

2.18 THE THIRTY-TWO POINT GROUPS

The thirty-two point groups are classified as listed in Table 2.18–1. They consist of rotations, reflections, rotatory-reflections, and/or inversion, no translations being included. The eleven point groups of the first column consist of (pure) rotations; the eleven point groups of the second column are isomorphic to the groups in the corresponding row in the first column. The ten point groups of the third column are direct-product groups between those of the first column in the corresponding row and $\mathbf{C}_i$ or $\mathbf{C}_s$.

Let us interpret the point groups in Table 2.18–1.

TABLE 2.18–1

CLASSIFIED THIRTY-TWO POINT GROUPS

First	Second	Third
$\mathbf{C}_1$		
$\mathbf{C}_2$	$\mathbf{C}_i$, $\mathbf{C}_s$	
$\mathbf{C}_3$		$\mathbf{S}_6 = \mathbf{C}_3 \times \mathbf{C}_i$, $\mathbf{C}_{3h} = \mathbf{C}_3 \times \mathbf{C}_s$
$\mathbf{C}_4$	$\mathbf{S}_4$	$\mathbf{C}_{4h} = \mathbf{C}_4 \times \mathbf{C}_i$
$\mathbf{C}_6$		$\mathbf{C}_{6h} = \mathbf{C}_6 \times \mathbf{C}_i$
$\mathbf{D}_2$	$\mathbf{C}_{2h}$, $\mathbf{C}_{2v}$	$\mathbf{D}_{2h} = \mathbf{D}_2 \times \mathbf{C}_i$
$\mathbf{D}_3$	$\mathbf{C}_{3v}$	$\mathbf{D}_{3d} = \mathbf{D}_3 \times \mathbf{C}_i$
$\mathbf{D}_4$	$\mathbf{C}_{4v}$, $\mathbf{D}_{2d}$	$\mathbf{D}_{4h} = \mathbf{D}_4 \times \mathbf{C}_i$
$\mathbf{D}_6$	$\mathbf{C}_{6v}$, $\mathbf{D}_{3h}$	$\mathbf{D}_{6h} = \mathbf{D}_6 \times \mathbf{C}_i$
$\mathbf{T}$		$\mathbf{T}_h = \mathbf{T} \times \mathbf{C}_i$
$\mathbf{O}$	$\mathbf{T}_d$	$\mathbf{O}_h = \mathbf{O} \times \mathbf{C}_i$

(i) $\mathbf{C}_p$ ($p = 1, 2, 3, 4,$ and 6): The group $\mathbf{C}_p$ possesses a single p-fold rotation axis, consisting of p rotations. They are Abelian. If the p-fold axis is chosen as the z-axis, a rotation by $2n\pi/p$ around the axis transforms ϕ into $\phi + 2n\pi/p$, leaving θ unaltered.

(ii) $\mathbf{C}_i$: The group $\mathbf{C}_i$ consists of two elements, i. e., the identity and inversion.

(iii) $\mathbf{C}_s$: The group $\mathbf{C}_s$ consists of the identity and reflection. If the xy-plane is chosen as the reflection plane, the reflection transforms θ into $\pi - \theta$ and leaves ϕ unaltered.

(iv) $\mathbf{S}_{2p}$ ($p = 2$ and 3): The group $\mathbf{S}_{2p}$ consists of $2p$ rotatory-reflections around the $2p$-fold axis. In particular, $\mathbf{S}_2$ is the same as $\mathbf{C}_i$; $\mathbf{S}_6$ is the direct-product group of $\mathbf{C}_3$ and $\mathbf{C}_i$.† If the $2p$-fold axis is chosen as the z-axis, the xy-plane is the rotatory-reflection plane. A rotatory-reflection by $n\pi/p$ transforms θ into $\pi - \theta$ and ϕ into $\phi + n\pi/p$.

(v) $\mathbf{C}_{ph}$ ($p = 2, 3, 4$, and 6): The group $\mathbf{C}_{ph}$ consists of $2p$ elements, i. e., p rotations and p rotatory-reflections around the p-fold axis at angles of π/p. In particular, $\mathbf{C}_{1h} = \mathbf{C}_s$.

(vi) $\mathbf{C}_{pv}$ ($p = 2, 3, 4$, and 6): The group $\mathbf{C}_{pv}$ possesses a p-fold axis and p symmetry planes intersecting the p-fold axis at angles of π/p. In particular $C_{1v} = C_s$.

(vii) $\mathbf{D}_p$ ($p = 2, 3, 4$, and 6): The group $\mathbf{D}_p$ possesses a p-fold axis and p twofold axes in the plane perpendicular to the p-fold axis. The p twofold axes intersect at angles π/p. If the p-fold axis is chosen as the z-axis, and one of the p twofold axes is chosen as the x-axis, a rotation around the x-axis transforms θ into $\pi - \theta$ and ϕ into $-\phi$. When p is even, the y-axis is also one of the p twofold axes; a rotation by π around the y-axis transforms θ into $\pi - \theta$ and ϕ into $\pi - \phi$.

(viii) $\mathbf{D}_{ph}$ ($p = 2, 3, 4$, and 6): The group $\mathbf{D}_{ph}$ consists of $4p$ elements, i. e., in addition to $2p$ elements of $\mathbf{D}_p$, p vertical planes which pass through the p-fold axis and intersect the horizontal plane along the p twofold axes, and p rotatory-reflections. The group $\mathbf{D}_{ph}$ is actually the directproduct group of $\mathbf{D}_p$ and $\mathbf{C}_s$. In particular, $\mathbf{D}_{2nh} = \mathbf{D}_{2n} \times \mathbf{C}_i$.

(ix) $\mathbf{D}_{pd}$ ($p = 2$ and 3): The group $\mathbf{D}_{pd}$ contains, in addition to $2p$ elements of $\mathbf{D}_p$, p vertical planes which pass through the p-fold axis and bisect angles between each adjacent pair of horizontal twofold axes. The p planes introduce p reflections and p reflections followed by a twofold rotation in the horizontal plane. The group $\mathbf{D}_{pd}$ consists of $4p$ elements. The group $\mathbf{D}_{3d}$ is the direct-product group of $\mathbf{D}_3$ and $\mathbf{C}_i$.

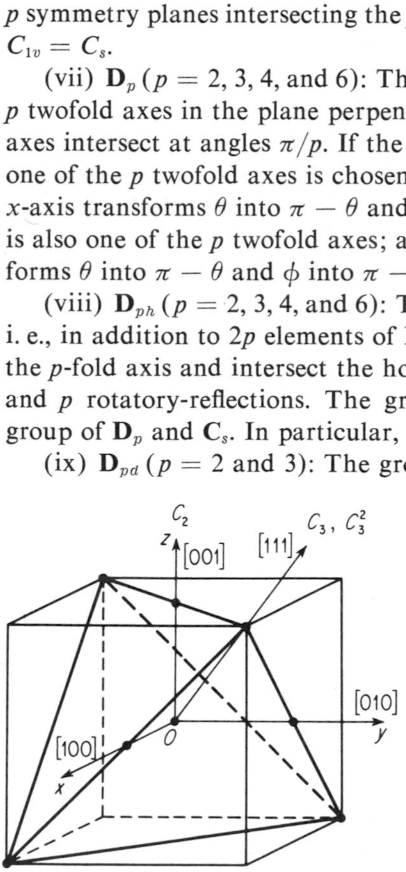

Fig. 2.18-1 Regular tetrahedron and cube. One rotation axis for each class is shown with the symbols C_2, C_3, and C_3^2.

(x) **T**(tetrahedral group): The tetrahedral group **T** consists of the rotations that rotate a regular tetrahedron into itself. The rotations are classified in four classes (see Fig. 2.18–1); that is,

C_1: E (identity),

†A direct-product group is defined between two groups G_1 and G_2. The g_1 elements of G_1 are to commute with the g_2 elements of G_2. The set of $g_1 \times g_2$ products of elements between G_1 and G_2 forms a group, which is called the *direct-product group.*

C_2: three rotations by π around [100] and the two other equivalent axes,
C_3: four rotations by $2\pi/3$ around [111] and the three other equivalent axes,
C_3^2: four rotations by $4\pi/3$ around [111] and the three other equivalent axes.

(xi) **O** (octahedral group): See Sec. 2.17.

(xii) $\mathbf{T}_d$: The point group $\mathbf{T}_d$ contains all symmetry transformations of the regular tetrahedron. The twenty-four transformations are classified in five classes:

C_1: E (identity),
C_2: three rotations by π around [100] and two other equivalent axes,
C_3: eight rotations by $2\pi/3$ and $4\pi/3$ around [111] and the other three equivalent axes,
σ_d: six reflection planes through the center and one of the six edges,
S_4: six rotatory-reflections around [100], [010], and [001].

The group $\mathbf{T}_d$ is isomorphic with the octahedral group **O**. The character table for $\mathbf{T}_d$ is the same as that for **O**, apart from the class classification. Characters for $\mathbf{T}_d$ with respect to ψ_{lm} are different from Table 2.17–2 for **O**; they are listed in Table 2.18–2. Decomposition of Γ_l into the irreducible representations of T_d is the same as Table 2.17–3 for even l, not for odd l; the latter is listed for $l = 1, 3$ and 5 in Table 2.18–3.

TABLE 2.18–2

CHARACTERS OF Γ_l WITH RESPECT TO $\mathbf{T}_d$

	E	C_3	C_2	σ_d	S_4
Γ_l	$2l+1$	$1(l=3n)$ $0(l=3n+1)$ $-1(l=3n+2)$	$(-1)^l$	1	$1(l=4n, 4n+3)$ $-1(l=4n+1, 4n+2)$

TABLE 2.18–3

DECOMPOSITION OF Γ_l FOR ODD l INTO $\mathbf{T}_d$

l	Direct sum
1	T_2
3	$A_1 + T_1 + T_2$
5	$E + T_1 + 2T_2$

(xiii) $\mathbf{T}_h$: The point group $\mathbf{T}_h$ is the direct-product group of **T** and $\mathbf{C}_i$. The twenty-four elements are classified in eight classes: four classes are the same as **T**; the other four are obtained by multiplying the classes of **T** by inversion I.

(xiv) $\mathbf{O}_h$: The point group $\mathbf{O}_h$ is the direct-product group of **O** and $\mathbf{C}_i$. The forty-eight transformations transform the regular octahedron into itself.

If character tables of the point groups in the first column of Table 2.18–1 are found, it is easy to find character tables for other point groups. First, the character tables for the second-column groups are the same as the corresponding ones for the first-column groups. Second, the character tables for the third-column groups are obtained by multiplying the characters for the first-column groups by $+1$ and -1 according to the definition of a direct-product group. For example, one obtains the character table

TABLE 2.18–4

CHARACTER TABLE FOR $\mathbf{O}_h$

$\mathbf{O}_h$	E	$8C_3$	$3C_2$	$6C_2'$	$6C_4$	I	$8IC_3$	$3IC_2$	$6IC_2'$	$6IC_4$
A_{1g}	1	1	1	1	1	1	1	1	1	1
A_{2g}	1	1	1	-1	-1	1	1	1	-1	-1
E_g	2	-1	2	0	0	2	-1	2	0	0
T_{1g}	3	0	-1	-1	1	3	0	-1	-1	1
T_{2g}	3	0	-1	1	-1	3	0	-1	1	-1
A_{1u}	1	1	1	1	1	-1	-1	-1	-1	-1
A_{2u}	1	1	1	-1	-1	-1	-1	-1	1	1
E_u	2	-1	2	0	0	-2	1	-2	0	0
T_{1u}	3	0	-1	-1	1	-3	0	1	1	-1
T_{2u}	3	0	-1	1	-1	-3	0	1	-1	1

for $\mathbf{O}_h$ by multiplying the characters of $\mathbf{C}_i$ by those of $\mathbf{O}$, as shown in Table 2.18–4. The subscripts g and u for the names of irreducible representations are to mean *even* and *odd* parity representations.

The eleven character tables for the twenty-two point groups in the first and second columns of Table 2.18–1 are given in Appendix 2.2.

2.19 DOUBLE POINT GROUPS

In Sec. 1.5 we saw that there is a two-to-one correspondence between characters for half-integral j and rotations of the xyz space. This is also the case for point groups. If angular momentum eigenvectors $|jm\rangle$ with half-integral j are chosen as bases, two distinct representation matrices correspond to every element of a given point group; such a representation is not faithful. The theory of group representation we have discussed is valid only for faithful representations. We can establish a one-to-one correspondence between the representation based on the $|jm\rangle$ and the group that is obtained by augmenting the point group with the artificial element Q introduced in Sec. 1.5. The representation based on the $|jm\rangle$ is then a faithful one for the augmented group, to which the results of the theory of representation can be applicable. Let the new element Q commute with rotations and inversion; then Q also commutes with reflection and rotatory-reflection. Let the square, Q^2, be equivalent to the identity E. The point group augmented by Q is called the *double point group* and is denoted by a prime, as $\mathbf{D}_3'$.

Let us show how to find the character table for the double point group $\mathbf{D}_3'$. Intuitive methods might lead to mistakes. Instead of finding the multiplication table by intuition, we construct the representation with respect to $|\frac{1}{2}m\rangle$. The representation matrices for the six rotations are, according to (1.4–2) and (1.4–4),

$$D^{1/2}(E) = \begin{bmatrix} 1 & 0 \\ 0 & 1 \end{bmatrix}, \qquad D^{1/2}(A) = \begin{bmatrix} 0 & -1 \\ 1 & 0 \end{bmatrix},$$

$$D^{1/2}(E) = \begin{bmatrix} 0 & \epsilon \\ \epsilon^2 & 0 \end{bmatrix}, \qquad D^{1/2}(C) = \begin{bmatrix} 0 & \epsilon^2 \\ \epsilon & 0 \end{bmatrix}, \tag{2.19–1}$$

$$D^{1/2}(D) = \begin{bmatrix} \epsilon^5 & 0 \\ 0 & \epsilon \end{bmatrix}, \qquad D^{1/2}(F) = \begin{bmatrix} \epsilon^4 & 0 \\ 0 & \epsilon^2 \end{bmatrix},$$

where $\epsilon = e^{i\pi/3}$.

The matrix for Q must be

$$D^{1/2}(Q) = \begin{bmatrix} -1 & 0 \\ 0 & -1 \end{bmatrix}, \tag{2.19–2}$$

since $D^{1/2}(Q)$ must be a scalar matrix whose square is the unit matrix. The other five matrices of D_3' are obtained by multiplying (2.19–2) by (2.19–1):

$$D^{1/2}(QA) = \begin{bmatrix} 0 & 1 \\ -1 & 0 \end{bmatrix}, \qquad D^{1/2}(QB) = \begin{bmatrix} 0 & \epsilon^4 \\ \epsilon^5 & 0 \end{bmatrix},$$

$$D^{1/2}(QC) = \begin{bmatrix} 0 & \epsilon^5 \\ \epsilon^4 & 0 \end{bmatrix}, \qquad D^{1/2}(QD) = \begin{bmatrix} \epsilon^2 & 0 \\ 0 & \epsilon^4 \end{bmatrix}, \tag{2.19–3}$$

$$D^{1/2}(QF) = \begin{bmatrix} \epsilon & 0 \\ 0 & \epsilon^5 \end{bmatrix}.$$

These twelve matrices are all distinct and must have the same multiplication table as D_3' (Table 2.19–1).

We can easily classify the twelve elements in six classes:

$$E; \quad Q; \quad C_2 = (A, B, QC); \quad C_2' = (QA, QB, C);$$

$$C_3 = (D, QF), \qquad C_3' = (QD, F).$$

Using relations (2.11–2), (2.11–8), (2.13–1), and (2.14–1), we find the character table for $\mathbf{D}_3'$ (Table 2.19–2). One may note that E_2' is equivalent to $D^{1/2}$, and that the character table for $\mathbf{D}_3$ is augmented by two irreducible representations E_1' and E_2'.

TABLE 2.19–1

MULTIPLICATION TABLE FOR $\mathbf{D}_3'$

	A	B	C	QA	QB	QC	D	F	QD	QF
A	Q	D	F	E	QD	QF	QB	QC	B	C
B	QF	Q	QD	F	E	D	C	A	QC	QA
C	QD	F	Q	D	QF	E	A	QB	QA	B
QA	E	QD	QF	Q	D	F	B	C	QB	QC
QB	F	E	D	QF	Q	QD	QC	QA	C	A
QC	D	QF	E	QD	F	Q	QA	B	A	QB
D	C	QA	B	QC	A	QB	F	Q	QF	E
F	B	QC	QA	QB	C	A	Q	QD	E	D
QD	QC	A	QB	C	QA	B	QF	E	F	Q
QF	QB	C	A	B	QC	QA	E	D	Q	QD

Character tables for double point groups of the first-column groups in Table 2.18–1 are given in Appendix 2.3. Character tables for other double point groups may be found from those for the first-column groups. Appendix 2.3 contains only the augmented characters.

Representations of $\mathbf{O}'$ referred to half-integral angular momentum eigenvectors $|jm\rangle$ may be decomposed into a direct sum of E_1', E_2', and G';

TABLE 2.19–2

CHARACTER TABLE FOR $\mathbf{D}_3'$

$\mathbf{D}_3'$	E	Q	C_2	C_2'	C_3	C_3'
A_1	1	1	1	1	1	1
A_2	1	1	-1	-1	1	1
E	2	2	0	0	-1	-1
E_1'	1	-1	i	$-i$	-1	1
	1	-1	$-i$	i	-1	1
E_2'	2	-2	0	0	1	-1

TABLE 2.19–3

CHARACTERS OF Γ_j FOR $\mathbf{O}'$, HALF-INTEGRAL j‡

	E	Q	C_3	C_3^2	C_2	C_2'	C_4	C_4^3
			1	$-1(3n+1)$			2	$-2(2n+1)$
Γ_j	$2j+1$	$-(2j+1)$	-1	$1(3n+2)$	0	0	0	$0(2n+2)$
			0	$0(3n)$			-2	$2(2n+3)$

‡Numbers in parentheses are $j + \frac{1}{2}$.

their characters are listed in Table 2.19–3. The decomposition is given in Table 2.19–4, up to $j = \frac{9}{2}$.

TABLE 2.19–4

DECOMPOSITION OF Γ_j FOR HALF-INTEGRAL j INTO $\mathbf{O}'$

j	Direct sum
1/2	E_1'
3/2	G'
5/2	$E_2' + G'$
7/2	$E_1' + E_2' + G'$
9/2	$E_1' + 2G'$

The decomposition of direct products among E_1', E_2', and G' is given in Table 2.19–5.

TABLE 2.19–5

DECOMPOSITION OF DIRECT PRODUCTS

	E_1'	E_2'	G'
E_1'	$A_1 + T_2$	$A_2 + T_1$	$E + T_1 + T_2$
E_2'	$A_2 + T_1$	$A_1 + T_2$	$E + T_1 + T_2$
G'	$E + T_1 + T_2$	$E + T_1 + T_2$	$A_1 + A_2 + E + 2T_1 + 2T_2$

2.20 APPLICATIONS TO QUANTUM MECHANICS

We shall briefly discuss how group theory is applied in quantum mechanics. A group of transformations that leave the Hamiltonian operator $\mathbf{H}$ of a given system invariant is called the *symmetry group* of the system. For example, the Hamiltonian operator for electrons in an atom is invariant under the three-dimensional rotation group. The single-electron states are classified with a set of quantum numbers $nlm_l m_s$. The $2l + 1$ orbital states with $m_l = l, l - 1, \ldots, -l$ are degenerate because of the symmetry. These $2l + 1$ orbital wave functions are transformed among themselves by a rotation R:

$$R\psi_{nlm_l} = \sum_{m_l'=-l}^{l} D_{m_l'm_l}(R)\psi_{nlm_l'}.$$

When a set of n wavefunctions is an irreducible basis for a symmetry group G of the system, these n wavefunctions must belong to the same eigenvalue of the Hamiltonian operator $\mathbf{H}$. Let the wavefunctions be ψ_i, $i = 1, 2, \ldots, n$. One of these is to satisfy the eigenvalue equation

$$\mathbf{H}\psi_i = E\psi_i. \tag{2.20–1}$$

A symmetry transformation R transforms ψ_i as follows:

$$R\psi_i = \sum_{j=1}^{n} D_{ji}(R)\psi_j. \tag{2.20–2}$$

Multiplying (2.20–2) by $(n/g)D_{ki}(R)^*$, and summing over all elements in G, we have according to Theorem 2.9–4

$$\frac{n}{g}\sum_{R} D_{ki}(R)^* R\psi_i = \psi_k.$$

Multiplying (2.20–1) by $(n/g)D_{ki}(R)^*R$, and summing over all elements, we find

$$\mathbf{H}\psi_k = E\psi_k.$$

This proves that the n wavefunctions are necessarily degenerate. Such a degeneracy due to the symmetry group is termed *due degeneracy*. There is also degeneracy that is not due degeneracy; this type of degeneracy is called *accidental degeneracy*. An example of accidental degeneracy is the hydrogen atom: the energy eigenvalue E_{nl} is independent of the azimuthal quantum number l. The degree of degeneracy is $2n^2$, not $2(2l + 1)$. These $2n^2$ wavefunctions are not wholly transformed among themselves under rotations. The degree of due degeneracy is simply determined by the dimension of the irreducible representation to which the eigenfunctions belong. When the dimensions of all the irreducible representations of a symmetry group are known, the degree of all due degeneracies is also known. This is one of the results of the application of group theory.

Eigenfunctions that are due degenerate are classified according to the transformation properties, which are explicitly specified by the representation matrices. Operators are also classified in the same way. These classified eigenfunctions and operators may be distinguished by a set of three labels $(u\alpha i)$, where the second Greek letter is to designate the αth irreducible representation Γ_α of d_α dimension. The third Roman letter is to designate the ith component of the d_α eigenfunctions or operators; the first Roman letter is to distinguish different types of eigenfunctions or operators that belong to the same irreducible representation. For example, the first Roman letter u is the principal quantum number n for atoms. An eigenfunction $\psi_{u\alpha i}$ is to be transformed by R according to

$$R\psi_{u\alpha i} = \sum_{i'}^{d_\alpha} D^{\alpha}_{i'i}(R)\psi_{u\alpha i'}. \tag{2.20–3}$$

A classified operator $\mathbf{O}(v\beta j)$ may also be transformed by R as follows:

$$R\mathbf{O}(v\beta j)R^{-1} = \sum_{j'}^{d_\beta} D^{\beta}_{j'j}(R)\mathbf{O}(v\beta j'). \tag{2.20–4}$$

Let us prove a theorem.

Theorem 2.20–1 An integral $\int \psi_{u\alpha i}\,d\tau$ is zero unless Γ_α is the identity representation.

Proof: Applying R to the integral and summing over all R, we have

$$g \int \psi_{u\alpha i}\, d\tau = \sum_{i'=1}^{d_\alpha} \int \psi_{u\alpha i'}\, d\tau \sum_{R} D^{\alpha}_{i'i}(R) = 0.$$

where we use Theorem 2.9–4.

In a similar manner, we can prove another theorem.

Theorem 2.20–2: An integral $\int \psi^*_{v\beta j} \psi_{u\alpha i}\, d\tau$ is zero unless $\Gamma_\beta = \Gamma_\alpha$, and $i = j$.

Proof: Apply R to the integral, and sum over all elements. Then, use Theorem 2.9–4.

The $d_\alpha \times d_\beta$ products $\psi^*_{v\beta j}\psi_{u\alpha i}$ are basis functions of the product representation $\Gamma^*_\beta \times \Gamma_\alpha$. According to Theorem 2.12–1, the product representation contains the identity representation only once if $\Gamma_\alpha = \Gamma_\beta$. We can state Theorem 2.20–2 in another way: the integral is zero unless the product representation contains the identity representation. We then have a theorem on the selection rule for symmetry classified operators, as a direct consequence of Theorem 2.20–2.

Theorem 2.20–3: A matrix element $\int \psi^*_{w\gamma k} O(v\beta j) \psi_{u\alpha i}\, d\tau$ is zero unless the direct product $\Gamma_\beta \times \Gamma_\alpha$ contains the irreducible representation Γ_γ, or in other words, unless the direct product $\Gamma^*_\gamma \times \Gamma_\beta \times \Gamma_\alpha$ contains the identity representation.

An irreducible representation of a group G is generally decomposed into a direct sum of irreducible representations of its subgroup H. Turning to basis vectors, we can say that a set of irreducible basis vectors of a group G is generally decomposed into sets of basis vectors for irreducible representations of its subgroup H. Examples of such a decomposition have already been listed in Tables 2.17–3, 2.18–3, and 2.19–4. With reference to Table 2.17–3 we can easily see how orbital degeneracies for a potential of spherical symmetry are removed when placed in an octahedral potential neglecting the spin degeneracy. The octahedral group **O** is a subgroup of the three-dimensional rotation group $\mathbf{R}_3$. When an electron having the orbital angular momentum $l = 1$ is placed in an octahedral potential, the threefold orbital degeneracy is not removed. If the electron has $l = 2$, the fivefold orbital states are split into two groups of orbital states, i. e., E and T_2. More generally, when a system subject to a potential of the symmetry group G is subjected to an additional perturbation potential of a symmetry group H, a subgroup of G, we can see from the decomposition or the compatibility relation between G and H whether, and how, the original degeneracies due to G are removed, apart from accidental degeneracies.

2.21 COUPLING OF TWO IRREDUCIBLE BASES

Two sets of basis vectors $|u\alpha i\rangle$ and $|v\beta j\rangle$ are to transform according to the irreducible representations Γ_α and Γ_β of a group G. The direct product is decomposed into a direct sum

$$\Gamma_\alpha \times \Gamma_\beta = \sum_\gamma n_\gamma \Gamma_\gamma.$$

Corresponding to this decomposition, the $d_\alpha \times d_\beta$ products between the two sets of basis vectors are classified in sets of basis vectors for Γ_γ. In other words, the products $|u\alpha i, v\beta j\rangle$ are linearly expressed in terms of $|u\alpha v\beta, w\gamma k\rangle$ in the form:

$$|u\alpha i, v\beta j\rangle = \sum_{\gamma k} |u\alpha v\beta, w\gamma k\rangle\langle u\alpha v\beta, w\gamma k|u\alpha i, v\beta j\rangle, \qquad (2.21\text{–}1)$$

where the basis vectors are assumed to be orthogonal and normalized:

$$\langle u\alpha i|v\beta j\rangle = \delta_{uv}\delta_{\alpha\beta}\delta_{ij}. \qquad (2.21\text{–}2)$$

We may assume that the transformation is unitary. The inverse relation of (2.21–1) is written as

$$|u\alpha v\beta, w\gamma k\rangle = \sum_{ij} |u\alpha i, v\beta j\rangle\langle u\alpha i, v\beta j|u\alpha v\beta, w\gamma k\rangle^*. \qquad (2.21\text{–}3)$$

The transformation coefficients in (2.21–1) and (2.21–3) may be called the Clebsch-Gordan coefficients of the group G, in analogy to angular momentum coupling. The Clebsch-Gordan coefficients depend on thc choice of basis vectors to which the representation matrices refer. The coefficients do not depend on u, v, or w.

Clebsch-Gordan coefficients for cubic groups are listed in Appendix 2.4. The basis vectors (or functions) used are of types listed in Table 2.17–5.

2.22 WIGNER-ECKART THEOREM

By analogy with (2.21–1), we have

$$\mathbf{O}(v\beta j)|u\alpha i\rangle = \sum_{\gamma k} |u\alpha v\beta, w\gamma k\rangle\langle u\alpha v\beta, w\gamma k|\mathbf{O}(v\beta j)|u\alpha i\rangle, \qquad (2.22\text{–}1)$$

where $\mathbf{O}(v\beta j)$ are classified operators [see (2.20–4)].

We find a set of equations for matrix elements $\langle u\alpha v\beta, w\gamma k|R\mathbf{O}(v\beta j)|u\alpha i\rangle$:

$$\sum_{i'}^{d_\alpha}\sum_{j'}^{d_\beta} D^\alpha_{i'i}(R)D^\beta_{j'j}(R)\langle u\alpha v\beta, w\gamma k|\mathbf{O}(v\beta j')|u\alpha i'\rangle$$
$$= \sum_{k'}^{d_\gamma} D^\gamma_{kk'}(R)\langle u\alpha v\beta, w\gamma k'|\mathbf{O}(v\beta j)|u\alpha i\rangle, \qquad (2.22\text{–}2)$$

where

$$i = 1, 2, \ldots, d_\alpha; \qquad j = 1, 2, \ldots, d_\beta;$$
$$k = 1, 2, \ldots, d_\gamma; \qquad \gamma = 1, 2, \ldots, r,$$

where r is the number of irreducible representations. There are $(d_\alpha \times d_\beta)^2$ homogeneous equations altogether. On the other hand, matrix elements $\langle u\alpha v\beta, w\gamma k|R|u\alpha i, v\beta j\rangle$ lead to equations

$$\sum_{i'}\sum_{j'} D^{\alpha}_{i'i}(R)D^{\beta}_{j'j}(R)\langle u\alpha v\beta, w\gamma k|u\alpha i', v\beta j'\rangle$$
$$= \sum_{k'} D^{\gamma}_{kk'}(R)\langle u\alpha v\beta, w\gamma k'|u\alpha i, v\beta j\rangle. \tag{2.22–3}$$

Equation (2.22–2) for matrix elements $\langle u\alpha v\beta, w\gamma k|\mathbf{O}(v\beta j)|u\alpha i\rangle$ is exactly the same as (2.22–3) for Clebsch-Gordan coefficients. We may conclude that the matrix elements are proportional to the Clebsch-Gordan coefficients:

$$\langle u\alpha v\beta, w\gamma k|\mathbf{O}(v\beta j)|u\alpha i\rangle$$
$$= \langle w\gamma\|\mathbf{O}(v\beta)\|u\alpha\rangle\langle u\alpha v\beta, w\gamma k|u\alpha i, v\beta j\rangle. \tag{2.22–4}$$

The relation (2.22–4) may also be called the Wigner-Eckart theorem for the classified operators.

3

THEORY OF THE SENIORITY SCHEME†

3.1 INTRODUCTION

Matrix elements between two determinants, discussed in Sec. 3.2, are of basic importance in quantum mechanical calculations of many-electron systems. One must note that single-electron wavefunctions used in determinants are orthogonal and normalized.

In subsequent sections we study the theory of the seniority scheme, originally introduced by Racah, by a more general approach. The concept of Kramers pairs, introduced in Sec. 3.3, is fundamental to this scheme, as interpreted in Sec. 3.6. We will make full use of the creation and annihilation operators, which are interpreted in Secs. 3.4 and 3.5. It should be emphasized that matrix relations in the seniority scheme are established in terms of factors that are determined by just three numbers: the total number of single-electron states in a shell, the number of electrons in a given system, and the seniority quantum number of the many-electron states concerned, as shown in Secs. 3.7 and 3.8.

In Sec. 3.9, the concept of the complementary states is introduced in terms of Kramers pair states within the seniority scheme. The complementary transformation, to be defined in Sec. 3.10, will lead to matrix relations between complementary states in Sec. 3.11. As a special case of

†This chapter is an extended version of the article by H. Watanabe, *Progr. Theorect. Phys. (Kyoto)* **32**, 106 (1964).

complementary configurations, half-filled shell systems are subject to several theorems that may be interpreted as a consequence of the symmetry between electrons and holes, as shown in Sec. 3.12.

The accompanying block diagram shows with arrows how each section depends logically on the preceding sections. The numbers refer to the sections.

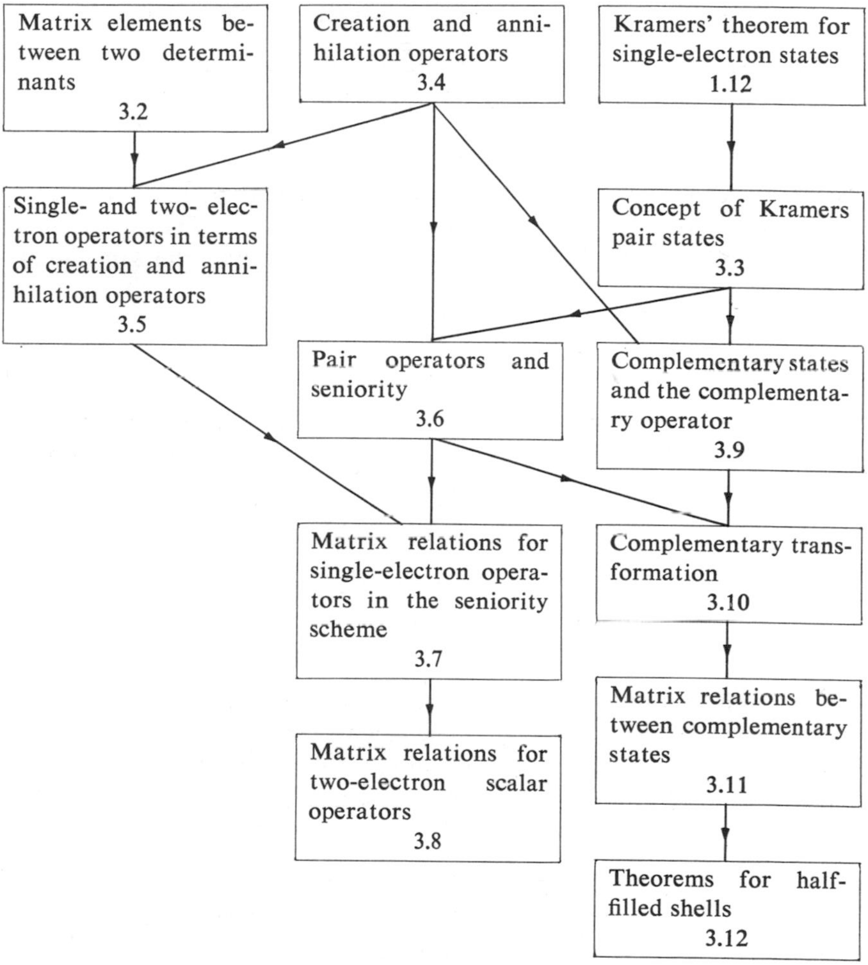

3.2 MATRIX ELEMENTS BETWEEN TWO DETERMINANTS

An n-electron determinant is, apart from its sign, determined by specifying which single-electron states are occupied by the n electrons.

In order to fix the sign, we name the single-electron states with $1, 2, \ldots, i, \ldots, j, \ldots, k, \ldots$, and arrange the order of single-electron states in the determinant

$$\Psi_{i, j, \ldots, k} = (n!)^{-1/2} \begin{vmatrix} \psi_i(x_1) & \psi_i(x_2) & \ldots & \psi_i(x_n) \\ \psi_j(x_1) & \psi_j(x_2) & \ldots & \\ \cdots & \cdots & \cdots & \cdots \\ \psi_k(x_1) & \psi_k(x_2) & \ldots & \end{vmatrix} \tag{3.2–1}$$

so that always $i < j < \cdots < k$. We shall call this sequence a *standard sequence*. The x_m stands for three coordinates and spin of the mth electron. The single-electron wavefunctions are to be orthogonal and normalized. The factor $(n!)^{-1/2}$ is for the normalization of the determinant. It is obvious that the determinant reverses its sign for every permutation of two electrons as well as of two single-electron states. The determinant identically vanishes when two electrons occupy one and the same single-electron state.

A *single-electron operator* **F** is defined as

$$\mathbf{F} = \sum_{\mu} f(x_\mu), \tag{3.2–2}$$

where μ is summed over n electrons, and $f(x_\mu)$ is an operator pertaining to the μth electron. The functional form of f is common to all the electrons. A *two-electron operator* **G** is defined by

$$\mathbf{G} = \sum_{\mu > \nu} g(x_\mu, x_\nu), \tag{3.2–3}$$

where the summation is over all electron pairs. The operator $g(x_\mu, x_\nu)$ is symmetric to the μth and νth electrons, i.e.,

$$g(x_\mu, x_\nu) = g(x_\nu, x_\mu). \tag{3.2–4}$$

Coulomb interaction between electrons $\sum e^2/r_{\mu\nu}$ is an example of **G**.

Let us list matrix elements of **F** and **G** with respect to two determinants. One can prove the relations by expanding the determinants by the Laplace expansion theorem.† When two determinants are the same, the matrix element of **F** is

$$\langle P|\mathbf{F}|P\rangle = \sum \langle p|f|p\rangle, \tag{3.2–5}$$

where P stands for a determinant, and p is summed over the single-electron states present in P. The matrix element $\langle p|f|p\rangle$ is

$$\langle p|f|p\rangle = \int \psi_p^*(x) f(x) \psi_p(x)\, dx, \tag{3.2–6}$$

where no particular electron name is needed. The integration over dx is to

†See, for instance, E. U. Condon and G. H. Shortley, *The Theory of Atomic Spectra* (London: Cambridge University Press, 1953), pp. 169–173.

contain the summation over two spin states. When single-electron states in two determinants P and P' are the same except that $r \neq s$, the matrix element of **F** is

$$\langle P|\mathbf{F}|P'\rangle = (-1)^{(r)-(s)}\langle r|f|s\rangle, \tag{3.2–7}$$

where $(r) - (s)$ is the number of row displacements to transfer s in P' to the row position that corresponds to the position of r in P. When two or more single-electron states differ between P and P'', matrix elements of **F** are all zero; i.e.,

$$\langle P|\mathbf{F}|P''\rangle = 0. \tag{3.2–8}$$

The diagonal element of a two-electron operator **G** is

$$\langle P|\mathbf{G}|P\rangle = \sum_{pq} \{\langle pq|g|pq\rangle - \langle pq|g|qp\rangle\}, \tag{3.2–9}$$

where the summation is over all single-electron state pairs present in the determinant P. The element

$$\langle pq|g|pq\rangle = \iint \psi_p^*(x_1)\psi_q^*(x_2)g(1, 2)\psi_p(x_1)\psi_q(x_2)\, dx_1\, dx_2$$

is called a *direct integral*; and the element

$$\langle pq|g|qp\rangle = \iint \psi_p^*(x_1)\psi_q^*(x_2)g(1, 2)\psi_q(x_1)\psi_p(x_2)\, dx_1\, dx_2$$

is called an *exchange integral*. When single-electron states in P and P' are the same except that $p \neq q$, the matrix element is

$$\langle P|\mathbf{G}|P'\rangle = (-1)^{(p)-(q)} \sum_{r} \{\langle pr|g|qr\rangle - \langle pr|g|rq\rangle\}, \tag{3.2–10}$$

where $(p) - (q)$ is the number of row displacements to displace q in p' to the row position corresponding to p in P. When two states P and P'' are the same except for two single-electron states p and q in P and r and s in P'', the matrix element is

$$\langle P|\mathbf{G}|P''\rangle = (-1)^{(p)+(q)-(r)-(s)}\{\langle pq|g|rs\rangle - \langle pq|g|sr\rangle\}. \tag{3.2–11}$$

When two states P and P''' differ by three or more single-electron states, then

$$\langle P|\mathbf{G}|P'''\rangle = 0. \tag{3.2–12}$$

3.3 CONCEPT OF KRAMERS PAIR STATES

In Sec. 1.12, we learned Kramers' theorem. For a single-electron system, Kramers' theorem states that when the system is subject to a time-reversal invariant Hamiltonian operator **H**, the energy eigenstates are necessarily at least doubly degenerate. This is obvious since the number n of electrons is now one. The Hamilton operator may be an actual or effective single-electron operator. By "effective" we mean that the individual electrons are considered to move in a common potential in which a certain part of the mutual interaction between electrons is included. The residual part of the mutual interaction is then taken into account with reference to the single-electron states. This procedure is, of course, approximate and has restrictions, yet it is also widely used in studying electronic properties of atoms, molecules, and solids.

If a single-electron statevector $|j\rangle$ satisfies the eigenvalue equation

$$\mathbf{H}|j\rangle = E|j\rangle, \tag{3.3–1}$$

the time-reversed statevector $K|j\rangle$ also satisfies the same equation

$$\mathbf{H}K|j\rangle = EK|j\rangle, \tag{3.3–2}$$

where j is a set of quantum numbers. For example, a statevector $|nlm_l m_s\rangle$ is transformed by K into $|nl\,-m_l\,-m_s\rangle$ with an appropriate phase factor. The phase factor is necessary since otherwise we would have

$$K^2|nlm_l m_s\rangle = K|nl\,-m_l\,-m_s\rangle = |nlm_l m_s\rangle$$

contrary to the fact that K^2 must be -1 for every single-electron state. The statevector $|nl\,-m_l\,-m_s\rangle$ is to be written, just for convenience, as

$$|nl\,-m_l\,-m_s\rangle = |T(nlm_l m_s)\rangle, \tag{3.3–3}$$

where the capital letter T is to reverse the sign of the quantum number whose operator reverses the sign under time reversal. We shall introduce phase factors $\mathcal{E}_j$ of absolute value unity by defining

$$K|j\rangle = \mathcal{E}_j|Tj\rangle. \tag{3.3–4}$$

For instance, phase factors for the $nlm_l m_s$ scheme are

$$\mathcal{E}(m_l m_s) = (-1)^{m+m_s}, \tag{3.3–5}$$

in accordance with Sec. 1.11. Applying K to both sides of (3.3–4), we have

$$K^2|j\rangle = \mathcal{E}_j^* \mathcal{E}_{Tj}|j\rangle, \tag{3.3–6}$$

since $|T^2 j\rangle = |j\rangle$. On the other hand, K^2 must be -1 for every single-electron state; therefore, we find

$$\mathcal{E}_j^* \mathcal{E}_{Tj} = -1 \qquad \text{or} \qquad \mathcal{E}_j = -\mathcal{E}_{Tj}. \tag{3.3–7}$$

For the $nlm_l m_s$ scheme, we have

$$\mathcal{E}(m_l m_s) = -\mathcal{E}(-m_l\,-m_s). \tag{3.3–8}$$

In defining the phase factor $\mathcal{E}_j$, we tacitly assume that the state Tj has the same radial wavefunction as j. We are interested only in the relative phase in physical problems so we may choose

$$\mathcal{E}_j = -\mathcal{E}_{Tj} = i \qquad \text{or} \qquad \mathcal{E}_j = -\mathcal{E}_{Tj} = -i, \tag{3.3–9}$$

where i is $(-1)^{1/2}$. We shall call the two states j and Tj a *Kramers pair*.

We shall then define a *shell* to be a set of Kramers pairs which are due degenerate in energy. The total number N of single-electron states in a shell is necessarily even. We shall name the single-electron states in the shell so that state j is the jth in the set, and its partner Tj is the $(N - j + 1)$th in the set.

An example of such a shell is a set of $2(2l + 1)$ single-electron states degenerate in an nl shell in an atom. Kramers pairs are $(m_l\, m_s)$ and $(-m_l\ -m_s)$. It is convenient to name the $2(2l + 1)$ states in the following order:

name	1	2	...	$\frac{1}{2}N$	$\frac{1}{2}N+1$	...	N
$(m_l\, m_s)$	l	$l-1$	...	$-l$	$\bar{l}$	...	$-\bar{l}$

(3.3–10)

A letter without a bar is for positive spin; a letter with a bar is for negative spin. The $2l + 1$ orbital states are due degenerate on account of the three-dimensional rotation group; additional degeneracy due to two spin states doubles the degree of degeneracy, if we do not consider the spin-orbit interaction.

3.4 CREATION AND ANNIHILATION OPERATORS

Let us consider a shell consisting of N single-electron states. A determinantal function (3.2–1) corresponds to a statevector that only specifies which n single-electron states are occupied with n electrons. The statevector is written as

$$|i, j, \ldots, k\rangle, \tag{3.4–1}$$

where the n single-electron states $i, j, \ldots,$ and k are occupied. We shall call a statevector $|i, j, \ldots, k\rangle$ a *basic statevector* when the sequence is standard.

We define an *electron-creation operator* a_i^+ so that the operator creates an electron in the ith single-electron state into a given basic statevector; for instance,

$$a_i^+ |j, \ldots, k\rangle = |i, j, \ldots, k\rangle. \tag{3.4–2}$$

Equation (3.4–2) may also be written in the form

$$a_i^+ a_j^+ \ldots a_k^+ |0\rangle = |i, j, \ldots, k\rangle, \tag{3.4–3}$$

where the statevector $|0\rangle$ stands for the electron vacuum, which is the state with no electron present in the shell. If we do not have the labels of single-electron states in (3.4–3) in a standard sequence, we will have a phase factor $+1$ or -1, according to whether the permutation for the standard sequence is even or odd. In order to get the correct phase factor, it is sufficient to assume that creation operators a_i^+ and a_j^+ satisfy the anticommutation relation:

$$a_i^+ a_j^+ = -a_j^+ a_i^+ \qquad \text{or} \qquad a_i^+ a_j^+ + a_j^+ a_i^+ = 0. \tag{3.4–4}$$

For example, a two-electron determinant $\Psi_{i,j}$ is reversed in sign under interchange of i and j:

$$\Psi_{j,i} = -\Psi_{i,j};$$

we have the corresponding relation:

$$a_j^+ a_i^+ |0\rangle = -a_i^+ a_j^+ |0\rangle.$$

Let us write the adjoint of (3.4–3) as

$$\langle i, j, \ldots, k| = \langle 0|a_k \ldots a_j a_i, \tag{3.4–5}$$

where a_i is adjoint to a_i^+. The scalar product of (3.4–3) and (3.4–5) is to be normalized:

$$\langle 0|a_k \ldots a_j a_i a_i^+ a_j^+ \ldots a_k^+|0\rangle = 1.$$

The statevector $a_k \ldots a_j a_i a_i^+ a_j^+ \ldots a_k^+|0\rangle$ must be the electron vacuum statevector $|0\rangle$; that is, we may interpret that the adjoint operator a_i annihilates an electron present in the ith single-electron state. The adjoint operator is called the *electron-annihilation operator,* or simply the *annihilation operator*. Based on this interpretation, we have

$$a_j a_j^+ a_i a_i^+ |0\rangle = 0\rangle,$$

and

$$-a_j a_i a_j^+ a_i^+ |0\rangle = |0\rangle.$$

In order to have these two equations compatible, it is sufficient to assume that a_i and a_j^+ satisfy the anticommutation relation:

$$a_i a_j^+ = -a_j^+ a_i \qquad \text{or} \qquad a_i a_j^+ + a_j^+ a_i = 0. \tag{3.4–6}$$

According to (3.4–4) and (3.4–6), a product $a_i^+ a_i$ (or $a_i a_i^+$) commutes with a_j^+ if $i \neq j$. Taking the adjoint of (3.4–4), we have

$$a_i a_j = -a_j a_i \qquad \text{or} \qquad a_i a_j + a_j a_i = 0. \tag{3.4–7}$$

In accordance with the Pauli principle, we cannot have two electrons in one and the same single-electron state; this principle is written in terms of creation and annihilation operators as

$$a_i^+ a_i^+ = 0; \tag{3.4–8}$$

and the adjoint is

$$a_i a_i = 0. \tag{3.4–9}$$

A product operator $a_p^+ a_p$ has the eigenvalue 1 for a statevector $a_i^+ a_j^+ \ldots a_k^+|0\rangle$ if the state p is present among the n states $i, j, \ldots,$ and k:

$$a_p^+ a_p a_i^+ a_j^+ \ldots a_k^+|0\rangle = a_i^+ a_j^+ \ldots a_k^+|\rangle;$$

the product operator $a_p^+ a_p$ has the eigenvalue 0 if the state p is not present:

$$a_p^+ a_p a_i^+ a_j^+ \ldots a_k^+ |0\rangle = 0,$$

since it is impossible to annihilate an electron from an unoccupied state p. A product operator $a_i^+ a_i$ has the eigenvalue that corresponds to the occupation number in the state i. Let us introduce a *number operator* $\mathbf{n}_i$ in the state i such that

$$\mathbf{n}_i = a_i^+ a_i. \tag{3.4–10}$$

A product operator $a_i a_i^+$, on the other hand, has the eigenvalue 0 or 1 according to whether the state i is occupied or unoccupied; that is, we have

$$a_i a_i^+ = 1 - \mathbf{n}_i. \tag{3.4–11}$$

Adding (3.4–10) and (3.4–11), we have

$$a_i a_i^+ + a_i^+ a_i = 1. \tag{3.4–12}$$

Equations (3.4–6) and (3.4–12) are combined into a single relation

$$a_i a_j^+ + a_j^+ a_i = \delta_{ij}. \tag{3.4–13}$$

The *number operator* is defined in the shell as

$$\mathbf{n} - \sum_{i=1}^{N} a_i^+ a_i. \tag{3.4–14}$$

If the N single-electron wavefunctions are bases of an irreducible representation of a symmetry group G, they are transformed under an operator R as

$$R\psi_i = \sum_{k=1}^{N} D_{ki}(R)\psi_k, \qquad i = 1, \ldots, N, \tag{3.4–15}$$

where the set of $D(R)$ is the irreducible representation. In accordance with the transformation (3.4–15), we may define the same transformation for the creation operator a_i^+ as

$$Ra_i^+ R^{-1} = \sum_{k=1}^{N} D_{ki}(R) a_k^+. \tag{3.4–16}$$

The adjoint of (3.4–16) is

$$Ra_i R^{-1} = \sum D_{ki}(R)^* a_k = \sum D_{ik}(R^{-1}) a_k. \tag{3.4–17}$$

We assume that the operators R are unitary.

In a similar way, we may define the time-reversal property of a_i^+ by

$$Ka_i^+ K^{-1} = \varepsilon_i a_{Ti}^+; \tag{3.4–18}$$

and the adjoint is

$$Ka_i K^{-1} = \varepsilon_i^* a_{Ti}. \tag{3.4–19}$$

The number operator $\mathbf{n}$ is shown to be invariant under R and K.

We often have cases where the single-electron Hamiltonian contains no spin operator. The single-electron statevectors then are simply a product of orbital and spin parts. The whole N single-electron states are classified in two sets, each of which consists of $N/2$ states with same spin. We may choose a symmetry group of transformations so that each transformation is concerned only with the orbital part and leaves the spin part unaltered:

$$Ra_i^+ R^{-1} = \sum_k{}' D_{ki}(R) a_k^+, \tag{3.4–20}$$

where the primed summation is over $N/2$ states with same spin as the state i. The matrix $D(R)$ is $N/2$-dimensional, being the same for both two sets. The time reversal transforms a single electron statevector of one set into its corresponding statevector with opposite spin in the other set. The whole N single-electron states form the shell. We have already seen an example of a spin-independent case in (3.3–10) of an nl shell.

3.5 SINGLE- AND TWO-ELECTRON OPERATORS

We shall verify that the following operators are equivalent to a single-electron and two-electron operator within a given shell:

$$\mathbf{F} = \sum_{pq} \langle p|f|q\rangle a_p^+ a_q, \tag{3.5–1}$$

and

$$\mathbf{G} = \tfrac{1}{2} \sum_{pqrs} \langle pq|g|rs\rangle a_p^+ a_q^+ a_s a_r, \tag{3.5–2}$$

where the summation is over all N single-electron states in the shell. Let us prove the equivalence by comparing matrix elements of (3.5–1) and (3.5–2) with the corresponding matrix elements in Sec. 3.2.

A diagonal element of (3.5–1) with respect to a basic statevector $a_i^+ a_j^+ \ldots a_k^+|0\rangle$ is

$$\langle 0|a_k \ldots a_j a_i \sum_{pq} \langle p|f|q\rangle a_p^+ a_q a_i^+ a_j^+ \ldots a_k^+|0\rangle.$$

If q is present among the n single-electron states $i, j, \ldots, k$, the operator a_q multiplied by a_q^+ gives $(-1)^{(q)}$, where (q) is the number of permutations required to transfer a_q to the immediate left of a_q^+; if q is not present, the operator a_q results in the zero vector. In the same manner, if p is present among the n states, we have $(-1)^{(p)}$, where (p) is the number of permutations required to transfer a_p^+ to the immediate right of a_p. If q is different from p, we have the zero vector. When q is p, we have the vaccum statevector with the phase factor unity after all the operators operate. We then find

$$\langle i, j, \ldots, k|\mathbf{F}|i, j, \ldots, k\rangle = \sum_p{}' \langle p|f|p\rangle, \tag{3.5–3}$$

where the primed summation is over the single-electron states present among the n states. The result is exactly the same as (3.2–5).

An off-diagonal matrix element between two basic statevectors $\langle i, j, \ldots, r, \ldots, k|$ and $|i, j, \ldots, s, \ldots, k\rangle$ which differ by one single-electron state is found to be

$$(-1)^{(r)-(s)}\langle r|f|s\rangle. \tag{3.5–4}$$

This is exactly the same as (3.2–7). If two single-electron states differ in the two basic statevectors, we have the zero vector after we operate with all the operators. Matrix elements between two such states are zero in agreement with (3.2–8).

A diagonal matrix element of (3.5–2) with respect to a basic statevector $|i, j, \ldots, k\rangle$ is

$$\tfrac{1}{2} \sum \langle 0|a_k \ldots a_j a_i \langle pq|g|rs\rangle a_p^+ a_q^+ a_s a_r a_i^+ a_j^+ \ldots a_k^+|0\rangle.$$

There are four cases when resulting statevectors are the vacuum statevector with an appropriate phase factor:

1. $(p = i, q = j)$ and $(r = i, s = j)$;
2. $(p = j, q = i)$ and $(r = j, s = i)$;
3. $(p = i, q = j)$ and $(r = j, s = i)$;
4. $(p = j, q = i)$ and $(r = i, s = j)$.

The matrix elements for the first two cases are multiplied by a phase factor 1; those for the last two cases by a phase factor -1. We then find

$$\sum_{pq}{}' \{\langle pq|g|pq\rangle - \langle pq|g|qp\rangle\}, \tag{3.5–5}$$

where we use the relations

$$\langle pq|g|pq\rangle = \langle qp|g|qp\rangle \quad \text{and} \quad \langle pq|g|qp\rangle = \langle qp|g|pq\rangle. \tag{3.5–6}$$

The result (3.5–5) is also exactly the same as (3.2–9).

Other relations (3.2–10), (3.2–11), and (3.2–12) are also found to be in agreement with the corresponding matrix elements calculated using (3.5–2) in a similar way.

We conclude that within a given shell, the operators (3.5–1) and (3.5–2) are equivalent to the single-electron operator **F** and two-electron operator **G** introduced in Sec. 3.2.

The operator (3.5–1) is transformed under time reversal into

$$K\mathbf{F}K^{-1} = \sum \langle p|f|q\rangle^* \varepsilon_p a_{Tp}^+ \varepsilon_q^* a_{Tp} = \sum \langle p|f^K|q\rangle a_p^+ a_q = \mathbf{F}^K \tag{3.5–7}$$

where we use the relation

$$K\langle p|f|q\rangle = \langle p|f|q\rangle^* = \varepsilon_p^* \varepsilon_q \langle Tp|f^K|Tq\rangle, \tag{3.5–8}$$

and replace Tp and Tq by p and q in the second equality. The operator f^K is KfK^{-1}. We also have a similar transformation for the two-electron operator **G** as

$$KGK^{-1} = \tfrac{1}{2} \sum \langle pq|g^K|rs\rangle a_p^+ a_q^+ a_s a_r = \mathbf{G}^K. \tag{3.5–9}$$

Let us define a *scalar* and *tensor operator* with reference to the symmetry group. A scalar operator is to be invariant with respect to the symmetry group, or in other words, to commute with every element of the symmetry group. A scalar operator is to be invariant under time reversal, being written as $\mathbf{O}_s$;

$$R\mathbf{O}_s R^{-1} = \mathbf{O}_s \qquad \text{for every } R, \tag{3.5–10}$$

and

$$K\mathbf{O}_s K^{-1} = \mathbf{O}_s. \tag{3.5–11}$$

When $\mathbf{O}_s$ is a single-electron operator $\mathbf{F}_s$, it is shown that $\mathbf{F}_s$ is proportional to the number operator $\mathbf{n}$ within the shell. The single-electron scalar operator $\mathbf{F}_s$ is represented in an $N \times N$ matrix $D(\mathbf{F}_s)$ within the N single-electron states. The relation $R\mathbf{F}_s R^{-1} = \mathbf{F}_s$ implies matrix relations

$$D(R)D(\mathbf{F}_s)D(R)^{-1} = D(\mathbf{F}_s) \qquad \text{for every } R.$$

The set of matrices $D(R)$ is an irreducible representation; according to Theorem 2.9–2, the matrix $D(\mathbf{F}_s)$ must be a scalar matrix. We may write the operator $\mathbf{F}_s$ in the form

$$\mathbf{F}_s = f_s \sum a_p^+ a_p = f_s \mathbf{n}, \tag{3.5–12}$$

where f_s is a constant. We cannot obtain such a simple relation for a two-electron scalar operator, since two-electron operators are represented in a $\frac{1}{2}N(N-1) \times \frac{1}{2}N(N-1)$ matrix with respect to $\frac{1}{2}N(N-1)$ products of two single-electron statevectors.

A tensor operator $T(\alpha i)$, $i = 1, 2, \ldots, d_\alpha$, is to transform under the symmetry group as

$$RT(\alpha i)R^{-1} = \sum_{i'=1}^{d_\alpha} D^\alpha_{i'i}(R)T(\alpha i'), \qquad i = 1, \ldots, d_\alpha. \tag{3.5–13}$$

When such a tensor-operator is single-electron type, we can show that the diagonal-element sum is zero within the shell:

$$\begin{aligned}\sum_{p=1}^{N} \langle p|f(\alpha i)|p\rangle &= \frac{1}{g}\sum_{p=1}^{N}\sum_{R} \langle p|Rf(\alpha i)R^{-1}|p\rangle \\ &= \frac{1}{g}\sum_{p}^{N}\sum_{i'=1}^{d_\alpha} \langle p|f(\alpha i')|p\rangle \sum_{R} D^\alpha_{i'i}(R) = 0, \end{aligned}\tag{3.5–14}$$

where R is summed over all elements in the symmetry group, and we use Theorem 2.9–4.

When the symmetry group G is spin-independent, a scalar operator is defined so that the orbital part of the operator is invariant under the group. A tensor operator is also defined in the same way. The spin-orbit interaction $\sum \zeta(r_\mu)\mathbf{l}_\upsilon \cdot \mathbf{s}_\mu$ is a tensor operator with respect to the orbital part under the three-dimensional rotation group. The diagonal element sum is zero:

$$\sum_{p=1}^{2(2l+1)} \langle p|\mathbf{l}\cdot\mathbf{s}|p\rangle = 0. \tag{3.5–15}$$

In a similar way, the diagonal-element sum for the spherical harmonic operator Y_{nm}, except for $n = 0$, is zero:

$$\sum_{p=1}^{2(2l+1)} \langle p|\, Y_{nm}|\, p\rangle = 0. \tag{3.5–16}$$

3.6 PAIR OPERATORS AND SENIORITY

The concept of *seniority* was originally introduced into the theory of atomic spectra by Racah in 1943.† In this section, we shall introduce the seniority with the use of *pair operators* to be defined below: the *pair-creation operator* α^+ is defined by

$$\alpha^+ = (2N)^{-1/2} \sum_{j=1}^{N} \varepsilon_j a_j^+ a_{Tj}^+, \tag{3.6–1}$$

where j is summed over all N single-electron states in a shell. The operator α^+ thus creates Kramers pairs. The phase factor ε_j is included to make the operator invariant with respect to time reversal, i.e.,

$$K\alpha^+K^{-1} = (2N)^{-1/2} \sum_{j=1}^{N} \varepsilon_{Tj} a_{Tj}^+ a_j^+ = \alpha^+.$$

The pair-creation operator is also shown to be invariant under the symmetry group:

$$\begin{aligned} R\alpha^+R^{-1} &= (2N)^{-1/2} \sum_{j'} \sum_{Tj''} \sum_{j} \varepsilon_j D_{j'j}(R) D_{Tj''Tj}(R) a_{j'}^+ a_{Tj''}^+ \\ &= (2N)^{-1/2} \sum_{j'} \sum_{Tj''} \delta_{j'j''} \varepsilon_{Tj''} a_{Tj''}^+ a_{j'}^+ = \alpha^+, \end{aligned}$$

where we use the relation (3.3–7) and

$$\begin{aligned} D_{Tj''Tj}(R) &= \langle Tj''|R|Tj\rangle = (K\langle Tj''|R|Tj\rangle)^* \\ &= \varepsilon_{Tj''}\varepsilon_{Tj}^*\langle j''|R|j\rangle^* = \varepsilon_{Tj''}\varepsilon_{Tj}^* D_{j''j}(R)^*. \end{aligned} \tag{3.6–2}$$

Note that we do not need the irreducibility but rather the unitary nature of the representation, and that the pair-creation operator is highly symmetric.

Taking the adjoint of (3.6–1), we define the *pair-annihilation operator* α as

$$\alpha = (2N)^{-1/2} \sum_{j=1}^{N} \varepsilon_j^* a_{Tj} a_j. \tag{3.6–3}$$

The pair-annihilation operator annihilates Kramers pairs.

For example, the pair-creation operator is defined for an nl shell con-

†G. Racah, *Phys. Rev.* **63**, 367 (1943).

sisting of $2(2l+1)$ single-electron states $(m_l m_s)$ as

$$\alpha^+ = [4(2l+1)]^{-1/2} \sum_{m_l=-l}^{l} \sum_{m_s=1/2}^{-1/2} (-1)^{m_l+m_s} a^+_{m_l m_s} a^+_{-m_l -m_s}. \tag{3.6–4}$$

In particular, for the *d* shell, the pair-creation operator is

$$\alpha^+ = \frac{-i}{20^{1/2}} \sum_{j=1}^{10} (-1)^j a_j^+ a^+_{10-j+1}, \tag{3.6–5}$$

where we use the arrangement (3.3–10).

The pair-creation and pair-annihilation operators satisfy the commutation relation

$$[\alpha, \alpha^+] = 1 - \frac{2\mathbf{n}}{N}. \tag{3.6–6}$$

Proof: The nonvanishing terms on the left-hand side are those with $j=k$ or $j=Tk$: these are

$$\frac{1}{2N} \sum_{j=1}^{N} (a_{Tj} a_j a_j^+ a_{Tj}^+ - a_j^+ a_{Tj}^+ a_{Tj} a_j - a_{Tj} a_j a_{Tj}^+ a_j^+ + a_{Tj}^+ a_j^+ a_{Tj} a_j)$$
$$= \frac{1}{N} \sum_{j=1}^{N} (1 - \mathbf{n}_j - \mathbf{n}_{Tj}) = 1 - \frac{2\mathbf{n}}{N}.$$

The pair-creation operator α^+ is used to classify many-electron states differing by an even number of electrons, according to whether the statevectors are related through the pair-creation operator. Two-electron states, for instance, are classified in two: one is generated by applying α^+ upon the vacuum statevector $|0\rangle$ as

$$\alpha^+|0\rangle = N(2,0)^{1/2} \mathcal{E}_1 |2, 0, \gamma\rangle. \tag{3.6–7}$$

The statevector $|2, 0, \gamma\rangle$ is a linear combination of $N/2$ Kramers pair statevectors with proper phases. The other $N(N-1)/2 - 1$ states are not generated from the vacuum. The factor $N(2, 0)$ is for normalization; the phase factor $\mathcal{E}_1$ is for the definiteness of the phase relation between the parent state and the generated state. The first number, 2, in the statevector $|2, 0, \gamma\rangle$ refers to the number of electrons in the state; the second number, 0, is the number of electrons in the parent state. The last, Greek letter γ, is a set of other quantum numbers to specify the state. The quantum number γ is actually redundant for states having the second number zero. The remaining $N(N-1)/2 - 1$ statevectors are to be orthogonal to $|2, 0, \gamma\rangle$ and written as $|2, 2, \gamma'\rangle$:

$$\langle 2, 2, \gamma' | 2, 0, \gamma \rangle = 0 \qquad \text{or} \qquad \langle 0 | \alpha | 2, 2, \gamma' \rangle = 0.$$

This relation implies that the pair-annihilation operator acting upon $|2, 2, \gamma'\rangle$ generates a null vector. The four-electron system has three types of states: one is generated from the vacuum by operating twice with the pair-creation operator; $N(N-1)/2 - 1$ statevectors are generated from

$|2, 2, \gamma'\rangle$; the remaining statevectors are not generated from the statevectors of fewer-electron states. Applying the pair-creation operator on N single-electron statevectors, we have N three-electron statevectors:

$$\alpha^+|1, 1, \gamma\rangle = N(3, 1)^{1/2}\mathcal{E}_1|3, 1, \gamma\rangle.$$

The remaining statevectors $|3, 3, \gamma'\rangle$ must be orthogonal to $|3, 1, \gamma\rangle$. In so doing, we can classify many-electron states according to the number of electrons present in the parent state. We shall call this number the *seniority* of a whole series of states that are related through the pair-creation operator α^+. In general, we generate a normalized statevector with seniority v of an n-electron system through

$$|n, v, \gamma\rangle = \frac{[N(n, v)]^{-1/2}}{\mathcal{E}_1\mathcal{E}_2 \ldots \mathcal{E}_{(n-v)/2}}(\alpha^+)^{(n-v)/2}|v, v, \gamma\rangle, \tag{3.6–8}$$

where operators for the set of quantum numbers γ must commute with α^+, and the parent statevector $|v, v, \gamma\rangle$ is normalized. Note that

$$\alpha|v, v, \gamma\rangle = 0; \tag{3.6–9}$$

and the adjoint is

$$\langle v, v, \gamma|\alpha^+ = 0. \tag{3.6–10}$$

Let us calculate the normalization factor $N(n, v)$. Taking a scalar product of $\langle v, v, \gamma|\alpha^{(n-v)/2}$ and $(\alpha^+)^{(n-v)/2}|v, v, \gamma\rangle$, we have

$$N(n, v) = \langle v, v, \gamma|\alpha^{(n-v)/2}(\alpha^+)^{(n-v)/2}|v, v, \gamma\rangle. \tag{3.6–11}$$

A product $\alpha^p(\alpha^+)^p$, with an integer p, can be reduced to a sum:

$$\begin{aligned}\alpha^p(\alpha^+)^p &= \alpha^{p-1}\left(\alpha^+\alpha + 1 - \frac{2\mathbf{n}}{N}\right)(\alpha^+)^{p-1} \\ &= \alpha^{p-1}\sum_{i=0}^{p-1}(\alpha^+)^i\left(1 - \frac{2\mathbf{n}}{N}\right)(\alpha^+)^{p-i-1} + \alpha^{p-1}(\alpha^+)^p\alpha.\end{aligned} \tag{3.6–12}$$

The normalization constant $N(n, v)$ of (3.6–11) is related to $N(n-2, v)$ in a recurrent form:

$$\begin{aligned}N(n, v) &= \langle v, v, \gamma|\alpha^{[(n-v)/2]-1}(\alpha^+)^{[(n-v)/2]-1}|v, v, \gamma\rangle \\ &\quad \times \sum_{i=0}^{[(n-v)/2]-1}\left\{1 - \frac{2(n-2i-2)}{N}\right\} \\ &= \left\{\frac{(n-v)(N-n-v+2)}{2N}\right\}N(n-2, v).\end{aligned} \tag{3.6–13}$$

With successive products of (3.6–13), we finally obtain

$$N(n, v) = \prod_{i=1}^{(n-v)/2}\left\{\frac{i(N-2v-2i+2}{N}\right\}. \tag{3.6–14}$$

For example, we have

$$N(v+2, v) = \frac{N-2v}{N}, \tag{3.6–14a}$$

and

$$N(v+4, v) = \frac{2(N-2v)(N-2v-2)}{N^2}. \tag{3.6–14b}$$

We are now able to find a whole series of statevectors with the same seniority according to (3.6–8) and (3.6–14), if the parent statevectors are available.

According to (3.6–14), we have

$$N(n, v) = 0 \qquad \text{for } n > N - v; \tag{3.6–15}$$

that is,

$$(\alpha^+)^{(n-v)/2}|v, v, \gamma\rangle = 0 \qquad \text{for } n > N - v. \tag{3.6–16}$$

If the seniority is given, the number of electrons must be in the range:

$$N - v \geqslant n \geqslant v. \tag{3.6–17}$$

The maximum seniority $N/2$ is possible for a half-filled shell.

In a statevector $|N - v, v, \gamma\rangle$, there are $(N - 2v)/2$ Kramers pairs generated by applying $(\alpha^+)^{(N-2v)/2}$ upon $|v, v, \gamma\rangle$. If these pairs are annihilated by $\alpha^{(n-v)/2}$, the resulting statevector is

$$\alpha^{(n-v)/2}|N - v, v, \gamma\rangle = N(n, v)^{1/2}\delta(N - n, v)|N - n, v, \gamma\rangle, \tag{3.6–18}$$

where the phase factor $\delta(N - n, v)$ is given by

$$\delta(N - n, v) = \frac{\varepsilon_1 \ldots \varepsilon_{(N-n-v)/2}}{\varepsilon_1 \ldots \varepsilon_{(N-2v)/2}}. \tag{3.6–19}$$

We find the normalization factor of (3.6–18), using

$$(\alpha^+)^p\alpha^p = (\alpha^+)^{p-1}\left\{\alpha^p\alpha^+ - \sum_{i=0}^{p-1}\alpha^i\left(\frac{N-2\mathbf{n}}{N}\right)\alpha^{p-i-1}\right\}.$$

We find the phase factor (3.6–19) by taking a scalar product of the adjoint of (3.6–18) and

$$N(N-n, n)^{-1/2}(\alpha^+)^{(N-n-v)/2}|v, v, \gamma\rangle = \varepsilon_1 \ldots \varepsilon_{(N-n-v)/2}|N - n, v, \gamma\rangle.$$

Example of d shell. There are ten configurations possible. The Russell-Saunders multiplets are listed in Table 3.6–1. In Sec. 3.8, we shall show that the quantum numbers L, S, M_L, and M_S can be specified simultaneously with the seniority. If we name the ten single-electron states according to (3.3–10), we have the phase factors listed in Table 3.6–2. The pair-creation operator α^+ is

$$\alpha^+ = \frac{i}{(5)^{1/2}}(a_1^+a_{10}^+ - a_2^+a_9^+ + a_3^+a_8^+ - a_4^+a_7^+ + a_5^+a_6^+);$$

the pair-annihilation operator α is

$$\alpha = \frac{i}{(5)^{1/2}}(a_1 a_{10} - a_2 a_9 + a_3 a_8 - a_4 a_7 + a_5 a_6).$$

TABLE 3.6–1

RUSSELL-SAUNDERS MULTIPLETS OF d^n CONFIGURATIONS†

d^0, d^{10}	${}^1_0S$
d^2, d^8	${}^1_0S$ ${}^1_2DG$ ${}^3_2PF$
d^4, d^6	${}^1_0S$ ${}^1_2DG$ ${}^3_2PF$ ${}^1_4SDFGI$ ${}^3_4PDFGH$ ${}^5_4D$
d^1, d^9	${}^2_1D$
d^3, d^7	${}^2_1D$ ${}^2_3PDFGH$ ${}^4_3PF$
d^5	${}^2_1D$ ${}^2_3PDFGH$ ${}^4_3PF$ ${}^2_5SDFGI$ ${}^4_5DG$ ${}^6_5S$

†Multiplets are designated as ${}^{2S+1}_{v}L$, v being the seniority.

TABLE 3.6–2

NAMES AND PHASE FACTORS FOR TEN SINGLE-ELECTRON STATES OF d SHELL

Name	1	2	3	4	5	6	7	8	9	10
$m_l\, m_s$	2	1	0	−1	−2	$\bar{2}$	$\bar{1}$	$\bar{0}$	$-\bar{1}$	$-\bar{2}$
Phase	i	$-i$	i	$-i$	i	$-i$	i	$-i$	i	$-i$

Normalization factors are

$$N(2, 0) = 1, \qquad N(4, 0) = \tfrac{8}{5}, \qquad N(4, 2) = \tfrac{3}{5},$$

$$N(3, 1) = \tfrac{4}{5}, \qquad N(5, 1) = \tfrac{24}{25}, \qquad N(5, 3) = \tfrac{2}{5}.$$

The squared operator $(\alpha^+)^2$ is

$$(\alpha^+)^2 = \tfrac{2}{5}(a_1^+ a_{10}^+ a_2^+ a_9^+ - a_1^+ a_{10}^+ a_3^+ a_8^+ + a_1^+ a_{10}^+ a_4^+ a_7^+$$

$$- a_1^+ a_{10}^+ a_5^+ a_6^+ + a_2^+ a_9^+ a_3^+ a_8^+ - a_2^+ a_9^+ a_4^+ a_7^+ + a_2^+ a_9^+ a_5^+ a_6^+$$

$$+ a_3^+ a_8^+ a_4^+ a_7^+ - a_3^+ a_8^+ a_5^+ a_6^+ + a_4^+ a_7^+ a_5^+ a_6^+).$$

For example, a statevector $|d^5\,{}^2_1DM_L = 0, M_S = \tfrac{1}{2}\rangle$ is obtained by applying $(\varepsilon_1\varepsilon_2)^{-1}(N(5, 1))^{-1}(\alpha^+)^2$ upon $|d^1\,{}^2_1DM_L = 0, M_S = \tfrac{1}{2}\rangle = a_3^+|0\rangle$:

$$(\tfrac{1}{6})^{1/2}(|1, 2, 3, 9, 10\rangle - |1, 3, 4, 7, 10\rangle + |1, 3, 5, 6, 10\rangle$$

$$+ |2, 3, 4, 7, 9\rangle - |2, 3, 5, 6, 9\rangle + |3, 4, 5, 6, 7\rangle).$$

Statevectors for more than five electrons will be obtained using a complementary operator to be introduced in Sec. 3.9. Seniority-scheme statevectors for d^n configurations are listed for $n = 1$ to 5 in Appendix 3.1.

3.7 MATRIX RELATIONS FOR SINGLE-ELECTRON OPERATOR

We now know that a whole series of seniority statevectors is related through the pair operator. This observation leads us to the belief that if appropriate commutation relations between an electronic operator and the pair operators are found, matrix elements with respect to $|n, v, \gamma\rangle$ can be related to matrix elements with respect to $|v, v, \gamma\rangle$.

Let us first establish seniority selection rules for single-electron operators. A commutation relation between the pair-annihilation operator α and a single-electron operator **F** is easily found to be

$$[\alpha, \mathbf{F}] = 2^{1/2}N^{-1/2} \sum_{pq} \varepsilon_p^* \langle p|f|q\rangle a_{Tp} a_q. \tag{3.7–1}$$

This is proved by noting that nonvanishing terms are those with $j = p$ and $j = Tp$. In particular cases, we find a theorem:

Theorem 7–1: When **F** is a *t*-reversed,† hermitian operator, or when **F** is a *t*-invariant, antihermitian operator, the single-electron operator **F** commutes with the pair-annihilation operator.

Proof: When **F** is hermitian, we have

$$\begin{aligned}\langle p|f|q\rangle &= \langle q|f|p\rangle^* = K\langle q|f|p\rangle \\ &= \varepsilon_q^* \varepsilon_p \langle Tq|f^K|Tp\rangle.\end{aligned} \tag{3.7–2}$$

Substituting (3.7–2) into (3.7–1), we obtain

$$\begin{aligned}[\alpha, F] &= 2^{1/2}N^{-1/2} \sum \varepsilon_q^* \langle Tq|f^K|Tp\rangle a_{Tp} a_q \\ &= 2^{1/2}N^{-1/2} \sum \varepsilon_p^* \langle p|f^K|q\rangle a_{Tp} a_q,\end{aligned} \tag{3.7–3}$$

where we replace p and q by Tq and Tp in the last expression. If $f^K = -f$, the right-hand side of (3.7–3) becomes $-[\alpha, \mathbf{F}]$. This completes the proof for the first case. The reader may prove the second case in a similar way, using the matrix relation for an antihermitian operator:

$$\begin{aligned}\langle p|f|q\rangle &= -\langle q|f|p\rangle^* = -K\langle q|f|p\rangle \\ &= -\varepsilon_q^* \varepsilon_p \langle Tq|f^K|Tp\rangle.\end{aligned} \tag{3.7–4}$$

It is easily shown that these operators also commute with the pair-creation operator.

The pair-annihilation operator does not necessarily commute with a *t*-invariant, hermitian operator **F**, or with a *t*-reversed, antihermitian operator **F**.

These results are listed in Table 3.7–1.

†Time-reversal invariant is abbreviated as *t-invariant*; time-reversal sign reversed is abbreviated as *t-reversed*.

TABLE 3.7–1

COMMUTATION RELATION BETWEEN **F** AND α

	Hermitian	Antihermitian
t-invariant	$[\alpha, F] \neq 0$	$[\alpha, F] = 0$
t-reversed	$[\alpha, F] = 0$	$[\alpha, F] \neq 0$

Examples for t-reversed, hermitian **F** are the spin and orbital angular momentum operators, and the linear momentum operator.

It is obvious that an operator that commutes with the pair operators α and α^+ can have a simultaneous eigenvalue with the seniority.

We shall call an operator *even* that does not commute with the pair operators, and an operator *odd* that commutes with the pair operators.

A single-electron, odd operator has only matrix elements diagonal in seniority; a single-electron, even operator has matrix elements between states with seniority difference of 0 and 2. The latter statement is obvious since a single-electron operator can change the number of Kramers pairs, at most, by one. Seniority selection rules are

$$\Delta v = 0 \qquad \text{for odd } \mathbf{F},$$

and (3.7–5)

$$\Delta v = 0 \text{ and } \pm 2 \qquad \text{for even } \mathbf{F}.$$

Matrix elements of a single-electron scalar operator are trivial; that is, they are diagonal in the seniority and in the rest of the quantum numbers:

$$\langle n, v', \gamma | \mathbf{F}_s | n, v, \gamma \rangle = \frac{n}{s} \langle v, v', \gamma | \mathbf{F}_s | v, v, \gamma \rangle = \delta_{vv'} n f_s. \tag{3.7–6}$$

Matrix elements of an odd tensor operator **F** are related to matrix elements of the parent states through

$$\langle n, v, \gamma' | \mathbf{F} | n, v, \gamma \rangle = \langle v, v, \gamma' | F | v, v, \gamma \rangle. \tag{3.7–7}$$

This is easily proved if one takes (3.6–8) into account.

To find matrix relations for an even operator, we need more relations. The following two relations are proved by induction:

$$\alpha^p \mathbf{F} = \mathbf{F} \alpha^p + p[\alpha, \mathbf{F}] \alpha^{p-1}, \tag{3.7–8}$$

and

$$\mathbf{F}(\alpha^+)^p = (\alpha^+)^p \mathbf{F} + p(\alpha^+)^{p-1} [\mathbf{F}, \alpha^+], \tag{3.7–9}$$

where p is an integer. These relations are also written in the form:

$$[\alpha^p, \mathbf{F}] = p[\alpha, \mathbf{F}] \alpha^{p-1}, \tag{3.7–8a}$$

and

$$[\mathbf{F}, (\alpha^+)^p] = p(\alpha^+)^{p-1} [\mathbf{F}, (\alpha^+)]. \tag{3.7–9a}$$

Proof: The relation (3.7–8a) is obviously valid for $p = 1$. According to (3.7–1), the commutator $[\alpha, \mathbf{F}]$ contains no creation operator; therefore, we have

$$[[\alpha, \mathbf{F}], \alpha] = 0.$$

This relation is also written as

$$[\alpha^2, \mathbf{F}] = 2[\alpha, \mathbf{F}]\alpha,$$

which is the relation (3.7–8a) for $p = 2$. If we assume for $p - 1$

$$[\alpha^{p-1}, \mathbf{F}] = (p-1)[\alpha, \mathbf{F}]\alpha^{p-2},$$

then we can easily prove (3.7–8a). The relation (3.7–9a) is proved in a similar way.

Using (3.6–14a), we find

$$\alpha\alpha^+|v, v, \gamma\rangle = \left\{\frac{N-2v}{N}\right\}|v, v, \gamma\rangle. \tag{3.7–10}$$

Applying α^{-1} on both sides, we get

$$\alpha^{-1}|v, v, \gamma\rangle = \left\{\frac{N}{N-2v}\right\}\alpha^+|v, v, \gamma\rangle, \tag{3.7–11}$$

except for $v = N/2$, when Eq. (3.7–10) is simply for a null vector. Using (3.7–11), we find for $p = (n - v)/2$

$$\alpha^{p-1}(\alpha^+)^p|v, v, \gamma\rangle = \left\{N(n, v)\frac{N}{N-2v}\right\}\alpha^+|v, v, \gamma\rangle. \tag{3.7–12}$$

We then find a relation for an even operator $\mathbf{F}$:

$$[[\alpha, \mathbf{F}], \alpha^+] = \frac{2c - 4\mathbf{F}}{N}, \tag{3.7–13}$$

$$= -\frac{4\mathbf{F}}{N} \quad \text{for an even tensor operator,} \tag{3.7–13a}$$

where $c = \sum \langle p|f|p\rangle$. The reader may prove the relation (3.7–13), by noting that on the left-hand side there are six types of nonvanishing terms:

$$j = p = q; \qquad j = Tp = Tq; \qquad j = p \neq q;$$
$$j = Tp \neq Tq; \qquad j = q \neq p; \qquad j = Tq \neq Tp.$$

We are now in a position to find matrix relations diagonal in the seniority. Using (3.6–8), (3.7–8), (3.7–12), and (3.7–13) successively, we find

$$\begin{aligned}
&\langle n, v, \gamma'|\mathbf{F}|n, v, \gamma\rangle \\
&= \{N(n, v)\}^{-1}\langle v, v, \gamma'|\alpha^p\mathbf{F}(\alpha^+)^p|v, v, \gamma\rangle \\
&= [N(n, v)]^{-1}\langle v, v, \gamma'|\mathbf{F}\alpha^p(\alpha^+)^p + p[\alpha, \mathbf{F}]\alpha^{p-1}(\alpha^+)^p|v, v, \gamma\rangle \\
&= \langle v, v, \gamma'|\mathbf{F}|v, v, \gamma\rangle + \left[\frac{(n-v)N}{2(N-2v)}\right]\langle v, v, \gamma'|[\alpha, \mathbf{F}]\alpha^+|v, v, \gamma\rangle
\end{aligned}$$

$$= \frac{(N-2n)}{(N-2v)} \langle v, v, \gamma' | \mathbf{F} | v, v, \gamma \rangle + \left[\frac{(n-v)}{(N-2v)} \right] c. \qquad (3.7\text{–}14)$$

In the last equality of (3.7–14) we use the fact that $\alpha^+[\alpha, \mathbf{F}]$ leads the statevector $|v, v, \gamma\rangle$ to a null vector. The second term in the last expression of (3.7–14) vanishes for an even tensor operator; that is,

$$\langle n, v, \gamma' | \mathbf{F} | n, v, \gamma \rangle = \frac{(N-2n)}{(N-2v)} \langle v, v, \gamma' | \mathbf{F} | v, v, \gamma \rangle. \qquad (3.7\text{–}14a)$$

A matrix element $\langle n, v-2, v' | \mathbf{F} | n, v, \gamma \rangle$ is related to $\langle v, v-2, \gamma' | \mathbf{F} | v, v, \gamma \rangle$ with successive use of (3.6–8) and (3.7–8a):

$$\begin{aligned} &\langle n, v-2, \gamma' | \mathbf{F} | n, v, \gamma \rangle \\ &\quad = [N(n, v-2) N(n, v)]^{-1/2} \mathcal{E}_{(n-v+2)/2} \\ &\quad\quad \times \langle v-2, v-2, \gamma' | [\alpha^{(n-v+2)/2}, \mathbf{F}] (\alpha^+)^{(n-v)/2} | v, v, \gamma \rangle \\ &\quad = [N(n, v-2) N(n, v)]^{-1/2} \mathcal{E}_{(n-v+2)/2} [N(v, v-2)]^{1/2} \mathcal{E}_1^* \\ &\quad\quad \times N(n, v) \left[\frac{(n-v+2)}{2} \right] \langle v, v-2, \gamma' | \mathbf{F} | v, v, \gamma \rangle. \end{aligned}$$

We finally find

$$\begin{aligned} &\langle n, v-2, \gamma' | \mathbf{F} | n, v, \gamma \rangle = \mathcal{E}_1^* \mathcal{E}_{(n-v+2)/2} \\ &\quad \times \left[\frac{(n-v+2)(N-n-v+2)}{2(N-2v+2)} \right]^{1/2} \langle v, v-2, \gamma' | \mathbf{F} | v, v, \gamma \rangle. \qquad (3.7\text{–}15) \end{aligned}$$

In a similar way, we find

$$\begin{aligned} &\langle n, v+2, \gamma' | \mathbf{F} | n, v, \gamma \rangle = \mathcal{E}_1 \mathcal{E}_{(n-v)/2}^* \\ &\quad \left[\frac{(n-v)(N-n-v)}{2(N-2v-2)} \right]^{1/2} \langle v+2, v+2, \gamma' | \mathbf{F} | v+2, v, \gamma \rangle. \qquad (3.7\text{–}16) \end{aligned}$$

3.8 MATRIX RELATIONS FOR TWO-ELECTRON SCALAR OPERATOR

In this section we find matrix relations for a *two-electron scalar operator* that is defined through

$$\mathbf{G}_\alpha = \sum_{\mu > \nu} \sum_{i=1}^{d_\alpha} f_{\alpha i}^K(\mu) f_{\alpha i}(\nu), \qquad (3.8\text{–}1)$$

where the tensor operator $f_{\alpha i}$, $i = 1, 2, \ldots, d_\alpha$, is to transform under a transformation R of the symmetry group through the relation:

$$R f_{\alpha i} R^{-1} = \sum_{j=1}^{d_\alpha} D_{ji}^\alpha(R) f_{\alpha j}. \qquad (3.8\text{–}2)$$

The superscript K is for the time-reversed operator. The two-electron scalar operator (3.8–1) is invariant under the symmetry group:

$$RG_\alpha R^{-1} = G_\alpha,$$

where we use the relations

$$Rf^K_{\alpha i}R^{-1} = KRf_{\alpha i}R^{-1}K^{-1} = \sum_{j=1}^{d_\alpha} D_{ji}(R)^* f^K_{\alpha j},$$

and

$$\sum_{i=1}^{d_\alpha} D^\alpha_{ki}(R)^* D^\alpha_{ji}(R) = \delta_{jk}.$$

Using (3.5–2), the two-electron scalar operator $\mathbf{G}_\alpha$ is written in the form:

$$\mathbf{G}_\alpha = \tfrac{1}{2}\sum_{i=1}^{d_\alpha} F^K_{\alpha i}F_{\alpha i} - \tfrac{1}{2}f^2_\alpha \mathbf{n}, \qquad (3.8\text{–}3)$$

where

$$F_{\alpha i} = \sum_{pr=1}^{N} \langle p|f_{\alpha i}|r\rangle a^+_p a_r, \qquad (3.8\text{–}4)$$

and

$$f^2_\alpha = \sum_{q=1}^{N}\sum_{i=1}^{d_\alpha} \langle p|f^K_{\alpha i}|q\rangle\langle q|f_{\alpha i}|p\rangle. \qquad (3.8\text{–}5)$$

The second term in (3.8–3) is derived from the observation that it is a single-electron scalar operator. The quantity (3.8–5) is independent of any particular p.

When the operator f in $\mathbf{G}$ is scalar, the two-electron scalar operator is written as

$$\mathbf{G}_s = \tfrac{1}{2}\sum_{pq=1}^{N} f^2_s a^+_p a^+_q a_q a_p = \tfrac{1}{2}f^2_s \mathbf{n}(\mathbf{n}-1). \qquad (3.8\text{–}6)$$

The matrix elements are diagonal in every quantum number and are proportional to $n(n-1)/2$. These two types of operators (3.8–3) and (3.8–6) will appear in Sec. 4.9 in the expansion of Coulomb interaction between electrons.

If the tensor operator f is odd, the matrix elements of $\mathbf{G}_\alpha$ must be diagonal in the seniority, being given by

$$\langle n, v, \gamma|\mathbf{G}_\alpha|n, v, \gamma\rangle = \langle v, v, \gamma|\mathbf{G}_\alpha|v, v, \gamma\rangle - \tfrac{1}{2}f^2_\alpha(n-v). \qquad (3.8\text{–}7)$$

When the relation (3.8–3) lacks the second term, matrix relation (3.8–7) is simplified to

$$\langle n, v, \gamma|\mathbf{G}_\alpha|n, v, \gamma\rangle = \langle v, v, \gamma|\mathbf{G}_\alpha|v, v, \gamma\rangle. \qquad (3.8\text{–}7a)$$

An example of (3.8–7a) is the squared spin operator $\mathbf{S}^2$, which is written in the form

$$\mathbf{S}^2 = -\sum_{i=-1}^{1} S^K_{1i}S_{1i},$$

where

$$S_{11} = -(\tfrac{1}{2})^{1/2}(S_x + iS_y), \quad S_{10} = S_z, \quad S_{1-1} = (\tfrac{1}{2})^{1/2}(S_x - iS_y).$$

The quantum number for $\mathbf{S}^2$ is the same for both generated and parent states.

When the tensor operator f is even, matrix relations for $\mathbf{G}_\alpha$ are given as follows. Using (3.7–14a), (3.7–15), and (3.7–16), we have

$$\begin{aligned}\langle n, v, \gamma|\mathbf{G}_\alpha|n, v-4, \gamma\rangle &= \mathcal{E}_1\mathcal{E}_2\mathcal{E}^*_{(n-v+2)/2}\mathcal{E}^*_{(n-v+4)/2} \\ &\times \left[\frac{(n-v+2)(n-v+4)(N-n-v+2)(N-n-v+4)}{8(N-2v+2)(N-2v+4)}\right]^{1/2} \\ &\times \langle v, v, \gamma|\mathbf{G}_\alpha|v, v-4, \gamma\rangle, \end{aligned} \tag{3.8–8}$$

$$\begin{aligned}\langle n, v, \gamma|\mathbf{G}_\alpha|n, v-2, \gamma\rangle &= \mathcal{E}_1\mathcal{E}^*_{(n-v+2)/2}\frac{N-2n}{N-2v}\left[\frac{(n-v+2)(N-n-v+2)}{2(N-2v+2)}\right]^{1/2} \\ &\times \langle v, v, \gamma|\mathbf{G}_\alpha|v, v-2, \gamma\rangle. \end{aligned} \tag{3.8–9}$$

For matrix elements diagonal in the seniority, we find

$$\langle n, v, \gamma|\mathbf{G}_\alpha|n, v, \gamma\rangle = \langle v, v, \gamma|\mathbf{G}_\alpha|v, v, \gamma\rangle + G_\alpha(n, v) - \frac{f_\alpha^2(n-v)}{2}, \tag{3.8–10}$$

where

$$\begin{aligned}G_\alpha(n, v) = (n-v)(N-n-v)\sum_{i,\gamma'} &\left[\frac{-2}{(N-2v)^2}\langle v, v, \gamma|F^K_{\alpha i}|v, v, \gamma'\rangle\langle v, v, \gamma'|F_{\alpha i}|v, v, \gamma\rangle\right. \\ &+ \frac{1}{4(N-2v+2)}\langle v, v, \gamma|F^K_{\alpha i}|v, v-2, \gamma'\rangle\langle v, v-2, \gamma'|F_{\alpha i}|v, v, \gamma\rangle \\ &+ \frac{1}{4(N-2v-2)}\langle v+2, v, \gamma|F^K_{\alpha i}|v+2, v+2, \gamma'\rangle \\ &\left.\times \langle v+2, v+2, \gamma'|F_{\alpha i}|v+2, v, \gamma\rangle\right].\end{aligned}$$

An example is the electrostatic interaction between electrons. In the nlm_lm_s scheme, it is convenient to expand the interaction in terms of spherical harmonics:

$$\sum_{\mu>\nu}\frac{e^2}{r_{\mu\nu}} = \sum_{\mu>\nu}\sum_{n=0}^{\infty} e^2\frac{r_<^n}{r_>^{n+1}}\left(\frac{4\pi}{2n+1}\right)\sum_{m=-n}^{n}(-1)^m Y_{nm}(\mu)Y_{n-m}(\nu), \tag{3.8–11}$$

where $r_<$ is the lesser and $r_>$ is the greater of r_μ and r_ν from the origin. One may verify that spherical harmonic operators are even tensor operators, except for $n = 0$. Matrix elements for the electrostatic interaction are not necessarily diagonal in the seniority, yet they are diagonal in L, M_L, and S, M_S, since the interaction is invariant under the three-dimensional rotation group and independent of the spin. Theoretical electrostatic

TABLE 3.8–1

THEORETICAL ELECTROSTATIC ENERGIES FOR RUSSELL-SAUNDERS TERMS OF d^n, $n = 2$ TO 5

n	Term	Energy
2	${}^{3}_{2}F$	$A - 8B$
	${}^{3}_{2}P$	$A + 7B$
	${}^{1}_{2}G$	$A + 4B + 2C$
	${}^{1}_{2}D$	$A - 3B + 2C$
	${}^{1}_{0}S$	$A + 14B + 7C$
3	${}^{4}_{3}F$	$3A - 15B$
	${}^{4}_{3}P$	$3A$
	${}^{2}_{3}H$, ${}^{2}_{3}P$	$3A - 6B + 3C$
	${}^{2}_{3}G$	$3A - 11B + 3C$
	${}^{2}_{3}F$	$3A + 9B + 3C$
	${}^{2}_{3}D$, ${}^{2}_{1}D$	$3A + 5B + 5C \pm (193B^2 + 8BC + 4C^2)^{1/2}$
4	${}^{5}_{4}D$	$6A - 21B$
	${}^{3}_{4}H$	$6A - 17B + 4C$
	${}^{3}_{4}G$	$6A - 12B + 4C$
	${}^{3}_{4}F$, ${}^{3}_{2}F$	$6A - 5B + 5\frac{1}{2}C \pm \frac{3}{2}(68B^2 + 4BC + C^2)^{1/2}$
	${}^{3}_{4}D$	$6A - 5B + 4C$
	${}^{3}_{4}P$, ${}^{3}_{2}P$	$6A - 5B + 5\frac{1}{2}C \pm \frac{1}{2}(912B^2 - 24BC + 9C^2)^{1/2}$
	${}^{1}_{4}I$	$6A - 15B + 6C$
	${}^{1}_{4}G$, ${}^{1}_{2}G$	$6A - 5B + 7\frac{1}{2}C \pm \frac{1}{2}(708B^2 - 12BC + 9C^2)^{1/2}$
	${}^{1}_{4}F$	$6A + 6C$
	${}^{1}_{4}D$, ${}^{1}_{2}D$	$6A + 9B + 7\frac{1}{2}C \pm \frac{3}{2}(144B^2 + 8BC + C^2)^{1/2}$
	${}^{1}_{4}S$, ${}^{1}_{0}S$	$6A + 10B + 10C \pm 2(193B^2 + 8BC + 4C^2)^{1/2}$
5	${}^{6}_{5}S$	$10A - 35B$
	${}^{4}_{5}G$	$10A - 25B + 5C$
	${}^{4}_{3}F$	$10A - 13B + 7C$
	${}^{4}_{5}D$	$10A - 18B + 5C$
	${}^{4}_{3}P$	$10A - 28B + 7C$
	${}^{2}_{5}I$	$10A - 24B + 8C$
	${}^{2}_{3}H$	$10A - 22B + 10C$
	${}^{2}_{5}G$	$10A - 13B + 8C$
	${}^{2}_{3}G$	$10A + 3B + 10C$
	${}^{2}_{5}F$	$10A - 9B + 8C$
	${}^{2}_{3}F$	$10A - 25B + 10C$
	${}^{2}_{3}D$	$10A - 4B + 10C$
	${}^{2}_{5}D$, ${}^{2}_{1}D$	$10A - 3B + 11C \pm 3(57B^2 + 2BC + C^2)^{1/2}$
	${}^{2}_{3}P$	$10A + 20B + 10C$
	${}^{2}_{5}S$	$10A - 3B + 8C$

energies of d^n terms are listed in Table 3.8–1 for $n = 2$ to 5.† Parameters A, B, and C will be explained in Sec. 4.9. For example, two terms ${}^2_5D$ and ${}^2_1D$ of d^5 are admixed to give the eigenstates of two energies listed. The three ${}^2D$ terms are of seniority 1, 3, and 5. In Sec. 3.12, we shall show that the electrostatic interaction has nonzero matrix elements between states differing in seniority by four, if the system is a half-filled shell. The ${}^2_3D$ of d^5 has vanishing matrix elements with the other two ${}^2_5D$ and ${}^2_1D$ terms.

3.9 CONCEPT OF COMPLEMENTARY STATES AND THE COMPLEMENTARY OPERATOR

Two systems are called *complementary* when one of the two consists of n electrons, and the other consists of $N - n$ electrons in a shell. Complementary systems have many similarities in the statevectors and matrix elements; for instance, the number of states is the same for both systems. We shall introduce an operator that transforms a statevector of the n-electron system into a statevector of the $(N - n)$-electron system in a definite way. The operator is defined to transform a basic statevector $|i, j, \ldots, k\rangle$ into a basic statevector $|(Ti, Tj, \ldots, Tk)\rangle$ that lacks $Ti, Tj, \ldots,$ and Tk from the filled statevector. In other words, the operator is to annihilate, from the filled statevector, the Kramers partners of $i, j, \ldots,$ and k, to give the transformed basic statevector. In particular, the operator must transform the vacuum statevector into the filled statevector and vice versa; the operator must transform a statevector of a half-filled shell system into a statevector of a half-filled system.

These requirements are satisfied by a definition of the operator:

$$C|0\rangle = \mathcal{E}_1\mathcal{E}_2 \ldots \mathcal{E}_{N/2} a_1^+ a_2^+ \ldots a_N^+|0\rangle = \mathcal{E}_0|N\rangle, \qquad (3.9\text{–}1)$$

and

$$Ca_j^+ C^{-1} = \mathcal{E}_j^* a_{Tj}, \qquad j = 1, 2, \ldots, N, \qquad (3.9\text{–}2)$$

where $|N\rangle$ is the filled statevector $a_1^+ a_2^+ \ldots a_N^+|0\rangle$, and the phase factor $\mathcal{E}_0$ is

$$\mathcal{E}_0 = \mathcal{E}_1\mathcal{E}_2 \ldots \mathcal{E}_{N/2}. \qquad (3.9\text{–}3)$$

The phase factor $\mathcal{E}_0$ is introduced for definiteness of eigenvalue of the squared C^2 for statevectors of the half-filled system. The operator C is called the *complementary operator*, or simply the *C-operator*.

It is noted that

$$[N(N, 0)]^{-1/2}(\alpha^+)^{N/2}|0\rangle = \mathcal{E}_0|N\rangle = C|0\rangle. \qquad (3.9\text{–}4)$$

Equation (3.9–1) shows that the C-operator transforms the vacuum state into the filled state. If we further multiply (3.9–1) by the C-operator, we have with use of (3.9–2)

†For instance, see G. Racah, *Phys. Rev.* **62**, 438 (1942).

$$C^2|0\rangle = CCC^{-1}C|0\rangle = (-1)^{N/2}|0\rangle; \qquad (3.9\text{–}5)$$

that is, the C-operator transforms the filled state back to the vacuum state.

If we multiply a basic statevector $|i, j, \ldots, k\rangle$ by the C-operator, we obtain

$$Ca_i^+ a_j^+ \ldots a_k^+|0\rangle = \varepsilon_i^* \varepsilon_j^* \ldots \varepsilon_k^* \varepsilon_0(-1)^{i+j+\ldots+k+n(n-1)/2}|(Ti, Tj, \ldots, Tk)\rangle, \qquad (3.9\text{–}6)$$

where we use the fact that the state Tj is located at the $(N - j + 1)$th among the N single-electron states. Equation (3.9–6) actually shows that the C-operator satisfies the requirements for the definition. The C-operator is defined in the 2^N dimensional space that is spanned by 2^N statevectors for the vacuum through the filled state. Matrix elements of the C-operator are shown to be

$$\langle(Ti, Tj, \ldots, Tk)|C|i, j, \ldots, k\rangle = (-1)^{i+j+\ldots+k+n(n-1)/2}\varepsilon_i^* \varepsilon_j^* \ldots \varepsilon_k^* \varepsilon^0. \qquad (3.9\text{–}7)$$

The matrix for the C-operator is unitary.

Taking the adjoint of (3.9–2), we have

$$Ca_j C^{-1} = \varepsilon_j a_{Tj}^+. \qquad (3.9\text{–}8)$$

Again transforming (3.9–2) with the C-operator, we have

$$C^2 a_j^+ C^{-2} = \varepsilon_j^* Ca_{Tj} C^{-1} = -a_j^+, \qquad (3.9\text{–}9)$$

where we use (3.3–7). Taking the adjoint of (3.9–9), we have

$$C^2 a_j C^{-2} = -a_j. \qquad (3.9\text{–}10)$$

It is easily shown that

$$C^2|i, j, \ldots, k\rangle = (-1)^{(N/2)-n}|i, j, \ldots, k\rangle, \qquad (3.9\text{–}11)$$

since the left-hand side is

$$C^2 a_i^+ C^{-2} C^2 a_j^+ C^{-2} \ldots C^2 a_k^+ C^{-2} C^2|0\rangle.$$

Equations (3.9–5) and (3.9–11) imply that the squared C^2 is replaced by

$$C^2 = (-1)^{(N/2)-n}. \qquad (3.9\text{–}12)$$

In a particular case of $n = N/2$, i.e., a half-filled shell, we find

$$C^2 = 1. \qquad (3.9\text{–}13)$$

This equation suggests that statevectors for a half-filled system can be characterized with the eigenvalue 1 or -1 of the C-operator in some scheme; we shall show that this is the case in the seniority scheme, in the next section.

The C-operator is shown to commute with the time-reversal K and the symmetry group. It may be sufficient to show that KC and RC commute with an arbitrary a_j^+. Transforming (3.9–2) with K, we have

$$KCa_j^+ C^{-1} K^{-1} = \varepsilon_j \varepsilon_{Tj}^* a_j = -a_j.$$

Transforming (3.4–18) with the C-operator, we have

$$CKa_j^+K^{-1}C^{-1} = \mathcal{E}_j\mathcal{E}_{Tj}^*a_j = -a_j.$$

We may conclude that

$$KC = CK. \tag{3.9–14}$$

Transforming (3.9–2) with an element R of the symmetry group, we have

$$RCa_j^+C^{-1}R^{-1} = \mathcal{E}_j^* \sum_{k=1}^{N} D_{TkTj}(R)^* a_{Tk}$$

$$= \sum_{k=1}^{N} D_{kj}(R)\mathcal{E}_k^* a_{Tk},$$

where we use (3.4–17) and (3.6–2). Transforming (3.4–16) with the C-operator, we have

$$CRa_j^+R^{-1}C^{-1} = \sum_{k=1}^{N} D_{kj}(R)\mathcal{E}_k^* a_{Tk}.$$

We may conclude that

$$RC = CR. \tag{3.9–15}$$

We finally note how the pair-creation and pair-annihilation operators are transformed under the C-operator:

$$C\alpha^+C^{-1} = (2N)^{-1/2} \sum_{j=1}^{N} \mathcal{E}_{Tj}^* a_{Tj}a_j = -\alpha; \tag{3.9–16}$$

the adjoint is

$$C\alpha C^{-1} = -\alpha^+. \tag{3.9–17}$$

For an nl shell, Equation (3.9–2) is written in the form:

$$Ca_{m_lm_s}^+C^{-1} = (-1)^{-m_l-m_s}a_{-m_l-m_s}; \tag{3.9–18}$$

the phase product $\mathcal{E}_0$ is

$$\mathcal{E}_0 = i \times (-1)^l. \tag{3.9–19}$$

3.10 COMPLEMENTARY TRANSFORMATION

In this section we shall discuss how the C-operator transforms statevectors in the seniority scheme. It will be found that the C-operator transforms a parent statevector $|v, v, \gamma\rangle$ in the form:

$$C|v, v, \gamma\rangle = \mathcal{E}(v, v)|N - v, v, \gamma\rangle, \tag{3.10–1}$$

where $\mathcal{E}(v, v)$ is a phase factor of absolute value unity. The set of quantum numbers γ is assumed to be unaltered. This is the case if the set of quantum numbers is determined by the symmetry group. The seniority v is unaltered as shown below. The phase factor $\mathcal{E}(v, v)$ will be fixed later.

Let a parent statevector $|v, v, \gamma\rangle$ be transformed with the C-operator in the form:

$$C|v, v, \gamma\rangle = \mathcal{E}(v, v')|N - v, v', \gamma\rangle. \tag{3.10–2}$$

If we replace n with $N - v$ and v with v' in (3.6–17), we have

$$N - v' \geqslant N - v \geqslant v';$$

therefore, we find the requirement

$$v \geqslant v'. \tag{3.10–3}$$

If we transform (3.6–9) with the C-operator, we have

$$C\alpha|v, v, \gamma\rangle = -\mathcal{E}(v, v')\alpha^{+}|N - v, v', \gamma\rangle = 0.$$

Under the requirement (3.10–3), this equation is satisfied only when $v' = v$; we conclude that the C-operator does not alter the seniority.

Let us write a transformation of $|n, v, \gamma\rangle$ under the C-operator in a form

$$C|n, v, \gamma\rangle = \mathcal{E}(n, v)|N - n, v, \gamma\rangle. \tag{3.10–4}$$

We shall call two states *complementary* that are related through the C-operator. The ratio of two phases $\mathcal{E}(n, v)$ and $\mathcal{E}(v, v)$ is found to be

$$\mathcal{E}(n, v) = \mathcal{E}(v, v)\frac{(-1)^{(n-v)/2}\varepsilon_1 \ldots \varepsilon_{(N-n-v)/2}}{\varepsilon_1 \ldots \varepsilon_{(n-v)/2}\varepsilon_1 \ldots \varepsilon_{(N-2v)/2}}. \tag{3.10–5}$$

Proof: According to (3.6–8), the left hand side of (3.10–4) is rewritten as

$$C|n, v, \gamma\rangle = \frac{\mathcal{E}(v, v)(-1)^{(n-v)/2}}{N(n, v)^{1/2}\varepsilon_1 \ldots \varepsilon_{(n-v)/2}}\, \alpha^{(n-v)/2}|N - v, v, \gamma\rangle.$$

Using (3.6–18), we can prove (3.10–5).

Applying the C-operator on (3.6–18), we find

$$\mathcal{E}(N - n, v) = \mathcal{E}(N - v, v)\frac{(-1)^{(n-v)/2}\varepsilon_1 \ldots \varepsilon_{(n-v)/2}\varepsilon_1 \ldots \varepsilon_{(N-2v)/2}}{\varepsilon_1 \ldots \varepsilon_{(N-n-v)/2}}. \tag{3.10–6}$$

In particular, for $n = N/2$, the phase relation (3.10–5) becomes

$$\mathcal{E}\left(\frac{N}{2}, v\right) = \mathcal{E}(v, v)\frac{(-1)^{[(N/2)-v]/2}}{\varepsilon_1 \ldots \varepsilon_{(N-2v)/2}}. \tag{3.10–7}$$

Let us now fix the phase factor $\mathcal{E}(v, v)$ for parent statevectors. A parent statevector $|v, v, \gamma\rangle$ is written in a form of linear combination of basic statevectors $|i, j, \ldots, k\rangle$:

$$|v, v, \gamma\rangle = \sum_{i<j<\ldots<k} |i, j, \ldots, k\rangle\langle i, j, \ldots, k|v, v, \gamma\rangle. \tag{3.10–8}$$

Applying the C-operator on a basic statevector $|i, j, \ldots, k\rangle$, we have

$$C|i, j, \ldots k\rangle = \varepsilon_i^* \varepsilon_j^* \ldots \varepsilon_k^*(-1)^{v(v-1)/2}(-1)^{i+j+\ldots+k}\varepsilon_0|(Ti, Tj, \ldots, Tk)\rangle. \tag{3.10–9}$$

Let us introduce a particular ordering of N single-electron states so that the jth phase factor $\mathcal{E}_j$ is related to $\mathcal{E}_1$ as

$$\mathcal{E}_j = (-1)^{j-1}\mathcal{E}_1. \qquad (3.10\text{–}10)$$

This ordering is always possible on account of (3.3–9); for instance, the ordering (3.3–10) is actually the case. Equation (3.10–9) is then simplified to

$$C|i, j, \ldots, k\rangle = (-1)^{v(v-1)/2}\mathcal{E}_1^v\mathcal{E}_0|(Ti, Tj, \ldots, Tk)\rangle. \qquad (3.10\text{–}11)$$

According to the particular ordering (3.10–10), then relation (3.10–8) is written as

$$C|v, v, \gamma\rangle = (-1)^{v(v-1)/2}\mathcal{E}_1^v\mathcal{E}_0|N - v, v, \gamma\rangle, \qquad (3.10\text{–}12)$$

where we define a statevector $|N - v, v, \gamma\rangle$ through

$$|N - v, v, \gamma\rangle = \sum_{i<j<\ldots<k} |(Ti, Tj, \ldots Tk)\rangle\langle i, j, \ldots, k|v, v, \gamma\rangle; \qquad (3.10\text{–}13)$$

the statevector $|N - v, v, \gamma\rangle$, complementary to $|v, v, \gamma\rangle$, is to be expressed as a linear combination of the complementary basic statevectors with the same coefficients. We then fix the phase relation

$$\mathcal{E}(v, v) = (-1)^{v(v-1)/2}\mathcal{E}_1^v\mathcal{E}_0. \qquad (3.10\text{–}14)$$

This relation leads to

$$\mathcal{E}(v + 2, v + 2) = \mathcal{E}(v, v), \qquad (3.10\text{–}15)$$

where we use $\mathcal{E}_1^2 = -1$. For a particular case $n = v = N/2$, Eq. (3.10–14) becomes

$$\mathcal{E}\left(\frac{N}{2}, \frac{N}{2}\right) = (-1)^{N[(N/2)-1]/4}\mathcal{E}_1^{N/2}\mathcal{E}_0 = (-1)^{N/2}. \qquad (3.10\text{–}16)$$

With the particular ordering (3.10–10), the phase relation (3.10–7) becomes

$$\mathcal{E}\left(\frac{N}{2}, v\right) = (-1)^{[(N/2)-v]/2}\mathcal{E}(v, v). \qquad (3.10\text{–}17)$$

Using (3.10–15), (3.10–16), and (3.10–17), we find

$$\mathcal{E}\left(\frac{N}{2}, v = \frac{N}{2} - 4p\right) = (-1)^{N/2},$$

and (3.10–18)

$$\mathcal{E}\left(\frac{N}{2}, v = \frac{N}{2} - 2(2p + 1)\right) = (-1)^{(N/2)-1},$$

where p is an integer. These phase factors for a half-filled system confirm the suggestion that seniority-scheme statevectors for a half-filled system can be characterized with the eigenvalue 1 or -1 of the C-operator.

Multiplying (3.10–5) by (3.10–6), we obtain

$$\mathcal{E}(N - n, v)\mathcal{E}(n, v) = \mathcal{E}(N - v, v)\mathcal{E}(v, v), \qquad (3.10\text{–}19)$$

where we use the fact that $n - v$ is even. The right-hand side of (3.10–19) is further calculated as

$$\mathcal{E}(v, v)\mathcal{E}(N - v, v) = (-1)^{(N/2)-v}, \tag{3.10–20}$$

where we use (3.10–5) for $n = N - v$. Combining (3.10–19) and (3.10–20), we have

$$\mathcal{E}(N - n, v)\mathcal{E}(n, v) = (-1)^{(N/2)-n}, \tag{3.10–21}$$

since $n - v$ is even. Equation (3.10–21) is in agreement with (3.9–12).

For an nl shell, statevectors with seniority v of a half-filled system are characterized with the eigenvalue of the C-operator by

$$C|2l + 1, v, \gamma\rangle = (-1)^{(2l+1+v)/2}|2l + 1, v, \gamma\rangle.$$

3.11 MATRIX RELATIONS BETWEEN COMPLEMENTARY STATES

The C-operator transforms electronic operators as well as statevectors. We shall first examine commutation relations between the C-operator and single-electron tensor operators. The C-operator transforms a single-electron tensor operator $\mathbf{F}$ into

$$C\mathbf{F}C^{-1} = \mp\mathbf{F} \qquad \text{or} \qquad C\mathbf{F} = \mp\mathbf{F}C, \tag{3.11–1}$$

where the minus sign refers to an even operator, and the plus sign to an odd operator. In finding (3.11–1), we use the relation

$$\langle p|f|q\rangle = (K\langle p|f|q\rangle)^* = \pm\, \mathcal{E}_p\mathcal{E}_q^*\langle Tq|f|Tp\rangle,$$

where the plus sign is for even and the minus sign is for odd operators. According to (3.11–1), an even tensor operator anticommutes with the C-operator; an odd tensor operator commutes with the C-operator. The spin-orbit interaction is an even tensor operator; according to (3.11–1) it has opposite sign for less-than-half and more-than-half systems. This fact is well known for the largest S and L states in the Russell-Saunders scheme.†

If $\mathbf{F}$ is even, we find a matrix relation

$$\langle N - n, v', \gamma'|\mathbf{F}|N - n, v, \gamma\rangle = -\mathcal{E}(n, v')\mathcal{E}(n, v)^*\langle n, v', \gamma'|\mathbf{F}|n, v, \gamma\rangle, \tag{3.11–2}$$

where we use (3.10–4). This matrix relation is further simplified in terms of parent matrix elements according to (3.7–14a), (3.7–15), and (3.7–16). If $\mathbf{F}$ is odd, we find with the use of (3.7–7)

$$\langle N - n, v', \gamma'|\mathbf{F}|N - n, v, \gamma\rangle = \delta_{vv'}\langle v, v, \gamma'|\mathbf{F}|v, v, \gamma\rangle. \tag{3.11–3}$$

†Condon and Shortley, *The Theory of Atomic Spectra*, p. 209.

The relation (3.11–3) is a particularly simple, important result based on the complementary transformation. For example, the component $S_z = M_S$ of the spin angular momentum is unaltered under the complementary transformation, and so is the component $L_z = M_L$ of the orbital angular momentum. In the Russell-Saunders scheme, which is compatible with the seniority, complementary states are characterized with the same set of LSM_LM_S.

The C-operator transforms a two-electron hermitian operator $\mathbf{G}$ into

$$\begin{aligned} C\mathbf{G}C^{-1} &= \tfrac{1}{2}\sum_{pq}\{\langle pq|g|pq\rangle - \langle pq|g|qp\rangle\} \\ &\quad - \sum_{pq}\sum_{r}\{\langle pr|g^K|qr\rangle - \langle pr|g^K|rq\rangle\}a_p^+a_q \\ &\quad + \tfrac{1}{2}\sum_{pqrs}\langle pq|g^K|rs\rangle a_p^+a_q^+a_sa_r, \end{aligned} \tag{3.11–4}$$

where the first term is a constant; the second term is a single-electron operator.

When a two-electron operator $\mathbf{G}$ is written in the form (3.8–6), the C-operator transforms $\mathbf{G}_s$ into

$$C\mathbf{G}_sC^{-1} = \tfrac{1}{2}f_s^2(N - \mathbf{n})(N - \mathbf{n} - 1). \tag{3.11–5}$$

This is obvious since

$$C\mathbf{n}C^{-1} = N - \mathbf{n}. \tag{3.11–6}$$

When a two-electron operator $\mathbf{G}$ is expressed in the form (3.8–3), the C-operator transforms $\mathbf{G}_\alpha$ into

$$C\mathbf{G}_\alpha C^{-1} = \mathbf{G}_\alpha - \tfrac{1}{2}f_\alpha^2(N - 2\mathbf{n}). \tag{3.11–7}$$

The relation (3.11–7) implies that the electrostatic interaction between electrons has the same matrix elements for two complementary states, except for a constant term in the diagonal elements. We shall see an example in Sec. 4.9.

If $\mathbf{G}_\alpha$ lacks the second term of (3.11–7), as does the square $\mathbf{S}^2$, the C-operator commutes with $\mathbf{G}_\alpha$;

$$C\mathbf{G}_\alpha C^{-1} = \mathbf{G}_\alpha \qquad \text{or} \qquad C\mathbf{G}_\alpha = \mathbf{G}_\alpha C. \tag{3.11–8}$$

The eigenvalue of $\mathbf{S}^2$ is the same for complementary states, being $S(S + 1)$.

3.12 THEOREMS FOR HALF-FILLED SHELL SYSTEMS

The C-operator transforms the statevectors of a half-filled shell system into themselves when the statevectors are referred to the seniority scheme. The statevectors are classified in two groups according to the eigenvalue 1 or -1 of the C-operator. The eigenvalue is uniquely determined by the seniority. The C-operator commutes with a single-electron odd operator and anticommutes with a single-electron even operator. These observations lead us to an important theorem:

Theorem 3.12–1: Matrix elements of a single-electron even operator are zero when they are diagonal in the seniority.

Proof: Equation (3.11–2), when $n = N/2$ and $v' = v$, becomes

$$\langle \frac{N}{2}, v, \gamma' | \mathbf{F} | \frac{N}{2}, v, \gamma \rangle = -\langle \frac{N}{2}, v, \gamma' | \mathbf{F} | \frac{N}{2}, v, \gamma \rangle = 0. \qquad (3.12\text{–}1)$$

This proves the theorem.

An example for the Theorem 3.12–1 is the matrix elements of the spin-orbit interaction among Russell-Saunders multiplets of the configuration d^5. The elements diagonal in the seniority are zero, as seen in Table XIV of Racah's article.†

If we are interested in a calculation of energy by the method of perturbation expansion, Theorem 3.12–1 leads us to another theorem.

Theorem 3.12–2: If the perturbation Hamiltonian is a single-electron and t-invariant odd-order terms in the expansion are all zero within a shell.

We shall see an example for Theorem 3.12–2 in Sec. 4.7.

We can also find a theorem on a two-electron scalar operator.

Theorem 3.12–3: When a two-electron operator is hermitian and scalar, the operator **G** commutes with the C-operator for half-filled systems:

$$C\mathbf{G}C^{-1} = \mathbf{G} \qquad \text{or} \qquad C\mathbf{G} = \mathbf{G}C. \qquad (3.12\text{–}2)$$

Proof: Equation (3.11–4) is written for the assumed case

$$C\mathbf{G}C^{-1} = \text{const.} - \text{const.}\,\mathbf{n} + \mathbf{G}, \qquad (3.12\text{–}3)$$

where the second term must be proportional to the number operator since it is a single-electron scalar operator. The number operator **n** commutes with the C-operator when $n = N/2$. Transforming (3.12–3) again with the C-operator, we have

$$\mathbf{G} = \text{const.} - \text{const.}\,\mathbf{n} + C\mathbf{G}C^{-1}. \qquad (3.12\text{–}4)$$

Comparing (3.12–3) and (3.12–4), we conclude that the first two terms give zero, and that **G** commutes with the C-operator.

When a two-electron operator **G** is written in the form (3.8–1), the operator $\mathbf{G}_\alpha$ is shown to be hermitian, regardless of whether the single-electron tensor operator is even or odd. For the case of $n = N/2$, the operator $\mathbf{G}_\alpha$ is transformed with the C-operator into

$$C\mathbf{G}_\alpha C^{-1} = \tfrac{1}{2} \sum_i F_{\alpha i}^* F_{\alpha i} - \tfrac{1}{2} f_\alpha^2 \mathbf{n} = \mathbf{G}_\alpha.$$

Theorem 3.12–4: Matrix elements for a two-electron operator $\mathbf{G}_\alpha$ are zero for $\Delta v = \pm 2$:

†G. Racah, *Phys. Rev.* **63**, 367 (1943).

$$\left\langle \frac{N}{2}, v \pm 2, \gamma | \mathbf{G}_\alpha | \frac{N}{2}, v, \gamma \right\rangle = 0. \qquad (3.12\text{–}5)$$

Proof: According to (3.10–18), the left-hand side simply reverses the sign under the C-operator because of the previous Theorem 3.12–3.

Statevectors for a half-filled shell system are combined through a two-electron operator $\mathbf{G}_\alpha$ according to a theorem.

Theorem 3.12–5: Eigenvectors of $\mathbf{G}_\alpha$ are linear combinations of statevectors $|N/2, v, \gamma\rangle$ that differ in seniority by integral multiples of four.

The electrostatic interaction between electrons has nonvanishing matrix elements between states that differ in seniority by zero or four.

Another example for a two-electron scalar operator is the magnetic dipole interaction between electrons:

$$\mathbf{H}_m = -a^2 \sum_{\mu>\nu} r_{\mu\nu}^{-5}\{3(\mathbf{s}_\mu \cdot \mathbf{r}_{\mu\nu})(\mathbf{s}_\nu \cdot \mathbf{r}_{\mu\nu}) - (\mathbf{s}_\mu \cdot \mathbf{s}_\nu)\mathbf{r}_{\mu\nu}^2\},$$

where $a = \hbar e/mc$. The operator H_m is a scalar with respect to a three-dimensional rotation $e^{-i\varphi(n\cdot J)}$. The matrix elements must be diagonal in J and M_J. According to Theorem 3.12–4, matrix elements of $\mathbf{H}_m$ are zero for $\Delta v = \pm 2$ in the case of a half-filled shell. For example, for a p^3 configuration, there are five terms:

$${}^4_3S_{3/2}, \quad {}^2_3D_{3/2}, \quad {}^2_3D_{5/2}, \quad {}^2_1P_{3/2}, \quad {}^2_1P_{1/2}.$$

The nonvanishing matrix element of $\mathbf{H}_m$ is only between the first two terms.†

†L. H. Aller, C. W. Ufford, and J. H. Van Vleck, *Astrophys. J.* **109**, 42 (1949).

4

LIGAND FIELD THEORY

4.1 INTRODUCTION

In this chapter we shall be concerned with phenomenological theory of first transition-metal ions incorporated into crystalline lattices. We may classify existing phenomenological theories in two: (1) the theory of the *single-ion model* and (2) the theory of the *cluster* or *ligand complex model.* The single-ion model assumes that the outer-shell electrons of transition-metal ions are moving in an effective potential due to the rest of the lattice. The cluster model takes into account the outer-shell ligand electrons as well as the outer-shell metal electrons. The single-ion model is suitable for describing only those electronic properties that are determined by electronic clouds mainly localized in the vicinity of transition-metal ions; the model cannot provide parameters that describe electronic behavior around the ligand nucleus, e. g., the transferred hyperfine interaction (Sec. 4.11). The cluster model can more satisfactorily explain such a behavior and also other parameters (Sec. 4.12). In order to give an elementary introduction to ligand field theory, most parts of this chapter are devoted to the single-ion model.

4.2 CRYSTAL POTENTIAL

The single-ion model assumes that the environmental effects may be replaced with an effective potential, in which the electrons of the ion move. According to the electrostatic theory, the electrostatic potential satisfies the Poisson equation

$$\Delta V(\mathbf{r}) = -4\pi\rho(\mathbf{r}), \tag{4.2–1}$$

where $\rho(\mathbf{r})$ is charge density at $\mathbf{r}$ in the vicinity of the ion. The charge density $\rho(\mathbf{r})$ may be calculated using the appropriate wavefunctions for the electrons of the surrounding ions. The Poisson equation may then be solved numerically. This procedure is quite troublesome and has been shown to be unsuccessful for chromium in alum by Kleiner,† who used Slater radial functions for oxygen electrons around the chromium ion.

We shall neglect the density $\rho(\mathbf{r})$ in the vicinity of the ion to simplify discussions. This approximation is, of course, very crude from the point of view of first principles, yet it may provide us with qualitative insights into the symmetry properties in ligand field theory. Equation (4.2–1) then becomes the Laplace equation:

$$\Delta V(\mathbf{r}) = 0. \tag{4.2–2}$$

The potential $V(\mathbf{r})$ is expressed in terms of spherical harmonics in the form:

$$V(\mathbf{r}) = \sum_{n=0}^{\infty} \sum_{m=-n}^{n} A_{nm} r^n Y_{nm}(\theta\phi), \tag{4.2–3}$$

where r, θ, and ϕ are the polar coordinates referred to the ion nucleus as origin. The coefficients A_{nm} may be determined from experiments, e. g., absorption spectra of the ion. If we assume that the charges outside the ion are pointlike, the coefficients A_{nm} are found to be

$$A_{nm} = \frac{4\pi}{2n+1}(-1)^m \sum_j e_j r_j^{-n-1} Y_{n-m}(\theta_j, \phi_j), \tag{4.2–4}$$

where j is summed over point charges on the lattice points. The phase factor $(-1)^m$ is introduced because of the phase convention of spherical harmonics [see (1.6–6) and (1.6–7)]. The expression (4.2–4) is obtained by expanding $V(\mathbf{r}) = \sum e_j/|\mathbf{r}_j - \mathbf{r}|$ in terms of Legendre polynomials and using the spherical harmonic addition theorem.

The term with $n = 0$ in (4.2–3), i. e., $\sum e_j/r_j$, is called the *Madelung potential*. It is a constant for a particular lattice and simply shifts all the electronic energy levels by this constant amount. Since we are concerned with relative energies, the constant term may be ignored; yet the constant energy is considered to be the dominant part of the binding energy of ionic crystals. Values of the Madelung constant A are listed in Table 4.2–1. For example, the electrostatic energy per ZnS unit is given by $-Ae^2/R$, where

†W. H. Kleiner, *J. Chem. Phys.* **20**, 1784 (1952).

TABLE 4.2–1

VALUES OF MADELUNG CONSTANT A

Structure	Formula	Example	A
Simple cubic	M^+X^-	NaCl	1.748
Body-centered cubic	M^+X^-	CsCl	1.763
Fluorite	$N^{++}X_2^-$	CaF_2	5.039
Sphalerite	M^+X^-	ZnS	1.638
Wurtzite	M^+X^-	ZnS	1.641
Cuprite	$M_2^+X^{--}$	Cu_2O	4.116
Rutile	$M^{++}X_2^-$	TiO_2	4.816
Corundum	$M_2^{3+}X_3^{--}$	Al_2O_3	25.031

R is the smallest anion-cation distance. If we take out a zinc ion from its site in a sphalerite lattice and place an electron there instead, the electron gets an energy of about 16.5 electron volts. If we do the same at a sulphur site, the electron gets an energy of about -16.5 electron volts. Here we use $R = 2.36$Å, and $e^2/a_0 = 27.2$ electron volts for the first Bohr radius $a_0 = 0.529$Å. The expression (4.2–4) for A_{nm} may be used to estimate rough relative magnitudes of point charge potentials for the same ion in different host lattices; an example will be given in the next section. The general form (4.2–3), however, leads to qualitatively important discussions.

Since the electrostatic potential (4.2–3) must be real, the coefficients satisfy the relation

$$A_{nm} = (-1)^m A^*_{n-m}. \tag{4.2–5}$$

If the point charges e_j in (4.2–4) are replaced by point dipoles $\mathbf{p}_j$, the potential $V(\mathbf{r})$ takes the form

$$\begin{aligned} V(\mathbf{r}) &= \Sigma\, \mathbf{p}_j \cdot \text{grad}_j |\mathbf{r} - \mathbf{r}_j|^{-1} \\ &= \sum_{n=0}^{\infty} \sum_{m=-n}^{n} (-1)^m \frac{4\pi}{2n+1} r^n Y_{nm}(\theta\phi) \\ &\quad \times \sum_j \mathbf{p}_j \cdot \text{grad}_j \left\{ \frac{Y_{n-m}(\theta_j \phi_j)}{r_j^{n+1}} \right\}. \end{aligned}$$

If the point dipoles are all radially directed toward the transition-metal ion, the coefficients A_{nm} are simplified to

$$A_{nm} = \frac{4\pi}{2n+1} \sum_j (n+1)(-1)^m r_j^{-n-2} p_j Y_{n-m}(\theta_j \phi_j). \tag{4.2–6}$$

The crystal potential (4.2–3) is a single-electron even operator with respect to the three-dimensional rotation group, except for the term with $n = 0$. According to (3.5–14), a single-electron tensor operator has a zero sum of diagonal elements; the crystal potential does not shift the center of gravity of energy levels that are degenerate without the crystal potential, to the approximation linear in V.

4.3 SYMMETRY OF CRYSTAL POTENTIAL

A transition-metal site is characterized by a certain symmetry, i. e., one of the thirty-two point groups. The point symmetry reduces the number of independent coefficients A_{nm}. Every symmetry element transforms Y_{nm} into a linear combination of $Y_{nm'}$, within the same n. If an element transforms Y_{nm} into itself, we obtain a restriction on n and m. If an element transforms Y_{nm} into Y_{n-m}, we find a relation between A_{nm} and A_{n-m}. In the following, we shall find some symmetry relations for point groups.

(i) $\mathbf{C}_p$: If we choose the p-fold axis as the z-axis, (or the polar axis),† the potential must be unaltered by a rotation of angle $2\pi/p$ around the z-axis. This rotation transforms Y_{nm} into $e^{i2m\pi/p}\,Y_{nm}$. The exponential factor must be unity; i. e., m must be an integral multiple of p:

$$m = 0, \pm p, \pm 2p, \ldots. \tag{4.3–1}$$

(ii) $\mathbf{C}_i$: The inversion transforms Y_{nm} into $(-1)^n\,Y_{nm}$; we have

$$A_{nm} = 0 \qquad \text{for odd } n. \tag{4.3–2}$$

(iii) $\mathbf{C}_s$: If we choose the symmetry plane as the zx-plane, the reflection transforms Y_{nm} into $(-1)^m\,Y_{n-m}$; therefore, we have

$$A_{nm} = (-1)^m A_{n-m}. \tag{4.3–3}$$

(iv) $\mathbf{S}_{2p}$: A rotatory-reflection by $2\pi/2p$ transforms Y_{nm} into $e^{i\pi\{n+m+(m/p)\}}\,Y_{nm}$; therefore, we have

$$n + m + \frac{m}{p} = \text{even}. \tag{4.3–4}$$

Four combinations of n and m are listed in Table 4.3–1.

TABLE 4.3–1

FOUR COMBINATIONS OF n AND m FOR S_{2p}

n	m	m/p	
odd	odd		impossible, since m/p cannot be even.
odd	even	odd	p can only be 2; n must be not less than 3.
even	odd	odd	p can only be 3; n must be not less than 4.
even	even	even	p can be either 2 or 3.

†We shall hereafter choose the p-fold axis as the z-axis.

(v) $\mathbf{C}_{ph}$: The p-fold axis leads to the relation (4.3–1); inversion leads to the relation (4.3–2) for the case $p = 4$ and 6. A rotatory-reflection by $2\pi/p$ transforms Y_{nm} into $e^{i\pi\{n+m+(2m/p)\}}\, Y_{nm}$; we have

$$n + m + \frac{2m}{p} = \text{even}. \tag{4.3–5}$$

Four combinations of n and m are listed in Table 4.3–2.

TABLE 4.3–2

FOUR COMBINATIONS OF n AND m FOR $\mathbf{C}_{ph}$

n	m	$2m/p$	
odd	odd	even	p can only be 3, n must be not less than 3.
odd	even	odd	p can only be 4, n must be not less than 3.
even	odd	odd	p can be either 2 or 6.
even	even	even	p can be either 2, 3, 4, or 6.

(vi) $\mathbf{C}_{pv}$: The p-fold axis leads to (4.3–1); reflection in the zx-plane leads to (4.3–3). When p is even, the yz-plane is also a symmetry plane; reflection in the yz-plane transforms Y_{nm} into Y_{n-m}; therefore, we have

$$A_{nm} = A_{n-m}. \tag{4.3–6}$$

(vii) $\mathbf{D}_p$: The p-fold axis leads to (4.3–1). If we choose one of the p twofold axes as x-axis, the twofold rotation transforms Y_{nm} into $(-1)^n$ Y_{n-m}; therefore, we have

$$A_{nm} = (-1)^n A_{n-m}. \tag{4.3–7}$$

(viii) $\mathbf{D}_{ph}$: The relations (4.3–1), (4.3–3), (4.3–5), and (4.3–7) hold.

(ix) $\mathbf{D}_{pd}$: The relations (4.3–1), (4.3–3), (4.3–4), and (4.3–7) hold.

Note that a crystal potential takes varied forms, depending upon the relative arrangement of the x, y, and z axes with respect to the crystal axes, and that the number of independent coefficients A_{nm} is less for a potential of higher symmetry.

There are five point groups that have not been explained yet in detail. These are point groups $\mathbf{T}$, $\mathbf{O}$, $\mathbf{T}_d$, $\mathbf{T}_h$, and $\mathbf{O}_h$. Symmetry properties of a potential, pertaining to these point groups, are easily determined with use of the relations (4.3–1) through (4.3–7).

EXAMPLE: $\mathbf{T}_d$ and $\mathbf{O}_h$.

We shall determine the form of a crystal potential of $\mathbf{T}_d$ and $\mathbf{O}_h$ symmetry, for a particular choice of coordinates. We first choose x, y, and z axes as shown in Figs. 2.17–1 and 2.18–1; i. e., x parallel to [100]; y parallel to [010]; z parallel to [001].

The tetrahedron has a rotatory-reflection S_4 around the z-axis. We obtain a tetrahedral potential in the form up to $n = 4$:

$$V(\mathbf{T}_d) = A_{32}r^3(Y_{32} - Y_{3-2}) + A_{40}r^4 Y_{40} + A_{44}r^4(Y_{44} + Y_{4-4}). \quad (4.3\text{–}8)$$

We can further determine a relation between A_{40} and A_{44}, referring to particular directions along which the potential value is equal, and using spherical harmonics listed in Appendix 1.2. The result is

$$A_{44} = \left(\frac{5}{14}\right)^{1/2} A_{40}.$$

The tetrahedral potential (4.3–8) is also written in terms of Cartesian coordinates:

$$V(\mathbf{T}_d) = iA_{32}\left(\frac{105}{8\pi}\right)^{1/2} xyz + A_{40}\left(\frac{9}{4\pi}\right)^{1/2}\frac{1}{8}$$
$$\times \{35z^4 - 30r^2z^2 + 3r^4 + 5(x^4 - 6x^2y^2 + y^4)\}, \quad (4.3\text{–}9)$$

where the coefficient A_{32} is pure imaginary. If point charges, Ze, are placed on the vertices of a tetrahedron, the coefficient A_{32} is calculated to be

$$A_{32} = -i\left(\frac{5\pi}{14}\right)^{1/2}\frac{8}{3}\frac{Ze}{R^4},$$

where R is the distance between the center and a vertex.

The octahedral potential has the property of inversion and takes the form

$$V(\mathbf{O}_h) = A_{40}r^4\left\{Y_{40} + \left(\frac{5}{14}\right)^{1/2}(Y_{44} + Y_{4-4})\right\}$$
$$= A_{40}\left(\frac{9}{4\pi}\right)^{1/2}\frac{1}{8}\{35z^4 - 30r^2z^2 + 3r^4 + 5(x^4 - 6x^2y^2 + y^4)\}. \quad (4.3\text{–}10)$$

If we choose x, y, and z axes as shown in Fig. 4.3–1(a) and (b), we obtain a potential in a different form. The direction cosines of the new x, y, and z axes, referred to the [100], [010], and [001] directions, are

$$x: \quad \frac{1}{(6)^{1/2}}, \quad \frac{1}{(6)^{1/2}}, \quad -\frac{2}{(6)^{1/2}};$$
$$y: \quad -\frac{1}{(2)^{1/2}}, \quad \frac{1}{(2)^{1/2}}, \quad 0;$$
$$z: \quad \frac{1}{(3)^{1/2}}, \quad \frac{1}{(3)^{1/2}}, \quad \frac{1}{(3)^{1/2}}.$$

The z-axis is along the [111] direction, being threefold. The zx-plane is a symmetry plane. We have a tetrahedral potential in the form up to $n = 4$:

$$V(\mathbf{T}_d) = A_{30}r^3\left\{Y_{30} + \left(\frac{2}{5}\right)^{1/2}(Y_{33} - Y_{3-3})\right\}$$
$$+ A_{40}r^4\left\{Y_{40} - \left(\frac{10}{7}\right)^{1/2}(-Y_{43} + Y_{4-3})\right\}. \quad (4.3\text{–}11)$$

An octahedral potential is written in the form:

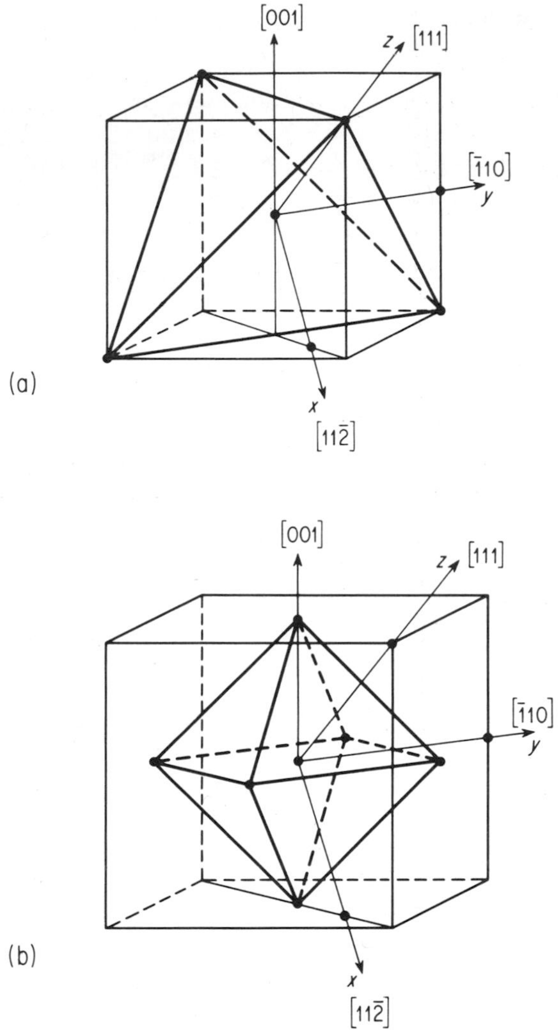

Figure 4.3-1

$$V(\mathbf{O}_h) = A_{40}r^4 \left\{Y_{40} - \left(\frac{10}{7}\right)^{1/2}(-Y_{43} + Y_{4-3})\right\}$$

$$= A_{40}\left(\frac{9}{4\pi}\right)^{1/2}\frac{1}{8}\{35z^4 - 30z^2r^2 + 3r^4 - 20(2)^{1/2}z(x^3 - 3xy^2)\}. \tag{4.3–12}$$

Let us calculate a coefficient A_{40} for octahedral, tetrahedral, and cube coordinations, assuming point charges Ze on the vertices of the regular polyhedrons, with reference to the choice of x, y, z axes shown in Figs.

2.17–1 and 2.18–1. The distance between the center and a vertex is to be R, being the same for all three coordinations. Using (4.2–4) and spherical harmonics of fourth order, we obtain

$$A_{40}(\mathbf{O}_h) = Ze\frac{7}{3}\frac{\pi^{1/2}}{R^5},$$

$$A_{40}(\mathbf{T}_d) = -\frac{4}{9}A_{40}(\mathbf{O}_h), \tag{4.3–13}$$

$$A_{40}(\text{cube}) = -\frac{8}{9}A_{40}(\mathbf{O}_h).$$

The absolute values of A_{40} may not be compared with experimentally observed crystal field splittings because of the crudeness of the point charge model, yet the ratio $A_{40}(\mathbf{O}_h)$: $A_{40}(\mathbf{T}_d)$: $A_{40}(\text{cube}) = 9: -4: -8$ appears to have some significance. The same ratio holds for point dipoles situated at the vertices.

Returning to less symmetrical potentials, when the z-axis is twofold, we have the crystal potential which involves terms Y_{nm} with $m =$ integral multiple of two. For example,

$$A_{20}r^2Y_{20} = A_{20}\left(\frac{5}{16\pi}\right)^{1/2}(3z^2 - r^2),$$

$$A_{22}r^2(Y_{22} + Y_{2-2}) = A_{20}\left(\frac{15}{8\pi}\right)^{1/2}(x^2 - y^2),$$

$$A_{42}r^4(Y_{42} + Y_{4-2}) = A_{42}\left(\frac{45}{32\pi}\right)^{1/2}(7z^2 - r^2)(x^2 - y^2).$$

4.4 MATRIX ELEMENTS AND OPERATOR EQUIVALENTS

When a transition-metal ion is placed in a crystal potential, the energy levels of the free ionic state are usually split into crystal levels. We assume that the magnitude of the crystal field splitting $\Delta E_{\text{cryst.}}$ is smaller than the energy separations associated with the principal and azimuthal numbers n and l, and that these quantum numbers are good to a first approximation in a crystal potential. The crystal field splitting $\Delta E_{\text{cryst.}}$ is, for example, given by $10Dq$ for the case of d-electron in a cubic field, where the parameter Dq is defined in the next section. We may classify four cases according to the relative magnitudes of the crystal field separation $\Delta E_{\text{cryst.}}$ compared to energy separations due to various interactions in free ions:

(i) strong field:

$$\Delta E(nl) > \Delta E_{\text{cryst.}} > \Delta E(SL);$$

the crystal field separation is smaller than the energy separation between nl states, and is larger than the separation between Russell-Saunders terms ${}^{2S+1}L$.

(ii) intermediate field:

$$\Delta E(nl) > \Delta E_{\text{cryst.}} \sim \Delta E(SL) > \Delta E_{\text{spin-orbit}};$$

the crystal field separation is comparable to the energy separation between Russell-Saunders terms ${}^{2S+1}L$, and is larger than the separation due to the spin-orbit interaction.

(iii) weak field:

$$\Delta E(SL) > \Delta E_{\text{cryst.}} > \Delta E_{\text{spin-orbit}};$$

the crystal field separation is between the two energies indicated.

(iv) very weak field:

$$\Delta E_{\text{spin-orbit}} > \Delta E_{\text{cryst.}}$$

An example for case (i) is the iron ion in a ferricyanide crystal or complex-ion. Case (ii) is commonly seen for iron-group ions in crystals; and so is case (iii). Case (iv) applies to rare-earth group ions in crystals.

This classification is only an approximation, yet it is convenient for calculating crystal field effects. Case (i) may be treated by the perturbation calculation; the crystal field effects on the *nl*-scheme energy states are calculated prior to the electrostatic interaction. Case (ii) must be treated by secular equation methods that involve both the crystal field and electrostatic interaction between electrons. The crystal field effects for case (iii) may be calculated within Russell-Saunders manifold ${}^{2S+1}L$; the crystal field effects for case (iv) may be taken into account within JM_J states.

In these four cases, matrix elements of a crystal potential are calculated with respect to eigenfunctions of angular momentum: cases (i) and (ii) are referred to those of l; case (iii) to those of L; and case (iv) to those of J. Each term in the crystal potential (4.2–3) is a spherical harmonic operator. In Sec. 1.9 we learned the Wigner-Eckart theorem on matrix elements of irreducible tensors with respect to angular momentum eigenfunctions:

$$\langle j_2 m_2 | Y_{nm} | j_1 m_1 \rangle = \langle j_2 \| Y_n \| j_1 \rangle \langle j_1 n, j_2 m_2 | j_1 m_1, nm \rangle, \qquad (4.4\text{–}1)$$

where we rearrange the names of quantum numbers and rank of tensor operator.

The selection rule (1.9–7) applies in the form: the matrix elements (4.4–1) are zero unless

$$m_1 + m = m_2 \qquad (4.4\text{–}2)$$

and

$$j_1 + n \geqslant j_2 \geqslant |j_1 - n|. \qquad (4.4\text{–}3)$$

When the orbital angular momentum eigenfunctions are used, an additional selection rule is obtained on account of parity:

$$\langle l_2 m_2 | Y_{nm} | l_1 m_1 \rangle = 0 \quad \text{unless } l_1 + l_2 + n = \text{even}. \qquad (4.4\text{–}4)$$

When $l_1 = l_2$, the selection rule becomes

$$\langle l_1 m_2 | Y_{nm} | l_1 m_1 \rangle = 0 \quad \text{unless } n \text{ is even.} \tag{4.4–5}$$

Terms with odd n in (4.2–3) have nonzero matrix elements only between states of opposite parity.

We are now concerned with the angular part of matrix elements of a crystal potential; the matrix elements of each term in (4.2–3) are factored into radial and angular parts. Calculation of the radial part requires precise knowledge about radial parts of eigenfunctions, e.g., self-consistent wavefunctions. The angular part is easily calculated if the Clebsch-Gordan coefficients are known. One may leave the radial part as a parameter to be determined by experiment.

There is a convenient technique to evaluate the angular part of the matrix elements. The technique is based on the replacement theorem (1.13–3), which is written in the form:

$$Y_{nm} = c(nj)T_{nm}. \tag{4.4–6}$$

The explicit forms of T_{nm} in terms of j_z, j_+, and j_- are listed in Appendix 1.3, up to $n = 6$. The factor $c(nj)$ can be obtained by comparing matrix elements of Y_{nm} and T_{nm} for particular values of m_1, m_2, and m; or it may be left as a parameter included in the radial part. For example, the octahedral potential (4.3–10) is replaced by the *equivalent operator*

$$35j_z^4 - 30j(j+1)j_z^2 + 25j_z^2 + 3j^2(j+1)^2 - 6j(j+1) + \tfrac{5}{2}(j_+^4 + j_-^4), \tag{4.4–7}$$

apart from a proportionality factor. It is then straightforward to evaluate matrix elements of the replaced form with respect to angular momentum eigenfunctions.

Note that the replacement is valid only within a manifold of a definite angular momentum. The replaced form has no meaning for matrix elements between different angular momentum states.

Let us show, by an example, how to calculate a proportionality factor. A quadratic term $(3z^2 - r^2)$ in a crystal potential is to be replaced by

$$\begin{aligned} \sum_{i=1}^{n} (3z_i^2 - r_i^2) &= \sum \gamma\overline{r^2}\{3l_z^2 - l(l+1)\} \\ &= \alpha\overline{r^2}\{3L_z^2 - L(L+1)\}, \end{aligned} \tag{4.4–8}$$

where the summation is over all the electrons. We assume that the empirical *Hund rule* is valid, i.e., that the ground state has the maximum spin S, under which requirement the state also has the maximum L. The number of electrons is to be less than $2l + 1$. The spin S is equal to $n/2$; the orbital L is equal to $S\cdot(2l + 1 - 4S)$. The state $|M_L = L, M_S = S\rangle$ is given by a single determinant

$$|M_L = L, M_S = S\rangle = |l, l-1, \ldots, l-2S+1\rangle. \tag{4.4–9}$$

The matrix element of (4.4–8) with respect to (4.4–9) is

$$\gamma\overline{r^2}L(2l+1-4S) = \alpha\overline{r^2}L(2L-1).$$

The coefficient γ is determined to be $-2/\{(2l-1)(2l+3)\}$, by a direct calculation:

$$\begin{aligned}\langle m_l = l|r^2(3\cos^2\theta - 1)|m_l = l\rangle &= \overline{r^2}\int_{-1}^{1} P_l^2(\cos\theta)(3\cos^2\theta - 1)d(\cos\theta)\\ &= -\frac{2\overline{r^2}l}{2l+3},\end{aligned}$$

where $\overline{r^2}$ is the radial average of r^2. We have the desired coefficient

$$\alpha = -\frac{2(2l+1-4S)}{(2l-1)(2l+3)(2L-1)}.$$

The sign must be reversed when we consider the complementary configurations, according to (3.11–1).

Some crystal potentials replaced by equivalent operators are listed in Table 4.4–1, in terms of L_z, L_+, and L_-. Matrix elements for the equivalent operators listed in Table 4.4–1 are given in Appendix 4.1.

TABLE 4.4–1

EQUIVALENT OPERATORS FOR SOME CRYSTAL POTENTIALS†

$\Sigma(3z^2 - r^2) =$	$\alpha\overline{r^2}\{3L_z^2 - L(L+1)\}$
$\Sigma(x^2 - y^2) =$	$\alpha\overline{r^2}(L_+^2 + L_-^2)$
$\Sigma(35z^4 - 30z^2r^2 + 3r^4) =$	$\beta\overline{r^4}\{35L_z^4 - 30L(L+1)L_z^2 + 25L_z^2 - 6L(L+1) + 3L^2(L+1)^2\}$
$\Sigma(7z^2 - r^2)(x^2 - y^2) =$	$\frac{1}{4}\beta\overline{r^4}[\{7L_z^2 - L(L+1) - 5\}(L_+^2 + L_-^2) + (L_+^2 + L_-^2)\{7L_z^2 - L(L+1) - 5\}]$
$\Sigma z(x^3 - 3xy^2) =$	$\frac{1}{4}\beta\overline{r^4}\{L_z(L_+^3 + L_-^3) + (L_+^3 + L_-^3)L_z\}$
$\Sigma(x^4 - 6x^2y^2 + y^4) =$	$\frac{1}{2}\beta\overline{r^4}(L_+^4 + L_-^4)$

†The proportionality factors α and β are calculated for the iron-group ions:

$\alpha = -2/21$, $\beta = 2/63$ for $d^1\ {}^2D$ and $d^6\ {}^5D$;
$\alpha = 2/21$, $\beta = -2/63$ for $d^9\ {}^2D$ and $d^4\ {}^5D$;
$\alpha = -2/105$, $\beta = -2/315$ for $d^2\ {}^3F$ and $d^7\ {}^4F$;
$\alpha = 2/105$, $\beta = 2/315$ for $d^8\ {}^3F$ and $d^3\ {}^4F$.

4.5 SINGLE *d* ELECTRON IN A CUBIC POTENTIAL

If a single *d* electron is placed in an octahedral field, the field effects are calculated by the secular equation method. Let us take the potential in the form:

$$\begin{aligned} V &= D\{x^4 + y^4 + z^4 - \tfrac{3}{5}r^4\} \\ &= \tfrac{1}{20}D\{35z^4 - 30z^2r^2 + 3r^4 + 5(x^4 - 6x^2y^2 + y^4)\}, \end{aligned} \tag{4.5–1}$$

where we need not consider terms higher than fourth order, on account of the selection rule (4.4–3). Using the equivalent operator (4.4–7), we have secular matrices

$$\begin{matrix} m_l = +2 & -2 & +1 & -1 & 0 \end{matrix}$$

$$\begin{bmatrix} 1 & 5 \\ 5 & 1 \end{bmatrix}, \quad (-4), \quad (-4), \quad (6), \tag{4.5–2}$$

where we use a unit Dq, a measure of cubic potential. The parameter q is given by the radial integral

$$q = \tfrac{2}{105}\overline{r^4},$$

where the average is with respect to the radial function of d orbital. The first secular matrix has two roots -4 and 6 in units of Dq. Two wavefunctions ψ_{21} and ψ_{2-1} must be degenerate, since the potential (4.5–1) is t-invariant and does not mix these states with other states, and since the two wavefunctions are transformed into each other under time reversal. The eigenfunctions of (4.5–2) are presented in a real form:

eigenvalue	*eigenfunction*	*name*
$6Dq$:	$\psi_{20} = \left(\frac{5}{4\pi}\right)^{1/2} \frac{1}{2} \frac{(3z^2 - r^2)}{r^2}$	*deu*
	$\left(\frac{1}{2}\right)^{1/2} (\psi_{22} + \psi_{2-2}) = \left(\frac{5}{4\pi}\right)^{1/2} \frac{1}{2} 3^{1/2} \frac{(x^2 - y^2)}{r^2}$	*dev*
$-4Dq$:	$i\left(\frac{1}{2}\right)^{1/2} (\psi_{21} + \psi_{2-1}) = \left(\frac{5}{4\pi}\right)^{1/2} 3^{1/2} \frac{yz}{r^2}$	$dt_2\xi$ (4.5–3)
	$\left(\frac{1}{2}\right)^{1/2} (-\psi_{21} + \psi_{2-1}) = \left(\frac{5}{4\pi}\right)^{1/2} 3^{1/2} \frac{zx}{r^2}$	$dt_2\eta$
	$-i\left(\frac{1}{2}\right)^{1/2} (\psi_{22} - \psi_{2-2}) = \left(\frac{5}{4\pi}\right)^{1/2} 3^{1/2} \frac{xy}{r^2}$	$dt_2\zeta$

where we omit the radial part. Inverse transformation of (4.5–3) is

$$\begin{aligned}
\psi_{22} &= (\tfrac{1}{2})^{1/2}\,(v + i\zeta),\\
\psi_{21} &= (\tfrac{1}{2})^{1/2}\,(-i\xi - \eta),\\
\psi_{20} &= u, \qquad\qquad (4.5\text{–}3a)\\
\psi_{2-1} &= (\tfrac{1}{2})^{1/2}\,(-i\xi + \eta),\\
\psi_{2-2} &= (\tfrac{1}{2})^{1/2}\,(v - i\zeta).
\end{aligned}$$

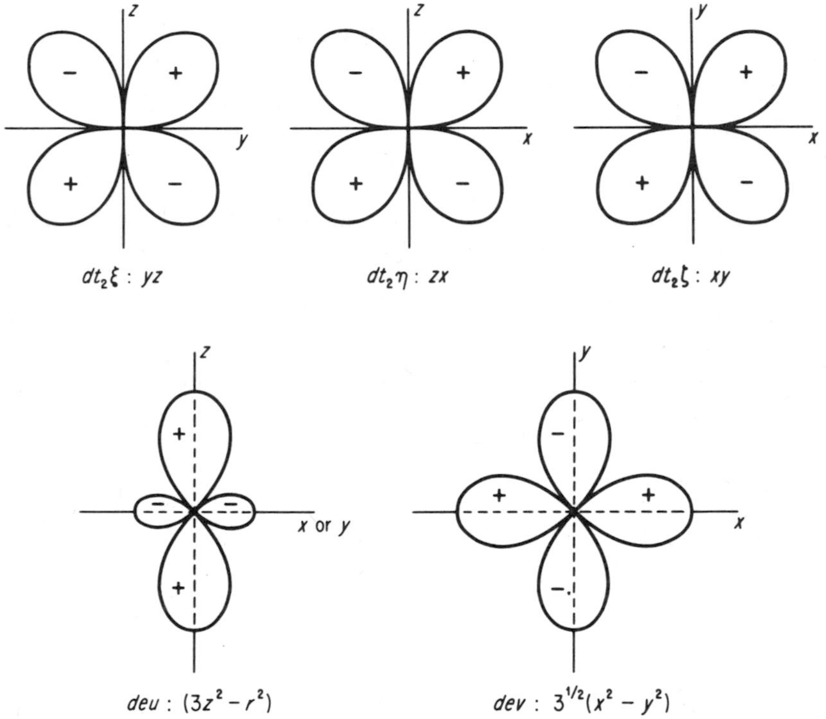

Figure 4.5-1

The real orbitals (4.5–3) are schematically illustrated in Fig. 4.5–1. Transformation properties of these five real orbitals are listed in Table 2.17–5 with respect to the point group **O**. Octahedral basis functions are listed in Appendix 2.1, being calculated in a manner similar to (4.5–3).

The splitting of five d orbitals into two sets, de and dt_2 is illustrated in Fig. 4.5–2, where the splitting in a tetrahedral potential is also shown in accordance with (4.3–3). The center of gravity of five d orbitals remains unaltered as mentioned in Sec. 4.2:

$$2 \times 6Dq + 3 \times (-4Dq) = 0.$$

In Fig. 4.5–2, we assume that the coefficient D is positive. This may be

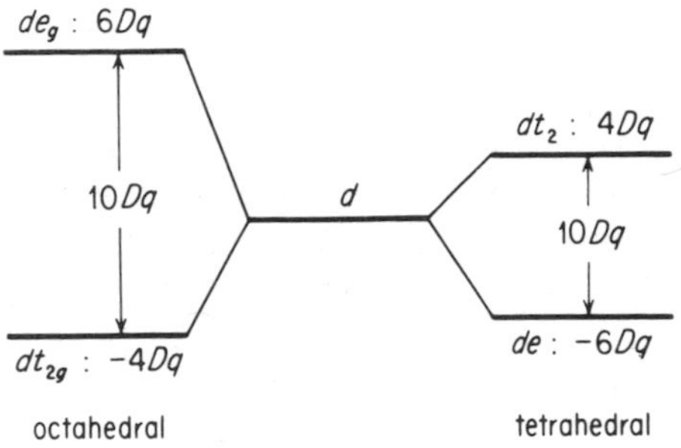

Figure 4.5-2

the case if the vertices of the octahedron are negatively charged. The two *de* orbitals are directed toward the negative charges while the three dt_2 orbitals escape them. This is the simplifying physical interpretation for the fact that *de* orbitals are higher in energy than dt_2 orbitals for octahedral coordination.

If the x, y, and z axes are chosen with respect to an octahedron as shown in Fig. 4.3–1, the octahedral potential is written in terms of operators of L_z, L_+, and L_- in the form:

$$V = -\frac{D}{30}\beta\overline{r^4}[35L_z^4 - 30L(L+1)L_z^2 + 25L_z^2 - 6L(L+1)$$
$$+ 3L^2(L+1)^2 - 5(2)^{1/2}\{L_z(L_+^3 + L_-^3) + (L_+^3 + L_-^3)L_z\}], \qquad (4.5\text{–}4)$$

where the coefficient D is the same as in (4.5–1). The eigenvalues of the octahedral potential must be independent of the choice of the coordinate axes, although the form of eigenfunctions depends on the choice. The five d orbitals are split in two groups and written as:

eigenvalue	*eigenfunction*	
$6Dq$	$(\frac{1}{3})^{1/2}\psi_{2-2} - (\frac{2}{3})^{1/2}\psi_{21}$	
	$(\frac{1}{3})^{1/2}\psi_{22} + (\frac{2}{3})^{1/2}\psi_{2-1}$	
$-4Dq$	ψ_{20}	(4.5–5)
	$(\frac{2}{3})^{1/2}\psi_{2-2} + (\frac{1}{3})^{1/2}\psi_{21}$	
	$(\frac{2}{3})^{1/2}\psi_{22} - (\frac{1}{3})^{1/2}\psi_{2-1}$.	

Note that two functions for $6Dq$ are degenerate owing to time-reversal degeneracy, and that the second and third functions for $-4Dq$ are transformed into each other under time reversal.

Let us next consider a single $3d$ electron in a tetrahedral potential (4.3–9), which contains an odd-order term of the form $C\,xyz$. The p_x, p_y, and p_z orbitals transform under the $\mathbf{T}_d$ group as $t_2\xi$, $t_2\eta$, and $t_2\zeta$. According to Theorem 2.20–3, the dt_2 orbitals can have nonvanishing elements of the odd-order term with the p orbitals. The elements are

$$\langle p_x|C\,xyz|dt_2\xi\rangle = \langle p_y|C\,xyz|dt_2\eta\rangle = \langle p_z|C\,xyz|dt_2\zeta\rangle.$$

The equality is proved by transforming one of the three by $C_3^{[111]}$ repeatedly. The $4p$ orbital is located about 10^5 cm^{-1} above the $3d$ orbital for iron-group ions in free space. The matrix element of $C\,xyz$ could be of the order of magnitude 10^4 cm^{-1} in some instances.† The odd-order term can admix the $4p$ orbital into the $3d$ orbital by an amount of the order of 10 per cent. The admixture of $4p$ orbital is formulated through the first-order perturbation procedure as

$$|t_2 i\rangle = |3dt_2 i\rangle - c|4pi\rangle, \qquad i = \xi, \eta, \zeta,$$

where

$$c = \frac{\langle 4p_x|C\,xyz|3dt_2\xi\rangle}{E(4p) - E(3d)}.$$

Let us introduce a concept of *effective orbital angular momentum.* Matrix representation of orbital angular momentum operators l_x, l_y, and l_z is given with respect to the five real orbitals (4.5–3):

$$l_x = \begin{bmatrix} 0 & 0 & 0 & -i3^{1/2} & -i \\ 0 & 0 & i & 0 & 0 \\ 0 & -i & 0 & 0 & 0 \\ i3^{1/2} & 0 & 0 & 0 & 0 \\ i & 0 & 0 & 0 & 0 \end{bmatrix},$$

$$l_y = \begin{bmatrix} 0 & 0 & -i & 0 & 0 \\ 0 & 0 & 0 & i3^{1/2} & -i \\ i & 0 & 0 & 0 & 0 \\ 0 & -i3^{1/2} & 0 & 0 & 0 \\ 0 & i & 0 & 0 & 0 \end{bmatrix}, \qquad (4.5\text{–}6)$$

$$l_z = \begin{bmatrix} 0 & i & 0 & 0 & 0 \\ -i & 0 & 0 & 0 & 0 \\ 0 & 0 & 0 & 0 & 2i \\ 0 & 0 & 0 & 0 & 0 \\ 0 & 0 & -2i & 0 & 0 \end{bmatrix}.$$

The dt_2 orbital is triply degenerate, as is the p orbital. Real forms of the p orbital are

$$\begin{aligned} p_x &= (\tfrac{1}{2})^{1/2}(-\psi_{11} + \psi_{1-1}), \\ p_y &= i(\tfrac{1}{2})^{1/2}(\psi_{11} + \psi_{1-1}), \qquad (4.5\text{–}7) \\ p_z &= \psi_{10}. \end{aligned}$$

†C. J. Ballhausen and A. D. Liehr, *J. Molecular Spectroscopy* **2**, 342 (1958).

Matrices for orbital angular momentum operators with respect to these real orbitals are

$$
\begin{array}{ccc} x & y & z \end{array}
$$

$$
l_x = \begin{bmatrix} 0 & 0 & 0 \\ 0 & 0 & -i \\ 0 & i & 0 \end{bmatrix}, \quad
l_y = \begin{bmatrix} 0 & 0 & i \\ 0 & 0 & 0 \\ -i & 0 & 0 \end{bmatrix}, \quad
l_z = \begin{bmatrix} 0 & -i & 0 \\ i & 0 & 0 \\ 0 & 0 & 0 \end{bmatrix}. \tag{4.5-8}
$$

The submatrices of (4.5–6) within the dt_2 orbitals are found to be the negative of the matrices (4.5–8). If we confine our interest within dt_2, the orbital angular momentum operator is regarded to be equivalent to the orbital angular momentum within the p orbital, with the proportionality factor -1:

$$
l' = -l \quad \text{with } l = 1. \tag{4.5-9}
$$

The submatrices of (4.5–6) within the de orbitals are null. The orbital angular momentum within de is thus regarded as being *quenched*.

NOTE 4.5–1: Note on *orbital quenching.*

When a single-electron Hamiltonian operator is t-invariant and spin-independent, the eigenvalue equation

$$
\mathbf{H}\psi = E\psi
$$

is satisfied by spin-independent eigenfunctions. If the energy E is nondegenerate, the eigenfunction is only multiplied by a phase factor under time reversal:

$$
K\psi = \psi^* = e^{i\delta}\psi,
$$

where the operator K acts on ψ simply as an operator of complex conjugation, since ψ is independent of spin. Within such an orbital singlet, the orbital angular momentum is quenched in the sense that the integral vanishes:

$$
\int \psi^* l_i \psi \, d\tau = 0, \qquad i = x, y, \text{ and } z. \tag{4.5-10}
$$

Proof: Transforming the integral on the left-hand side of (4.5–10) with K, we have

$$
K\int \psi^* l_i \psi \, d\tau = -\int \psi^* l_i \psi \, d\tau = \int \psi^* l_i \psi \, d\tau = 0,
$$

where we use the property that a diagonal element of a hermitian operator is real.

4.6 DEFORMATION OF AN OCTAHEDRON; SPIN-ORBIT INTERACTION

When a regular octahedron is stretched along the [001] direction, the symmetry reduces to the point group $\mathbf{D}_{4h}$. The compatibility relation,

Table 4.6–1, between the point groups $\mathbf{O}_h$ and $\mathbf{D}_{4h}$ shows how the octahedral crystal levels are split. The *de* orbitals are split into two nondegenerate orbitals a_1 and b_1; the dt_2 orbitals are split into a nondegenerate b_2 and a doubly degenerate e orbital. The basis functions are listed in the last column of Table 4.6–1.

TABLE 4.6–1

COMPATIBILITY RELATION BETWEEN $\mathbf{O}_h$ AND $\mathbf{D}_{4h}$†

$\mathbf{O}_h$	$\mathbf{D}_{4h}$	Basis function for $\mathbf{D}_{4h}$
A_1	A_1	$(3z^2 - r^2)$
A_2	B_1	$(3)^{1/2}(x^2 - y^2)$
E	$A_1 + B_1$	
T_1	$A_2 + E$	
T_2	$B_2 + E$	(xy), $(yz$ and $zx)$

†Even and odd parities are not explicitly indicated, since the parity must be unaltered.

If we write the tetragonal potential in terms of operators L_z, L_+, and L_- in the form

$$V = B\overline{r^2}\{3L_z^2 - L(L+1)\} + F\overline{r^4}\{35L_z^4 - 30L(L+1)L_z^2 + 25L_z^2 - 6L(L+1) + 3L^2(L+1)^2\}, \quad (4.6\text{–}1)$$

the energy eigenvalues and the eigenfunctions are

$$\begin{array}{lll} A_1 & 6Dq + 2Bs + 6Ft: & deu, \\ B_1 & 6Dq - 2Bs + Ft: & dev, \\ E & -4Dq + Bs - 4Ft: & dt_2\xi \text{ and } dt_2\eta, \\ B_2 & -4Dq - 2Bs + Ft: & dt_2\xi, \end{array} \quad (4.6\text{–}2)$$

where $s = 2\overline{r^2}/7$, and $t = 8\overline{r^4}/21$. The names of the octahedral bases are retained.

If the spin-orbit interaction is added, and if the effects are smaller than the tetragonal potential, we may treat the spin-orbit interaction by the perturbation method. The spin-orbit interaction is invariant under the three-dimensional rotation group, which rotates both the orbital and spin parts. The basis functions are to be a product of orbital and spin functions. The product representations are the representations of the double point group $\mathbf{D}'_{4h}$. The pertinent product representations are

$$A_1 \times D^{1/2} = E_1'; \quad A_2 \times D^{1/2} = E_1'; \quad B_1 \times D^{1/2} = E_2';$$
$$B_2 \times D^{1/2} = E_2'; \quad E \times D^{1/2} = E_1' + E_2', \quad (4.6\text{–}3)$$

where we use the matrices $D^{1/2}$ for the transformations of $\mathbf{D}_{4h}$, referring to (1.4–2) and (1.4–4), and Appendix 2.3. As is shown in Sec. 4.5, an orbitally singlet state has a zero matrix element of the orbital angular momentum; therefore, the three orbital singlets are unperturbed by the linear effect of the spin-orbit interaction. The orbital doublet E is split into two by the linear effect. These are explicitly shown in (4.6–3). The levels belonging to the same irreducible representation disturb each other through higher-order perturbation processes. In Fig. 4.6–1 the linear effects both in the

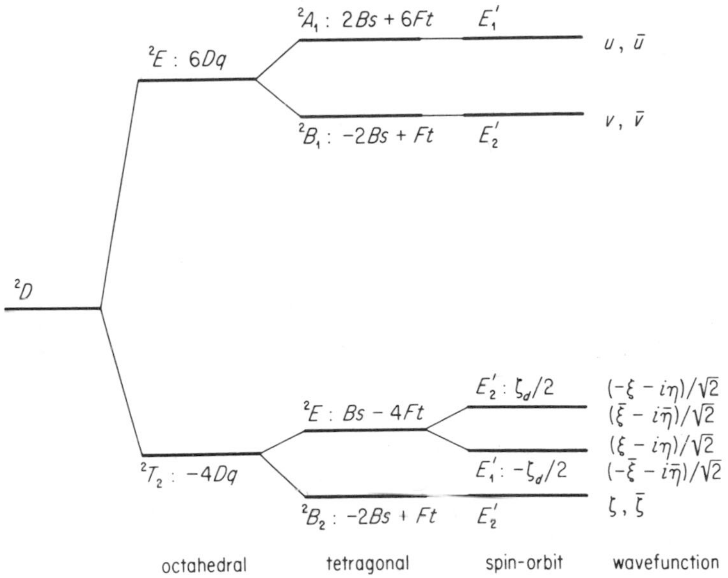

Figure 4.6-1

tetragonal potential and the spin-orbit interaction are schematically shown. The reader may work out the case of Fig. 4.6–2, where the spin-orbit effects are greater than the tetragonal potential. On the right of the levels, wavefunctions are labeled with bar for negative spin and without bar for positive spin; the names of the octahedral bases are retained.

If the spin-orbit interaction is comparable to the tetragonal potential, one has to find eigenvalue of a secular matrix, which involves matrix elements of both the spin-orbit interaction and the tetragonal potential. The six-by-six secular matrix is decomposed into two three-dimensional matrices. Each level must be at least doubly degenerate on account of Kramers' theorem (Sec. 1.12).

According to (3.11–1), an even tensor operator reverses the sign under the complementary transformation. Within the $3d$ shell, the complementary transformation transforms a system d^n into d^{10-n}; the single d electron system is transformed into the nine-electron system d^9. The crystal potential and the spin-orbit interaction are both even operators. Energy-level diagrams in Figs. 4.6–1 and 4.6–2 are inverted if one goes from a single d

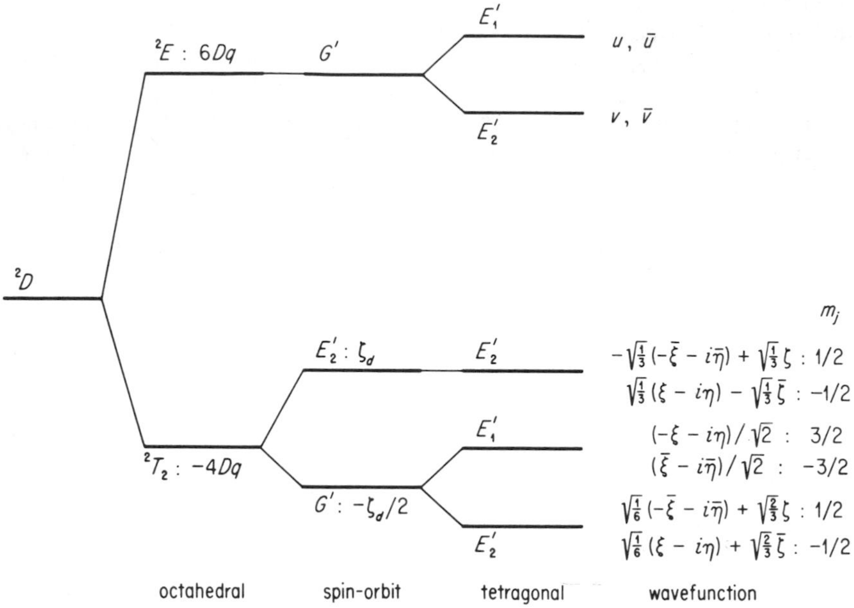

Figure 4.6-2

electron system to a single-hole system, i.e., d^9. An example for a pair of complementary systems is $3d^1$ Ti^{3+} and $3d^9$ Cu^{2+}.

Let an octahedron be subjected to a simple elongation along the [111] direction. Refer to Fig. 4.3–2(b). The two triangles Δ123 and Δ456 are left unaltered in shape. The symmetry of the potential then reduces from $\mathbf{O}_h$ to $\mathbf{D}_{3d}$. In order to calculate the effects of the additional trigonal potential, it is convenient to use the octahedral basis functions (4.5–5). The compatibility relation between $\mathbf{D}_{3d}$ and $\mathbf{O}_h$ is listed in Table 4.6–2. The trigonal potential may be expressed in the form (4.6–1). The octahedral ^2E states are unsplit; the $^2T_2$ are split into $^2A_1$ and ^2E of $\mathbf{D}_{3d}$.

TABLE 4.6–2

COMPATIBILITY RELATION BETWEEN $\mathbf{O}_h$ AND $\mathbf{D}_{3d}$†

$\mathbf{O}_h$	$\mathbf{D}_{3d}$
A_1	A_1
A_2	A_2
E	E
T_1	$A_2 + E$
T_2	$A_1 + E$

†Parities of irreducible representations are not explicitly indicated, since they are unaltered.

If the linear effects of the spin-orbit interaction are considered, the orbital doublet E remains the same in energy as the doublet of $\mathbf{D}_{3d}$, even though the product representation $E \times D^{1/2}$ is decomposed into $E_1' + E_2'$:

$$\begin{array}{lcccccc} & E & Q & C_2 & C_2' & C_3 & C_3' \\ E \times D^{1/2} = & 4 & -4 & 0 & 0 & -1 & 1 = E_1' + E_2'. \end{array}$$

The reason is as follows. The wavefunctions (4.5–5) are simply a unitary transformation of wavefunctions (4.5–3). The orbital doublet E has a null matrix for the orbital angular momentum, as shown in Sec. 4.5. The null matrix remains the same under the unitary transformation. The matrix elements of the spin-orbit interaction within the doublet E are all zero.

The irreducible representation E_1' actually consists of two one-dimensional irreducible representations that are complex conjugate. The eigenfunction belonging to one of the two is transformed with time reversal into the eigenfunction belonging to the other representation. These two eigenfunctions must be degenerate since the trigonal potential and the spin-orbit interaction are both t-invariant.

4.7 MANY d ELECTRONS IN AN OCTAHEDRAL POTENTIAL—WEAK FIELD

When an ion has more than one d electron, the electrons interact through electrostatic forces. In Sec. 4.4 we classified cases according to the magnitudes of the crystal potential relative to the electrostatic energies. The electrostatic energies are listed in Table 3.8–1. If the crystal field is considered to be weak, calculation of the crystal field effects is carried out referred to the Russell-Saunders multiplets ^{2S+1}L. There are L values ranging from 0 through 6. Crystal terms for octahedral potential are listed for $L = 0$ to 6 in Table 2.17–3. As far as the linear effects are considered, the equivalent operator method is applied.

The octahedral potential is written in the form:

$$V = \frac{B_4}{60}\{35L_z^4 - 30L(L+1)L_z^2 + 25L_z^2 - 6L(L+1) + 3L^2(L+1)^2 + \frac{5}{2}(L_+^4 + L_-^4)\}.$$

The eigenvalues and eigenvectors are straightforwardly calculated, being listed in Appendix 4.2. The sign and magnitudes of B_4 must be determined for every multiplet. The three states of T_1 are named T_11, T_10, and $T_1\,-1$, which are related to T_1x, T_1y, and T_1z through

$$T_11 = -\frac{T_1x + iT_1y}{\sqrt{2}}, \quad T_10 = T_1z, \quad T_1\,-1 = \frac{T_1x - iT_1y}{\sqrt{2}}.$$

The three states of T_2 are termed T_21, T_20, and $T_2\,-1$, which are related to $T_2\xi$, $T_2\eta$, and $T_2\zeta$ through

$$T_21 = -\frac{T_2\xi + iT_2\eta}{\sqrt{2}}, \quad T_20 = T_2\zeta, \quad T_2 - 1 = \frac{T_2\xi - iT_2\eta}{\sqrt{2}}.$$

Russell-Saunders ground states for d^n configurations, except for $n = 5$, are split in a first approximation under octahedral potential. Splitting patterns are inverted in a tetrahedral potential compared with an octahedral potential. These are schematically illustrated in Fig. 4.7–1. Russell-

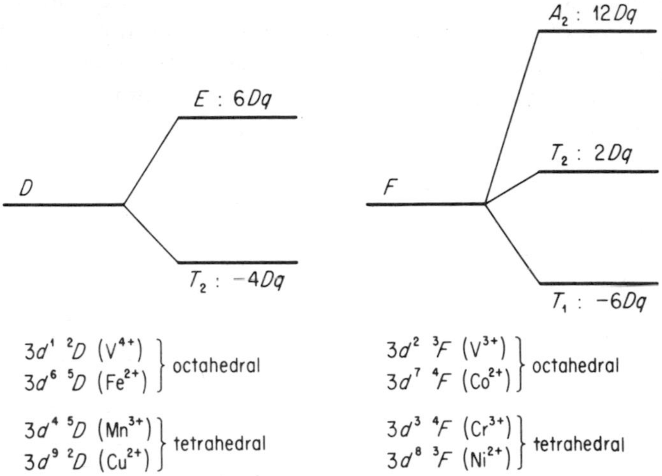

Figure 4.7-1

Saunders multiplets of d^5 are not split in any crystal potential, provided only the linear effects are considered.

Crystal eigenvectors for $d^2\ {}^3F$ are explicitly given in terms of dt_2 and de orbitals:

$$|{}^3T_1 z\ M_S = 1\rangle = -\frac{1}{5^{1/2}}(2|\xi\eta\rangle - |\zeta v\rangle),$$

$$|{}^3T_2 \zeta\ M_S = 1\rangle = |\zeta u\rangle,$$

$$|{}^3A_2\ M_S = 1\rangle = |uv\rangle,$$

where we use $d^2\ {}^3F$ wavefunctions in terms of single-electron functions in Appendix 3.1, and rewrite the d orbitals in terms of dt_2 and de orbitals. Other crystal eigenvectors for T_1 and T_2 terms can easily be found by applying $C_3^{[111]}$ with reference to Table 2.17–5.

The T_1 term consists of two configurations t_2^2 and t_2e in the ratio four to one. The crystal energy is found to be

$$(\tfrac{4}{5})(-8Dq) + (\tfrac{1}{5})(2Dq) = -6Dq \qquad \text{for } {}^3T_1.$$

The T_2 term consists of single configuration t_2e; the crystal energy is $2Dq$. The A_2 term consists of e^2; the crystal energy is $12Dq$. These energies are in agreement with those calculated by the equivalent operator method.

In a similar manner, we find crystal statevectors for $d^3\ {}^4F$ as

$$|{}^4A_2\ M_S = \tfrac{3}{2}\rangle = |\xi\eta\zeta\rangle,$$
$$|{}^4T_2\zeta\ M_S = \tfrac{3}{2}\rangle = |\xi\eta v\rangle,$$
$$|{}^4T_1 z\ M_S = \tfrac{3}{2}\rangle = (\tfrac{1}{5})^{1/2}(2|\zeta uv\rangle + |\xi\eta u\rangle).$$

The ${}^4A_2$ term consists of t_2^3; the crystal energy is $-12Dq$. The ${}^4T_2$ term consists of t_2^2e; the crystal energy is $-2Dq$. The ${}^4T_1$ term consists of two configurations t_2e^2 and t_2^2e in the ratio four to one; the crystal energy is $6Dq$.

When higher-order effects are considered, one has to calculate matrix elements between same component states of same symmetry, and of the same spin multiplicity. For example, a half-filled configuration $3d^5$ has no linear effects of crystal fields since all the diagonal matrix elements vanish (Theorem 3.12–1). The quartet states ${}^4G, {}^4F,$ and ${}^4P$ have ${}^4T_1$ terms in common. These terms perturb each other through the octahedral potential. The secular matrix is

	${}^4GT_1$	${}^4FT_1$	${}^4PT_1$
${}^4GT_1$	0	$2(5)^{1/2}Dq$	$4(5)^{1/2}Dq$
${}^4FT_1$	$2(5)^{1/2}Dq$	E_1	0
${}^4PT_1$	$4(5)^{1/2}Dq$	0	E_2

where E_1 and E_2 are the electrostatic energy difference between ${}^4G$ and ${}^4F$, and between ${}^4G$ and ${}^4P$ (see Table 3.8–1). Three ${}^4T_2$ terms from ${}^4G, {}^4F,$ and ${}^4D$ have a secular matrix of the octahedral potential:

	${}^4GT_2$	${}^4FT_2$	${}^4DT_2$
${}^4GT_2$	0	$10(\frac{3}{7})^{1/2}Dq$	0
${}^4FT_2$	$10(\frac{3}{7})^{1/2}Dq$	E_1	$20(7)^{-1/2}Dq$
${}^4DT_2$	0	$20(7)^{-1/2}Dq$	E_2

where E_1 and E_2 are the electrostatic energy difference between ${}^4G$ and ${}^4F$, and between ${}^4G$ and ${}^4D$. Matrix elements of the octahedral potential between two terms ${}^4E$ from ${}^4G$ and ${}^4D$ are shown to be zero. In calculating the matrix elements of the octahedral potential, we can use the equivalent operator in terms of $l_z, l_+,$ and l_-, not in terms of $L_z, L_+,$ and L_-. Assuming that the Racah parameters B and C for electrostatic interaction remain unchanged under the potential, we find the splitting pattern of these quartets versus the cubic field parameter Dq as shown in Fig. 4.7–2. The parameters B and C should actually depend on the magnitude of the potential, but it would be difficult to find the dependence from first principles at this time. Note that the initial slope of the levels is zero, indicating no linear effects.

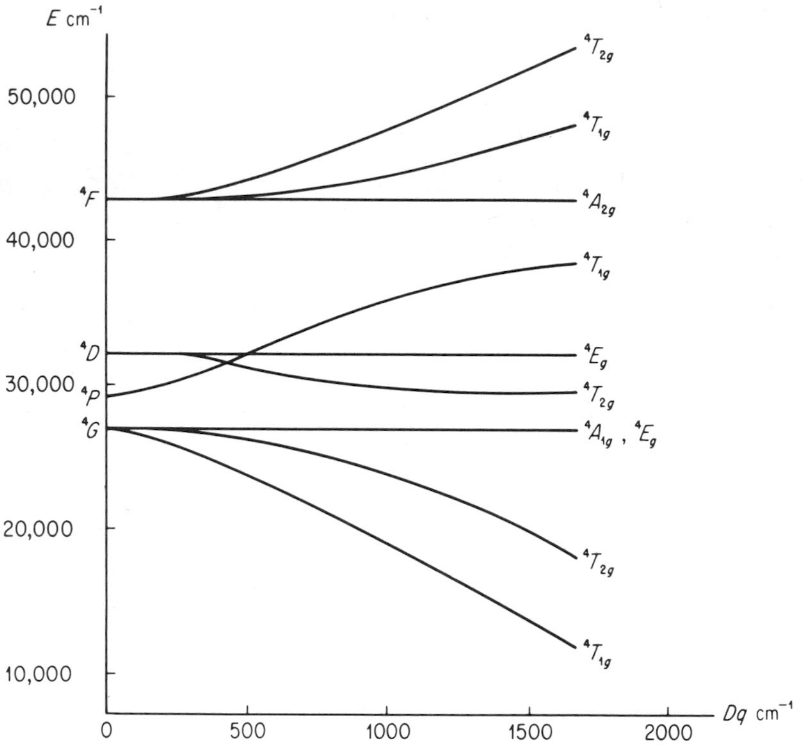

Figure 4.7-2

Higher-order effects for other configurations are calculated in a similar way.†

4.8 MANY d ELECTRONS IN AN OCTAHEDRAL POTENTIAL—STRONG FIELD

When the crystal energy is much greater than the electrostatic energy between electrons, the electrons are first placed in the t_2 orbitals and then in the e orbitals. The crystal energy for a configuration $t_2^m e^n$ is $(-4m + 6n)Dq$. Wavefunctions for strong-field crystal terms are obtained with full use of Clebsch-Gordan coefficients tabulated in Appendix 2.4, and symmetry properties listed in Table 2.17–5 for octahedral group. The wavefunctions are listed in Appendix 4.3, for configurations $t_2^m e^n$ with $m + n = 1$ to 5. For T_1 and T_2 terms, only the z component and ζ component are given, since the other two components are easily obtained by applying $C_3^{[111]}$. The ground crystal terms for four, five, six, and seven electrons are

†L. E. Orgel, *J. Chem. Phys.* **23**, 1004 (1955).

$$t_2^4\,{}^3T_1;\quad t_2^5\,{}^2T_2;\quad t_2^6\,{}^1A_1;\quad \text{and}\quad t_2^6e\,{}^2E.$$

These are compared with the corresponding weak-field ground crystal terms:

$$t_2^3e\,{}^5E;\quad t_2^3e^2\,{}^6A_1;\quad t_2^4e^2\,{}^5T_2;\quad \text{and}\quad \tfrac{1}{5}t_2^4e^3 + \tfrac{4}{5}t_2^5e^2\,{}^4T_1,$$

where the last term contains two configurations in the ratio indicated. Ground crystal terms for other systems are the same for both weak and strong fields. Yet, the two-electron weak-field term ${}^3T_1$ contains two configurations as shown in the previous section.

The strong-field ground and excited terms are perturbed by the electrostatic interaction $\mathbf{G} = \sum e^2/r_{\mu\nu}$ between the electrons. The electrostatic interaction is invariant under the transformations of the octahedral group $\mathbf{O}_h$, belonging to the identity representation A_1. The nonvanishing matrix elements

$$\langle ab|g|cd\rangle = \iint a(1)\,b(2)\frac{e^2}{r_{12}}\,c(1)d(2)\,d\tau_1 d\tau_2$$

arc between two products ab and cd that belong to the same irreducible representation (Theorem 2.20–3). There are fifteen linearly independent products:

$$\xi^2, \eta^2, \zeta^2, u^2\ v^2, \xi\eta, \eta\zeta, \zeta\xi, \xi u, \eta u, \zeta u, \xi v, \eta v, \zeta v, \text{ and } uv.$$

Linear combinations of these products are classified according to the irreducible representations of $\mathbf{O}_h$:

$$\begin{aligned}
a_1&: \quad \frac{\xi^2+\eta^2+\zeta^2}{\sqrt{3}}, \frac{u^2+v^2}{\sqrt{2}},\\
eu&: \quad \frac{-\xi^2-\eta^2+2\zeta^2}{\sqrt{6}}, \frac{u^2-v^2}{\sqrt{2}},\\
ev&: \quad \frac{\xi^2-\eta^2}{\sqrt{2}}, -(2)^{1/2}\,uv,\\
t_1x&: \quad -\tfrac{1}{2}(3)^{1/2}\xi u - \tfrac{1}{2}\xi v,\\
t_1y&: \quad \tfrac{1}{2}(3)^{1/2}\eta u - \tfrac{1}{2}\eta v,\\
t_1z&: \quad \zeta v,\\
t_2\xi&: \quad \eta\zeta, -\tfrac{1}{2}\xi u + \tfrac{1}{2}(3)^{1/2}\xi v,\\
t_2\eta&: \quad \zeta\xi, -\tfrac{1}{2}\eta\mu + \tfrac{1}{2}(3)^{1/2}\eta v,\\
t_2\zeta&: \quad \xi\eta, \zeta u.
\end{aligned}$$

There are ten direct products that contain the identity representation A_1: three from $A_1 \times A_1$; three from $E \times E$; one from $T_1 \times T_1$; and three from $T_2 \times T_2$. There are, therefore, ten independent matrix elements, to which other elements are somehow related. The t_2 and e orbitals are real; we have a relation $\langle ab|g|ba\rangle = \langle aa|g|bb\rangle$. Matrix relations are listed in Table 4.8–1, being found with full use of Table 2.17–5. The ten parameters $a, b,$

TABLE 4.8–1

MATRIX RELATIONS AMONG ELECTROSTATIC INTERACTION INTEGRALS $\langle ab|g|cd\rangle$†

$$
\begin{aligned}
\langle\xi\xi|g|\xi\xi\rangle &= \langle\eta\eta|g|\eta\eta\rangle = \langle\zeta\zeta|g|\zeta\zeta\rangle = a = A + 4B + 3C,\\
\langle\xi\xi|g|\eta\eta\rangle &= \langle\eta\eta|g|\zeta\zeta\rangle = \langle\zeta\zeta|g|\xi\xi\rangle = \langle\xi\eta|g|\eta\xi\rangle\\
&= \langle\eta\zeta|g|\zeta\eta\rangle = \langle\zeta\xi|g|\xi\zeta\rangle = j = 3B + C,\\
\langle\xi\eta|g|\xi\eta\rangle &= \langle\eta\zeta|g|\eta\zeta\rangle = \langle\zeta\xi|g|\zeta\xi\rangle = b = A - 2B + C,\\
\langle\xi u|g|\xi v\rangle &= -\langle\eta u|g|\eta v\rangle = c = 2(3)^{1/2}B,\\
\langle\xi v|g|\xi v\rangle &= \langle\eta v|g|\eta v\rangle = d = A - 2B + C,\\
\langle\xi u|g|\xi u\rangle &= \langle\eta u|g|\eta u\rangle = 2(3)^{-1/2}c + d = A + 2B + C,\\
\langle\zeta u|g|\zeta u\rangle &= d - (3)^{-1/2}c = A - 4B + C,\\
\langle\zeta v|g|\zeta v\rangle &= d + (3)^{1/2}c = A + 4B + C,\\
\langle uu|g|uu\rangle &= \langle vv|g|vv\rangle = e = A + 4B + 3C,\\
\langle uu|g|vv\rangle &= \langle uv|g|vu\rangle = f = 4B + C,\\
\langle uv|g|uv\rangle &= e - 2f = A - 4B + C,\\
\langle\xi\xi|g|uu\rangle &= \langle\eta\eta|g|uu\rangle = g = B + C,\\
-\langle\xi\xi|g|uv\rangle &= \langle\eta\eta|g|uv\rangle = h = (3)^{1/2}B,\\
\langle\xi\xi|g|vv\rangle &= \langle\eta\eta|g|vv\rangle = g + 2(3)^{-1/2}h = 3B + C,\\
\langle\zeta\zeta|g|uu\rangle &= g + (3)^{1/2}h = 4B + C,\\
\langle\zeta\zeta|g|vv\rangle &= g - (3)^{-1/2}h = C,\\
\langle\xi\eta|g|\zeta u\rangle &= \langle\eta\xi|g|\zeta u\rangle = \langle\zeta\xi|g|\eta u\rangle = \langle\zeta\eta|g|\xi u\rangle = i = (3)^{1/2}B,\\
\langle\eta\zeta|g|\xi u\rangle &= \langle\xi\zeta|g|\eta u\rangle = -2i = -2(3)^{1/2}B,\\
\langle\xi\eta|g|\zeta v\rangle &= -\langle\eta\xi|g|\zeta v\rangle = (3)^{1/2}i = 3B,\\
\langle\zeta\xi|g|\eta v\rangle &= -\langle\zeta\eta|g|\xi v\rangle = -(3)^{1/2}i = -3B,\\
\langle\eta\zeta|g|\xi v\rangle &= -\langle\xi\zeta|g|\eta v\rangle = 0.
\end{aligned}
$$

†The parameters $a, b, \ldots, j$ are the same as those given by J. S. Griffith, *The Theory of Transition Metal Ions* (London: Cambridge University Press, 1961), p. 409.

$\ldots, j$ are often too many for practical analysis of experimental observation. It may be more or less convenient to express the ten parameters in terms of Racah parameters A, B, and C, even though these three parameters are not necessarily the same as those for free states.

The electrostatic interaction $\mathbf{G}$ is expanded in terms of spherical harmonics [see (3.8–11)]:

$$\mathbf{G} = \sum_{\mu>\nu} \sum_{n=0}^{\infty} \frac{r_<^n}{r_>^{n+1}} \sum_{m=-n}^{n} (-1)^m C_{nm}(\mu) C_{n-m}(\nu), \tag{4.8–1}$$

where

$$C_{nm} = \left(\frac{4\pi}{2n+1}\right)^{1/2} Y_{nm}. \tag{4.8–2}$$

If the wavefunctions are separated into radial and angular parts, matrix elements are also separated in two. The radial integrals F^n are written in the form

$$F^n = e^2 \iint \frac{r_<^n}{r_>^{n+1}} f^2(1) f^2(2) r_1^2\, dr_1\, r_2^2\, dr_2$$
$$= 2e^2 \int_0^\infty r^{-(n+1)} f^2 r^2\, dr \int_0^r r'^n f^2 r'^2\, dr'.\dagger$$

The Racah parameters A, B, and C are related to F^0, F^2, and F^4 by

$$A = F_0 - 49F_4, \quad B = F_2 - 5F_4, \quad \text{and} \quad C = 35F_4,$$

where

$$F_0 = F^0, \quad F_2 = \frac{F^2}{49}, \quad \text{and} \quad F_4 = \frac{F^4}{441}.$$

The angular parts are calculated with use of equivalent operators listed in Table 4.8–2 for $n = 2$ and 4. The matrix elements of operators C_{nm} are

TABLE 4.8–2
EQUIVALENT OPERATORS FOR C_{nm}, $n = 2$ AND 4†

C_{nm}	Equivalent operator
$C_{20} =$	$\frac{1}{2}\alpha\{3l_z^2 - l(l+1)\}$
$C_{2\pm1} =$	$\mp\left(\frac{3}{8}\right)^{1/2} \alpha l_\pm(2l_z \pm 1)$
$C_{2\pm2} =$	$\left(\frac{3}{8}\right)^{1/2} \alpha l_\pm^2$
$C_{40} =$	$\frac{1}{8}\beta\{35l_z^4 - 30l(l+1)l_z^2 + 25l_z^2 - 6l(l+1) + 3l^2(l+1)^2\}$
$C_{4\pm1} =$	$\mp\frac{1}{8}\beta(5)^{1/2} l_\pm\{14l_z^3 \pm 21l_z^2 + 19l_z - 6l(l+1)l_z \mp 3l(l+1) \pm 6\}$
$C_{4\pm2} =$	$\frac{1}{8}\beta(10)^{1/2} l_\pm^2\{7l_z^2 \pm 14l_z - l(l+1) + 9\}$
$C_{4\pm3} =$	$\mp\frac{1}{8}\beta(35)^{1/2} l_\pm^3(2l_z \pm 3)$
$C_{4\pm4} =$	$\frac{1}{8}\beta\left(\frac{35}{2}\right)^{1/2} l_\pm^4$

†For d electrons $\alpha = -2/21$, $\beta = 2/63$.

listed in Table 4.8–3, for d electrons.

Electrostatic interaction energies for the two-electron system are calculated with the use of wavefunctions in Appendix 4.3 and Table 8–1. They are simply given by the diagonal elements:

t_2^2 configuration:

$$\langle {}^3T_1|\mathbf{G}|{}^3T_1\rangle = b - j \quad (= A - 5B),$$

†See, for instance, O. Laporte, *Phys. Rev.* **61**, 302 (1942).

TABLE 4.8–3†

MATRIX ELEMENTS OF C_{nm}, $m = m_1 - m_2$

m_1	m_2	$n = 0$	2	4
± 2	± 2	1	$-\left(\frac{4}{49}\right)^{1/2}$	$\left(\frac{1}{441}\right)^{1/2}$
± 2	± 1	0	6‡	$-$ 5‡
± 2	0	0	-4	15
± 1	± 1	1	1	-16
± 1	0	0	1	30
0	0	1	4	36
± 2	∓ 2	0	0	70
± 2	∓ 1	0	0	-35
± 1	∓ 1	0	-6	-40

†More tables are available, for instance, in Condon and Shortley, *The Theory of Atomic Spectra*, sec. 6-9.

‡Square root and denominator are omitted in the remainder of the column.

$$\langle {}^1E|\mathbf{G}|{}^1E\rangle = a - j \quad (= A + B + 2C),$$
$$\langle {}^1T_2|\mathbf{G}|{}^1T_2\rangle = b + j \quad (= A + B + 2C),$$
$$\langle {}^1A_1|\mathbf{G}|{}^1A_1\rangle = a + 2j \quad (= A + 10B + 5C),$$

t_2e configuration:

$$\langle {}^3T_1|\mathbf{G}|{}^3T_1\rangle = d + (3)^{1/2}c - g + (3)^{-1/2}h \quad (= A + 4B),$$
$$\langle {}^3T_2|\mathbf{G}|{}^3T_2\rangle = d - (3)^{-1/2}c - g - (3)^{1/2}h \quad (= A - 8B),$$
$$\langle {}^1T_1|\mathbf{G}|{}^1T_1\rangle = d + (3)^{1/2}c + g - (3)^{-1/2}h \quad (= A + 4B + 2C),$$
$$\langle {}^1T_2|\mathbf{G}|{}^1T_2\rangle = d - (3)^{-1/2}c + g + (3)^{1/2}h \quad (= A + 2C),$$

e^2 configuration:

$$\langle {}^3A_2|\mathbf{G}|{}^3A_2\rangle = e - 3f \quad (= A - 8B),$$
$$\langle {}^1A_1|\mathbf{G}|{}^1A_1\rangle = e + f \quad (= A + 8B + 4C),$$
$$\langle {}^1E|\mathbf{G}|{}^1E\rangle = e - f \quad (= A + 2C).$$

In a similar way, we find the electrostatic energies for crystal terms of t_2^3 configuration:

$$^4A_2 = 3b - 3j \qquad (= 3A - 15B),$$
$$^2E = 3b \qquad (= 3A - 6B + 3C),$$
$$^2T_1 = a + 2b - 2j \quad (= 3A - 6B + 3C),$$
$$^2T_2 = a + 2b \qquad (= 3A + 5C).$$

One may proceed with similar calculations; yet, the complementary transformation relates relative energy between two complementary states. This will be shown in the next section.

Ground term energies for strong- and weak-field cases are listed in Table 4.8–4. Strong-field ground terms for four, five, six, and seven electrons are characterized by lower spin than the corresponding weak-field terms.

TABLE 4.8–4

GROUND TERMS AND ENERGIES FOR STRONG- AND WEAK-FIELD CASES

Strong field		Weak field	
$t_2\ ^2T_2$	$-4Dq$	$d\ ^2T_2$	$-4Dq$
$t_2^2\ ^3T_1$	$-8Dq+b-j$ $=-8Dq+A-5B$	$d^2\ ^3T_1$	$-6Dq+A-5B$
$t_2^3\ ^4A_2$	$-12Dq+3b-3j$ $=-12Dq+3A-15B$	$d^3\ ^4A_2$	$-12Dq+3A-15B$
$t_2^4\ ^3T_1$	$-16Dq+a+5b-3j$ $=-16Dq+6A-15B+5C$	$d^4\ ^5E$	$-6Dq+6A-21B$
$t_2^5\ ^2T_2$	$-20Dq+2a+8b-4j$ $=-20Dq+10A-20B+10C$	$d^5\ ^6A_1$	$10A-35B$
$t_2^6\ ^1A_1$	$-24Dq+3a+12b-6j$ $=-24Dq+15A-30B+15C$	$d^6\ ^5T_2$	$-4Dq+15A-35B+7C$
$t_2^6e\ ^2E$	$-18Dq+3a+12b-6j+6d$ $+2(3)^{1/2}c-3g-(3)^{1/2}h$ $=-18Dq+21A-36B+18C$	$d^7\ ^4T_1$	$-6Dq+21A-40B+14C$
$t_2^6e^2\ ^3A_2$	$-12Dq+3a+12b-6j+12d$ $+4(3)^{1/2}c+e-3f-6g-2(3)^{1/2}h$ $=-12Dq+28A-50B+21C$	$d^8\ ^3A_2$	$-12Dq+28A-50B+21C$
$t_2^6e^3\ ^2E$	$-6Dq+3a+12b-6j+18d+6(3)^{1/2}c$ $+3e-5f-9g-3(3)^{1/2}h$ $=-6Dq+36A-56B+28C$	$d^9\ ^2E$	$-6Dq+36A-56B+28C$
$t_2^6e^4\ ^1A_1$	$3a+12b-6j+24d+8(3)^{1/2}c$ $+6e-10f-12g-4(3)^{1/2}h$ $=45A-70B+35C$	$d^{10}\ ^1A_1$	$45A-70B+35C$

Such low-spin states are experimentally found in potassium ferricyanide $K_3Fe(CN)_6$ from measurements of its magnetic susceptibility.†

4.9 ELECTROSTATIC ENERGY FOR COMPLEMENTARY CONFIGURATIONS

By analogy with (3.8–1), we expand the electrostatic interaction (4.8–1) in terms of operators that transform as irreducible basis functions of the octahedral group:

$$\mathbf{G} = \sum_{\mu<\nu} \sum_{n} \frac{r_<^n}{r_>^{n+1}} \sum_{\gamma,\, i} C_{n\gamma i}(\mu) C_{n\gamma i}(\nu), \tag{4.9–1}$$

where $C_{n\gamma i}$ is a linear combination of spherical harmonic operators of order

†For example, M. Kotani, *Suppl. Progr. Theoret. Phys.* (*Kyoto*) no. 14, 1 (1960).

n and transforms as the component i of the γth irreducible representation. If we consider t_2 and e orbitals to be of even parity, we need not consider the odd-order terms in (4.9–1). Relevant operators $C_{n\gamma i}$ with $n = 0, 2$, and 4 are classified to A_1 for $n = 0$ and 4; to E for $n = 2$ and 4; to T_1 for $n=4$; and to T_2 for $n = 2$ and 4.

In the case of two shells t_2 and e, the expression (3.5–2) for a two-electron operator is written in the form

$$\begin{aligned}\mathbf{G} = {} & \tfrac{1}{2}\sum (t_2)\langle pq|g|rs\rangle a_p^+ a_q^+ a_s a_r \\ & + \tfrac{1}{2}\sum (e)\langle pq|g|rs\rangle a_p^+ a_q^+ a_s a_r \\ & + \sum_{pr} (t_2) \sum_{qs} (e)\langle pq|g|rs\rangle a_p^+ a_q^+ a_s a_r \end{aligned} \tag{4.9–2}$$

where the summation $\sum (t_2)$ stands for the summation over six single-electron states in the t_2 shell. Each term can be separated into two parts, i.e., scalar-scalar product and tensor-tensor product terms. The scalar-scalar product term is written, according to (3.8–6), in the form

$$G_s(\alpha) = \tfrac{1}{2}\sum_n G^n(\alpha)\langle \alpha i|C_{nA_1}|\alpha i\rangle^2 \times \mathbf{n}(\mathbf{n}-1), \tag{4.9–3}$$

where α is either a t_2 or an e orbital, and $\mathbf{n}$ is the number operator in either orbital. The parameter $G^n(\alpha)$ is the radial integral with respect to a t_2 or an e orbital; it becomes F^n if a d radial function is used for the radial part of the t_2 and e orbitals. The scalar-scalar term for the last term in (4.9–2) is

$$\mathbf{G}_s(t_2e) = \sum_n G^n(t_2e)\langle t_2 i|C_{nA_1}|t_2 i\rangle \langle ei|C_{nA_1}|ei\rangle \times \mathbf{n}(t_2)\mathbf{n}(e), \tag{4.9–4}$$

where $G^n(t_2e)$ is a radial integral corresponding to the matrix product involved. The component i may be an arbitrary component of three components of t_2 or of two components of e.

The tensor-tensor product term for the first two terms in (4.9–2) is, according to (3.8–3), written as

$$\begin{aligned}\mathbf{G}_t(\alpha) = {} & \tfrac{1}{2}\sum_n \sum_{\gamma i} F_{n\gamma i}(\alpha)F_{n\gamma i}(\alpha) \\ & - \tfrac{1}{2}\sum_n \sum_{\beta j} G^n(\alpha\beta\alpha\beta)\sum_{\gamma k}\langle \alpha i|C_{n\gamma k}|\beta j\rangle\langle \beta j|C_{n\gamma k}|\alpha i\rangle \times \mathbf{n}(\alpha), \end{aligned} \tag{4.9–5}$$

where β is summed over t_2 and e orbitals. The parameter $G^n(\alpha\beta\alpha\beta)$ is a radial integral corresponding to the matrix product, being equal to $G^n(\alpha)$ if $\alpha = \beta$. The operator $F_{n\gamma i}(\alpha)$ is

$$F_{n\gamma i}(\alpha) = \sum_{pr}\langle p|C_{n\gamma i}|r\rangle a_p^+ a_r, \tag{4.9–6}$$

where the summation is over the t_2 shell or e shell. The tensor-tensor product term for the last term in (4.9–2) lacks the term proportional to the number operator:

$$\mathbf{G}_t(t_2e) = \sum_{n\gamma i} F_{n\gamma i}(t_2)F_{n\gamma i}(e). \tag{4.9–7}$$

The matrix elements $\langle \alpha i|C_{n\gamma k}|\beta j\rangle$ are related through symmetry transformations. Using Table 2.17–5, we find the relations, which are independent of n:

$$\begin{aligned}
\langle\xi|A_1|\xi\rangle &= \langle\eta|A_1|\eta\rangle = \langle\zeta|A_1|\zeta\rangle,\\
\langle u|A_1|u\rangle &= \langle v|A_1|v\rangle,\\
\langle\xi|Eu|\xi\rangle &= \langle\eta|Eu|\eta\rangle = -\tfrac{1}{2}\langle\zeta|Eu|\zeta\rangle = -(\tfrac{1}{3})^{1/2}\langle\xi|Ev|\xi\rangle\\
&= (\tfrac{1}{3})^{1/2}\langle\eta|Ev|\eta\rangle,\\
\langle\zeta|Ev|\zeta\rangle &= 0,\\
\langle u|Eu|u\rangle &= -\langle v|Eu|v\rangle = -\langle u|Ev|v\rangle = -\langle v|Ev|u\rangle,\\
\langle u|Ev|u\rangle &= \langle v|Ev|v\rangle = 0,\\
\langle\xi|T_1x|v\rangle &= \langle\eta|T_1y|v\rangle = -\tfrac{1}{2}\langle\zeta|T_1z|v\rangle = (\tfrac{1}{3})^{1/2}\langle\xi|T_1x|u\rangle\\
&= -(\tfrac{1}{3})^{1/2}\langle\eta|T_1y|u\rangle,\\
\langle\zeta|T_1z|u\rangle &= 0,\\
\langle\xi|T_2\eta|\zeta\rangle &= \langle\eta|T_2\zeta|\xi\rangle = \langle\zeta|T_2\xi|\eta\rangle,\\
\langle\xi|T_2\xi|u\rangle &= \langle\eta|T_2\eta|u\rangle = -\tfrac{1}{2}\langle\zeta|T_2\zeta|u\rangle\\
&= -(\tfrac{1}{3})^{1/2}\langle\xi|T_2\xi|v\rangle = (\tfrac{1}{3})^{1/2}\langle\eta|T_2\eta|v\rangle,
\end{aligned}$$

where the notations α, β, and C are omitted for brevity, since no confusion can occur. If we assume that the angular dependence of t_2 and e orbitals is the same as that of dt_2 and de orbitals (4.5–3), we can calculate the matrix elements $\langle\alpha i|C_{n\gamma k}|\beta j\rangle$, referring to Appendix 2.1 and Table 4.8–3. For instance,

$$C_4(Eu) = (\tfrac{10}{24})^{1/2}C_{40} - (\tfrac{7}{24})^{1/2}(C_{44} + C_{4-4}).$$

The numerical values are listed in Table 4.9–1.

TABLE 4.9–1

NUMERICAL VALUES OF MATRIX ELEMENTS $\langle\alpha i|C_{n\gamma k}|\beta j\rangle$; NOTATIONS α, β, AND C ARE OMITTED

$n =$	0	2	4
$\langle\xi\|A_1\|\xi\rangle$	1	0	$-\left(\frac{14}{24}\right)^{1/2}\left(\frac{16}{441}\right)^{1/2}$
$\langle u\|A_1\|u\rangle$	1	0	$\left(\frac{14}{24}\right)^{1/2}\left(\frac{36}{441}\right)^{1/2}$
$\langle\xi\|Eu\|\xi\rangle$	0	$\left(\frac{1}{49}\right)^{1/2}$	$-\left(\frac{10}{24}\right)^{1/2}\left(\frac{16}{441}\right)^{1/2}$
$\langle u\|Eu\|u\rangle$	0	$\left(\frac{4}{49}\right)^{1/2}$	$\left(\frac{10}{24}\right)^{1/2}\left(\frac{36}{441}\right)^{1/2}$
$\langle\xi\|T_1x\|v\rangle$	0	0	$-\left(\frac{1}{8}\right)^{1/2}\left(\frac{70}{441}\right)^{1/2}$
$\langle\xi\|T_2\eta\|\zeta\rangle$	0	$\left(\frac{3}{49}\right)^{1/2}$	$\left(\frac{1}{2}\right)^{1/2}\left(\frac{40}{441}\right)^{1/2}$
$\langle\xi\|T_2\xi\|u\rangle$	0	$\left(\frac{1}{49}\right)^{1/2}$	$-\left(\frac{1}{4}\right)^{1/2}\left(\frac{15}{441}\right)^{1/2}$

Inserting the numerical values of $\langle\alpha i|C_{nA_1}|\alpha i\rangle$ into (4.9–3), we have the scalar-scalar product terms:

$$\mathbf{G}_s(t_2) = \tfrac{1}{2}\{G_0(t_2) + \tfrac{28}{3}G_4(t_2)\}\mathbf{n}(t_2)\{\mathbf{n}(t_2) - 1\},$$
$$\mathbf{G}_s(e) = \tfrac{1}{2}\{G_0(e) + 21G_4(e)\}\mathbf{n}(e)\{\mathbf{n}(e) - 1\}, \quad (4.9\text{–}8)$$
$$\mathbf{G}_s(t_2e) = \{G_0(t_2e) - 14G_4(t_2e)\}\mathbf{n}(t_2)\mathbf{n}(e),$$

where $G_0 = G^0$, and $G_4 = G^4/441$. Calculating the second term of (4.9–5), we find the tensor-tensor product terms to be

$$\mathbf{G}_t(t_2) = \tfrac{1}{2}\sum_n \sum_{\gamma i} F_{n\gamma i}(t_2)F_{n\gamma i}(t_2)$$
$$-\tfrac{1}{2}\{10G_2(t_2) + 4G_2(t_2et_2e) + 66\tfrac{2}{3}G_4(t_2) + 50G_4(t_2et_2e)\}\mathbf{n}(t_2),$$

and

$$\mathbf{G}_t(e) = \tfrac{1}{2}\sum_n \sum_{\gamma i} F_{n\gamma i}(e)F_{n\gamma i}(e)$$
$$-\tfrac{1}{2}\{8G_2(e) + 6G_2(t_2et_2e) + 30G_4(e) + 75G_4(t_2et_2e)\}\mathbf{n}(e),$$

where $G_2 = G^2/49$. If we assume the same radial function for t_2 and e orbitals, the parameters G_0, G_2, and G_4 become F_0, F_2, and F_4.

Since we have two shells t_2 and e, the complementary transformation transforms a configuration $t_2^m e^n$ into $t_2^{6-m}e^{4-n}$. The C-operator transforms $n(t_2)$ into $6 - n(t_2)$, and $n(e)$ into $4 - n(e)$. The C-operator commutes with the product $F_{n\gamma i}F_{n\gamma i}$ in (4.9–5) and (4.9–7); the first terms in (4.9–5) and (4.9–7) are invariant under the C-operator and contribute the same amount of electrostatic energy to two complementary states. The energy difference between two complementary states arises from other terms containing the number operators. It is straightforward to find the difference as

$$E(t_2^{6-m}e^{4-n}) - E(t_2^m e^n)$$
$$= (-5m + 15)G_0(t_2) + (-3n + 6)G_0(e) + (24 - 6n - 4m)G_0(t_2e)$$
$$+ (-30 + 10m)G_2(t_2) + (-16 + 8n)G_2(e) + (-24 + 4m + 6n)G_2(t_2et_2e)$$
$$+ (-60 + 20m)G_4(t_2) + (66 - 33n)G_4(e) + (-336 + 56m + 84n)G_4(t_2e)$$
$$+ (-300 + 50m + 75n)G_4(t_2et_2e).$$

If we put the parameters G_n equal to F_n, we have the energy difference

$$E(t_2^{6-m}e^{4-n}) - E(t_2^m e^n)$$
$$= \{45 - 9(m + n)\}A + \{-70 + 14(m + n)\}B + \{35 - 7(m + n)\}C, \quad (4.9\text{–}9)$$

i.e., the energy difference is determined only by the total number $(m + n)$ of electrons among t_2 and e orbitals, not by the individual number in the respective orbitals.

4.10 MANY d ELECTRONS IN AN OCTAHEDRAL POTENTIAL: INTERMEDIATE FIELD

When the electrostatic energy and the crystal potential energy are comparable, we have to treat these effects by solving secular determinants that involve matrix elements of both interactions. We may choose one of two schemes—one that diagonalizes the crystal energy or one that diagonalizes the electrostatic interaction. Tanabe and Sugano carried out extensive calculations using the first scheme.† Orgel treated the problem by the second scheme, and calculated energy diagrams for V^{+++}, Cr^{+++}, Mn^{++}, Co^{++}, and Ni^{++} in octahedral and tetrahedral potentials.‡ Following the literature, we call the first scheme the *strong-field coupling scheme* and the second scheme the *weak-field coupling scheme*. An example of the weak-field coupling scheme has already been given in Sec. 4.7, i.e., Mn^{++} in an octahedral potential field. We shall now show a strong-field coupling scheme calculation.

Let us consider an ion with two electrons distributed among the t_2 and e shells. According to Appendix 4.3, there are eleven crystal terms:

$$\begin{aligned} t_2^2 &: \ {}^3T_1,\ {}^1E,\ {}^1T_2,\ {}^1A_1, \\ t_2e &: \ {}^3T_1,\ {}^1T_1,\ {}^3T_2,\ {}^1T_2, \\ e^2 &: \ {}^1E,\ {}^1A_1,\ {}^3A_2. \end{aligned}$$

One notes that there are crystal terms that belong to the same irreducible representation and to the same spin quantum number, e.g., two ${}^3T_1$ terms arising from t_2^2 and t_2e configurations. The electrostatic interaction between electrons results in admixing such two terms since it has nonvanishing matrix elements between them. In order to find the energy eigenvalues of the pairs of admixed terms, it is necessary to solve secular determinants which involve both the crystal energy and the electrostatic energy. The crystal energy appears along the diagonal, being given by $(-4m + 6n)Dq$ for the $t_2^m e^n$ configuration. The diagonal matrix elements of the electrostatic interaction have already been obtained in Sec. 4.8. The off-diagonal elements are calculated using the wavefunctions listed in Appendix 4.3, Eq. (3.2–11), and Table 4.8–1. For example, the matrix element between two crystal terms $t_2^2\,{}^3T_2$ and $t_2e\ {}^3T_1$ is calculated as follows:

$$\begin{aligned} &\langle t_2^2\,{}^3T_1 z M_S = 1|\mathbf{G}|t_2e\,{}^3T_1 z M_S = 1\rangle && \text{(see Appendix 4.3)} \\ &= \langle \xi\eta|g|\zeta v\rangle - \langle \xi\eta|g|v\zeta\rangle && \text{[see Eq. (3.2–11)]} \\ &= 6B, && \text{(see Table 4.8–1)} \end{aligned}$$

where $\mathbf{G}$ is the electrostatic interaction. The crystal term ${}^3T_1$ is ninefold degenerate, i.e., threefold both in the orbital and spin states. The nonvanishing elements are obtained only between the states that are characterized by the same label of the irreducible representation T_1 and by the same spin component M_S. These elements take the same value by the following reasoning. If we transform the matrix element given above with

†Y. Tanabe and S. Sugano, *J. Phys. Soc. Japan* **9**, 753, 766 (1954).
‡L. E. Orgel, *J. Chem. Phys.* **23**, 1004 (1955).

the rotation $C_3^{[111]}$, we obtain

$$\langle t_2^2\,{}^3T_1x\;M_S = 1|\mathbf{G}|t_2e\,{}^3T_1x\;M_S = 1\rangle,$$

which must be equal to the original element since it is a scalar quantity. The operator **G** commutes with the spin shift operator, i.e., $\mathbf{G}S_- = S_-\mathbf{G}$ or $S_-^{-1}\mathbf{G}S_- = \mathbf{G}$, where S_-^{-1} is defined to operate in the range $S > M_S \geqslant -S+1$. If **G** in the matrix element is replaced by $S_-^{-1}\mathbf{G}S_-$, we obtain

$$\langle t_2^2\,{}^3T_1z\;M_S = 0|\mathbf{G}|t_2e\,{}^3T_1z\;M_S = 0\rangle,$$

which must be equal to the original value.

The other nonvanishing matrix elements are calculated in a similar way; they are

$$\langle t_2^2\,{}^1E|\mathbf{G}|e^2\,{}^1E\rangle = 2(3)^{1/2}B,$$

$$\langle t_2^2\,{}^1T_2|\mathbf{G}|t_2e\,{}^1T_2\rangle = 2(3)^{1/2}B,$$

and

$$\langle t_2^2\,{}^1A_1|\mathbf{G}|e^2\,{}^1A_1\rangle = (6)^{1/2}(2B + C).$$

The secular matrix for the two ${}^3T_1$ states, apart from the common term A along the diagonal, is

$$\begin{array}{cc} t_2^2 & t_2e \end{array}$$
$$\begin{bmatrix} -8Dq - 5B & 6B \\ 6B & 2Dq + 4B \end{bmatrix}.$$

The eigenvalues for the two admixed ${}^3T_1$ states are

$$\mathcal{E} = \tfrac{1}{2}[-6Dq - B \pm \{(10Dq + 9B)^2 + 144B^2\}^{1/2}].$$

In a similar way, we find for other admixed states

$$\mathcal{E} = \tfrac{1}{2}[4Dq + B + 4C \pm \{(20Dq - B)^2 + 48B^2\}^{1/2}] \qquad \text{for } {}^1E \text{ states,}$$

$$\mathcal{E} = \tfrac{1}{2}[-6Dq + B + 4C \pm \{(10Dq - B)^2 + 48B^2\}^{1/2}] \qquad \text{for } {}^1T_2 \text{ states,}$$

and

$$\mathcal{E} = \tfrac{1}{2}[4Dq + 18B + 9C \pm \{(20Dq - 2B - C)^2 + 24(2B + C)^2\}^{1/2}] \qquad \text{for } {}^1A_1 \text{ states.}$$

The other crystal terms that have no partner to be admixed have the energies, apart from A,

$$12Dq - 8B \qquad \text{for } e^2\,{}^3A_2,$$

$$2Dq - 8B \qquad \text{for } t_2e\,{}^3T_2,$$

and

$$2Dq + 4B + 2C \qquad \text{for } t_2e\,{}^1T_1.$$

These energy values are easily converted to those for an ion with eight electrons distributed among the t_2 and e shells since this ion is complementary to the ion with two electrons. The sign of Dq in the above expressions should be reversed since the crystal energy reverses the sign. For example, the configuration t_2^2 has the crystal energy $-8Dq$ while its complementary configuration $t_2^4e^4$ has $+8Dq$. According to (4.9–9), the complementary transformation simply shifts the electrostatic energy of the whole terms by the constant amount which is $27A - 42B + 21C$.

If we take the energy of $t_2^6e^2\ {}^3A_2$ to be zero, we find the relative energies of the crystal terms which are listed in Table 4.10–1.

TABLE 4.10–1

ENERGIES OF CRYSTAL TERMS OF $t_2^m e^n$, $m + n = 8$

Terms	Energy
$t_2^6e^2\ {}^3A_2$	0
$t_2^5e^3\ {}^3T_2$	Δ†
$(t_2^4e^4 + t_2^5e^3)_{a,b}\ {}^3T_1$‡	$\frac{5}{2}\Delta + \frac{15}{2}B \mp \frac{1}{2}\{(9B - \Delta)^2 + 144B^2\}^{1/2}$
$(t_2^4e^4 + t_2^6e^2)_{a,b}\ {}^1E$	$\Delta + \frac{17}{2}B + 2C \mp \frac{1}{2}\{(2\Delta + B)^2 + 48B^2\}^{1/2}$
$(t_2^4e^4 + t_2^5e^3)_{a,b}\ {}^1T_2$	$\frac{5}{2}\Delta + \frac{17}{2}B + 2C \mp \frac{1}{2}\{(\Delta + B)^2 + 48B^2\}^{1/2}$
$(t_2^4e^4 + t_2^6e^2)_{a,b}\ {}^1A_1$	$\Delta + 17B + \frac{9}{2}C$
	$\mp\frac{1}{2}\{(2\Delta + 2B + C)^2 + 24(2B + C)^2\}^{1/2}$
$t_2^5e^3\ {}^1T_1$	$\Delta + 12B + 2C$

†$\Delta = 10Dq$.

‡The subscripts *a* and *b* refer to the minus and plus sign, respectively.

Knox, Shulman, and Sugano† used these expressions to analyze the Ni^{2+} absorption bands in $KNiF_3$, in which the Ni^{2+} ion is surrounded by six fluorine ions octahedrally. They determined the parameter Δ from the transition ${}^3A_2 \longrightarrow {}^3T_2$, the energy separation of which is exactly Δ, and the parameters B and C from two transitions ${}^3A_2 \longrightarrow {}^3_bT_1$ and ${}^3A_2 \longrightarrow {}^1_aE$. The parameter values thus determined are

$$\Delta = 7250\text{cm}^{-1}, \quad B = 955\text{cm}^{-1}, \quad \text{and} \quad C = 4234\text{cm}^{-1}.$$

The B value is reduced from the free-ion value of 1030cm^{-1} by 7 per cent, and C is reduced from the estimated free-ion value of 4850cm^{-1} by about 13 per cent. They could favorably fit other observed transitions with the corresponding values calculated with these parameter values. The reader should refer to the original paper for details. The experimental data do not seem to be so precise that we can determine the ten parameters $a, b, \ldots, j$ which were introduced in Sec. 4–8.

According to Appendix 4.3, ions with three, four, and five electrons distributed among the t_2 and e shells have more than two crystal terms with the same spin that belong to the same irreducible representation. This is also the case for the complementary ions of the first two ions, i.e., those with seven and six electrons. To find the energy values of such

†K. Knox, R. G. Shulman, and S. Sugano, *Phys. Rev.* **130**, 512 (1963).

crystal terms, we have to solve the secular equations of more than two dimensions, usually by numerical methods. We could solve the secular equations if we could find reasonable values of the parameters involved from the transitions the energy separations of which are available in analytical forms.

For example, the crystal terms of an ion with three electrons are listed in Table 4.10–2 together with the energies or secular matrices apart from the common term $3A$. The reader may calculate himself the energies and matrix elements.

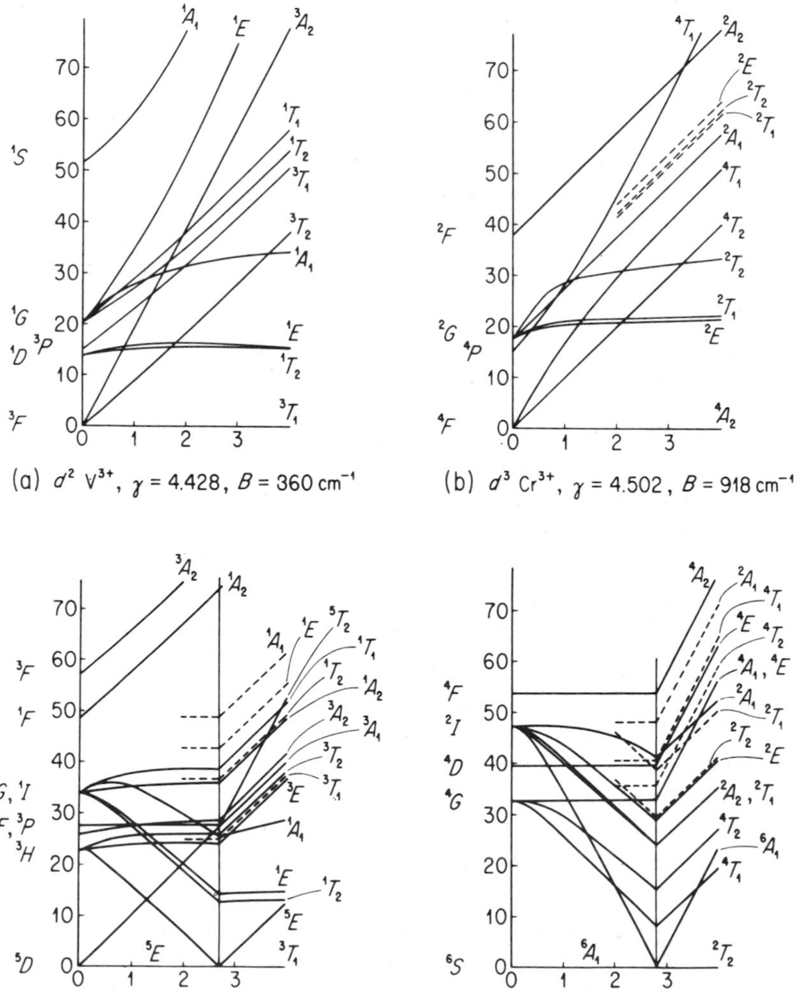

(a) d^2 V^{3+}, $\gamma = 4.428$, $B = 360\ cm^{-1}$

(b) d^3 Cr^{3+}, $\gamma = 4.502$, $B = 918\ cm^{-1}$

(c) d^4 Mn^{3+}, $\gamma = 4.611$, $B = 965\ cm^{-1}$

(d) d^5 Mn^{2+}, $\gamma = 4.477$, $B = 860\ cm^{-1}$

Figure 4.10-1

Tanabe and Sugano† tabulated crystal terms, energies and secular matrices for $t_2^m e^n$ configurations with $m + n = 3, 4, \ldots, 7$; they calculated the matrix elements of electrostatic interaction with the use of formulas established by the irreducible tensor method. They also calculated energy diagrams for $m + n = 2, 3, \ldots 8$, using reasonable values of the parameter B and the ratio C/B for free ions. The diagrams are reproduced in Fig. 4.10–1, where the energies are plotted against Dq (in units of B),

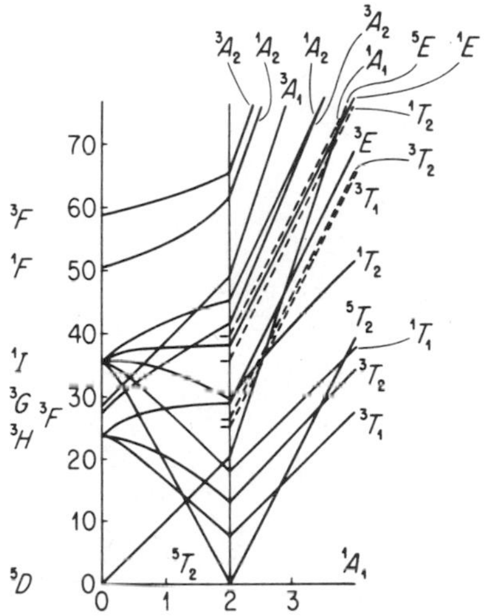

(e) d^6 Co^{3+}, $\gamma = 4.808$, $B = 1{,}065\ cm^{-1}$

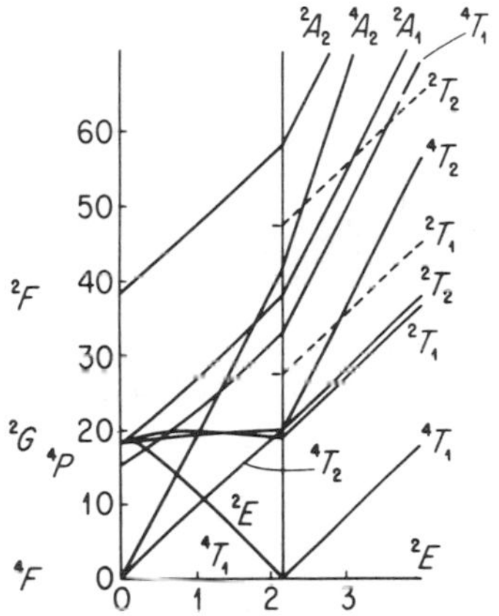

(f) d^7 Co^{2+}, $\gamma = 4.633$, $B = 971\ cm^{-1}$

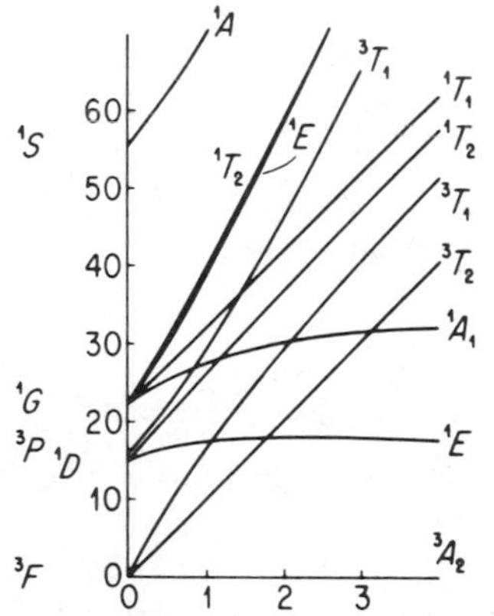

(g) d^8 Ni^{2+}, $\gamma = 4.709$, $B = 1{,}030\ cm^{-1}$

Figure 4.10-1 (cont.)

†Y. Tanabe and S. Sugano, *J. Phys. Soc. Japan* **9**, 753 (1954).

showing the relative positions of energy levels. The parameter A does not appear in the relative energies, being common to all levels in the approximation considered here. Note that a crossover of low-spin states and high-spin states occurs for ions with d^4, d^5, d^6, and d^7 at certain value of Dq, beyond which low-spin states become the ground states.

TABLE 4.10–2†

CRYSTAL TERMS, ENERGIES, AND SECULAR MATRICES FOR $t_2^m e^n$, WITH $m + n = 3$

Term	Energy			
$t_2^3\ {}^4A_2$	$-12Dq - 15B$			
$t_2^2\ {}^4T_2$	$-2Dq - 15B$			
$t_2^2\ {}^2A_1$	$-2Dq - 11B + 3C$			
$t_2^2 e\ {}^2A_2$	$-2Dq + 9B + 3C$			
$(t_2^2 e + t_2 e^2)\ {}_{a,b}^{\ 4}T_1$	$-3Dq + \frac{15}{2}B \mp \frac{1}{2}\{(10Dq - 9B)^2 + 144B^2\}^{1/2}$			
$^2E : t_2^3$	$t_2^2(^1A_1)e$	$t_2^2(^1E)e$	e^3	
$-12Dq - 6B + 3C$	$-6(2)^{1/2}B$	$-3(2)^{1/2}B$	0	
	$-2Dq + 8B + 6C$	$10B$	$(3)^{1/2}(2B + C)$	
		$-2D - B + 3C$	$2(3)^{1/2}B$	
			$18Dq - 8B + 4C$	
$^2T_1 : t_2^3$	$t_2^2(^1T_2)e$	$t_2^2(^3T_1)e$	$t_2e^2(^3A_2)$	$t_2e^2(^1E)$
$-12Dq-6B+3C$	$-3B$	$3B$	0	$-2(3)^{1/2}B$
	$-2Dq-6B+3C$	$-3B$	$-3B$	$(3)^{1/2}B$
		$-2Dq + 3C$	$3B$	$-3(3)^{1/2}B$
			$8Dq-6B+3C$	$-2(3)^{1/2}B$
				$8Dq-2B+3C$
$^2T_2 : t_2^3$	$t_2^2(^1T_2)e$	$t_2^2(^3T_1)e$	$t_2e^2(^1A_1)$	$t_2e^2(^1E)$
$-12Dq+5C$	$5(3)^{1/2}B$	$-3(3)^{1/2}B$	$4B+2C$	$-2B$
	$-2Dq+4B+3C$	$-3B$	$(3)^{1/2}B$	$(3)^{1/2}B$
		$-2Dq-6B+3C$	$-3(3)^{1/2}B$	$3(3)^{1/2}B$
			$8Dq+6B+5C$	$-10B$
				$8Dq-2B+3C$

†The secular matrices are symmetrical, and the elements below the diagonal are omitted.

Stephens and Drickamer applied high hydrostatic pressure on K_3CoF_6 and $FeSiF_6 \cdot 6H_2O$ systems and observed the shift in energy levels of the Co and Fe ions. They did not arrive at the crossover point, but estimated that the crossover should occur at 220–250 Kbar.†

Before leaving this section, one should note the following. Tanabe and Sugano showed in their diagrams general features of energy levels of ions

†D. R. Stephens and H. G. Drickamer, *J. Chem. Phys.* **35**, 424 (1961).

with the configurations $t_2^m e^n$ with the value of $m + n$ fixed, assuming that B and C are independent of the crystal field parameter Dq. Some of the values of parameters Dq, B, and C that are determined from experiments are listed in Table 4.10–3. Zahner and Drickamer determined the values of Dq and B for the Ni^{2+} and Co^{2+} ions from transitions that do not involve

TABLE 4.10–3

VALUES OF Dq, B, AND C DETERMINED FROM EXPERIMENTS (IN UNITS OF cm^{-1})

Ion	Host	Dq	B	B/B_f†	C	C/C_f	Reference
V^{2+}	Al_2O_3	1455	590	0.78	$\left(\frac{C}{B} = 4.5\right)$‡		a
Cr^{3+}	Al_2O_3	1667	700	0.76	$\left(\frac{C}{B} = 4\right)$‡		b
Mn^{4+}	Al_2O_3	2130	700	0.7			c
Co^{2+}	$CoCl_2$	750	766	0.79			d
	$CoBr_2$	697	713	0.73			d
Ni^{2+}	$Ni(NH_3)_6Cl_2$	1090	887	0.86			d
	$NiCl_2$	755	823	0.80			d
	$NiBr_2$	728	730	0.70			d
	$KNiF_3$	725	955	0.93	4234	0.87	e

†B_f and C_f are free-ion parameters. Numerical values of B_f and C_f for some of the first transition ions are available in Fig. 4.10-1 and in D. S. McClure, *Solid State Physics*, vol. 9 (New York: Academic Press, 1959).

‡The ratio in parentheses is assumed.

a. M. D. Sturge, *Phys. Rev.* **130**, 639 (1963). Dr. Sturge in a private communication made the correction that the values $Dq = 1360\,cm^{-1}$ and $B = 550\,cm^{-1}$ should be increased by about 7 per cent. The values listed are the corrected ones.

b. S. Sugano and M. Peter, *Phys. Rev.* **122**, 381 (1961).

c. S. Geschwind *et al.*, *Phys. Rey.* **126**, 1684 (1962).

d. J. C. Zahner and H. G. Drickamer, *J. Chem. Phys.* **35**, 1483 (1961). They used optical transitions involving no C parameter but Dq and B.

e. K. Knox, R. G. Shulman, and S. Sugano, *Phys. Rev.* **130**, 512 (1963).

the parameter C, i.e.,

$$^3A_2 \longrightarrow {}^3T_2, \quad {}^3A_2 \longrightarrow {}^3_aT_1, \quad \text{and} \quad {}^3A_2 \longrightarrow {}^3_bT_1 \qquad \text{for } Ni^{2+},$$

and

$$^4_aT_1 \longrightarrow {}^4T_2\colon \quad 5Dq - \tfrac{15}{2}B + \tfrac{1}{2}\{(10Dq + 9B)^2 + 144B^2\}^{1/2},$$
$$^4_aT_1 \longrightarrow {}^4A_2\colon \quad 15Dq - \tfrac{15}{2}B + \tfrac{1}{2}\{(10Dq + 9B)^2 + 144B^2\}^{1/2},$$
$$^4_aT_1 \longrightarrow {}^4_bT_1\colon \quad \{(10Dq + 9B)^2 + 144B^2\}^{1/2} \qquad \text{for } Co^{2+}.$$

The calculation of these energy separations is left for the reader's exercise. From the values of Dq, B, and C in Table 4.10–3, it appears that the values of B and C depend on the value of Dq, or in other words, that the values of B and C actually depend on the ligand ions surrounding the transition ion.

4.11 ELECTRON PARAMAGNETIC RESONANCE

The single-ion model is used to interpret the electron spin resonance experiment with transition-metal ions, to a good zero-order approximation. The electron possesses the magnetic moment $-2.0023\,\beta\mathbf{s}$ where the value of the Bohr magneton β is 0.9273×10^{-20} erg gauss^{-1}. The energy of the magnetic moment is quantized in an applied magnetic field H, and the energy separation between two states $m = \frac{1}{2}$ and $-\frac{1}{2}$ is given by $2.0023 \times \beta H$. Paramagnetic transition ions also possess a magnetic moment of the same order of magnitude as the electron and absorb microwave energy when placed in an external magnetic field of the order of a few thousand gauss. We will not go into detail but will give some discussions pertaining to the ligand field theory. The reader is referred for details to the literature on electron paramagnetic resonance.†

Electron paramagnetic resonance is usually concerned with the ground state splitting of paramagnetic ions in a magnetic field. Excited levels are located far above the ground level compared with the microwave energy. The effects of the excited levels on the microwave absorption are treated by the perturbation method. We consider here for simplicity only those cases where the ground level is an orbital singlet with a spin degeneracy. The Hamiltonian operator of iron-group ions that are situated in a cubic crystal potential is conveniently written in the form

$$H = g\mathbf{H}\cdot\mathbf{S} + A\mathbf{S}\cdot\mathbf{I} + \sum_{n} A^{n}\mathbf{S}\cdot\mathbf{I}^{n}. \tag{4.11-1}$$

The first term in (4.11-1) is the so-called Zeeman term; the factor g is called the *g-factor*. The second term stands for the interaction between the electron and nuclear magnetic moments if the ion has the nuclear spin $\mathbf{I}$, being called the *hyperfine interaction*. It has been found that the electrons interact with the nuclear magnetic moments of the surrounding ligands. This interaction is represented by the third term, the summation being taken over the magnetic nuclei. This interaction is called the *superhyperfine interaction*. There are also additional terms which are quartic in the spin operators; however, we ignore them for simplicity.

The g-factor, which is a measure of the magnetic moment of the ion, is often shifted from the free-spin value 2.0023. The shift is due to the contribution of the orbital magnetic moment. The shift is calculated by the second-order perturbation method. The ground state is designated by $|0\rangle$; the excited states which have the the same spin as $|0\rangle$ are designated by

†B. Bleaney and K. W. H. Stevens, *Rep. Progr. Phys.* **16**, 108 (1953); W. Low, *Paramagnetic Resonance in Solids* (New York: Academic Press,1960).

$|n\rangle$. The magnetic moment of the ion is given by $-\partial E(\mathbf{S}, \mathbf{H})/\partial \mathbf{H}$, where $E(\mathbf{S}, \mathbf{H})$ is the energy of the ground state. The calculation of the magnetic moment is therefore reduced to that of $E(\mathbf{S}, \mathbf{H})$ as follows. The starting Hamiltonian is

$$H = \beta(2.0023S_z + L_z)H + \lambda \mathbf{L} \cdot \mathbf{S} \tag{4.11-2}$$

where the z direction is taken to be that of the applied magnetic field. The energy of (4.11–2) is, to the second order,

$$E(S_z, H) = 2.0023\beta S_z H - \sum_n 2\langle 0|L_z|n\rangle\langle n|L_z|0\rangle \frac{\lambda\beta S_z H}{\Delta E_n}, \tag{4.11-3}$$

where ΔE_n is the energy separation of the excited levels from the ground state. In this calculation we do not calculate the spin part but only the orbital one. The g-shift is given to the second order by

$$\Delta g_z = -2\lambda \sum_n \frac{|\langle 0|L_z|n\rangle|^2}{\Delta E_n}. \tag{4.11-4}$$

We assume that the ion is placed in a cubic potential; therefore, the g-shift is isotropic, i.e., $\Delta g_x = \Delta g_y = \Delta g_z$.

Let us give an example of the Ni^{2+} ion in an octahedral potential. The Russell-Saunders ground state ^3F is split into three crystal levels; the energy diagram in Fig. 4.7–1 should be reversed. The crystal eigenfunctions are available in Appendix 4.2. It is only

$$|T_2 0\rangle = (\tfrac{1}{2})^{1/2}\{|32\rangle + |3\text{-}2\rangle\}$$

which has a nonvanishing matrix element in (4.11–3) with the ground state

$$|A_2\rangle = (\tfrac{1}{2})^{1/2}\{|32\rangle - |3\text{-}2\rangle\}.$$

The g-shift is simply given by

$$\Delta g = -\frac{8\lambda}{10Dq}. \tag{4.11-5}$$

One obtains the same formula for the V^{2+} and Cr^{3+} ions in an octahedral potential. In nickel Tutton salts, the Ni^{2+} ion is surrounded by six water molecules in an approximately octahedral arrangement. The g-shift observed is reported to be 0.25 ± 0.05. The energy separation $10Dq$ is available from the optical transitions, being about 8400cm^{-1}. On the other hand, we know that the spin-orbit constant λ_f is -335cm^{-1} for the free ion. These three values cannot be compatible simultaneously unless λ_f is replaced by an effective spin-orbit constant $\lambda_{eff} = -270 \text{cm}^{-1}$. Griffiths and Owen estimated the effective spin-orbit constant to be -250cm^{-1} to fit the magnetic susceptibility tensor of the Ni^{2+} ions in Tutton salts.†

†J. E. Griffiths and J. Owen, *Proc. Roy. Soc.* **A213**, 459 (1952).

Such a reduction of the spin-orbit constant has also been found in other ions, some of which are listed in Table 4.11–1.

Mechanisms for the hyperfine interaction are explained as follows. Fermi in 1930 successfully explained hyperfine structures observed in

TABLE 4.11–1

REDUCTION OF THE SPIN-ORBIT CONSTANT FOR SOME TRANSITION-ELEMENT IONS IN A NEARLY CUBIC POTENTIAL

Ion	Host	$\lambda_{\text{eff}}(\text{cm}^{-1})$	$\lambda_f(\text{cm}^{-1})$	$\lambda_{\text{eff}}/\lambda_f$	Reference
V^{2+}	Tutton salt	44	55.5	0.83	a
	MgO	34		0.61	b
V^{3+}	alum	64†	104	0.62	c
Cr^{3+}	alum	57	91	0.63	a
	MgO	63		0.72	d
Ni^{2+}	Tutton salt	−270	−324	0.83	a
		−250†		0.77	e

†These values are estimated from magnetic susceptibility data which are independent of optical data.

a. J. Owen, *Proc. Roy. soc.* **A227**, 183 (1955).
b. W. Low, *Phys. Rev.* **101**, 1827 (1956).
c. J. Van den Handel and A. Sigert, *Physica* **4**, 871 (1937).
d. W. Low, *Phys. Rev.* **105**, 801 (1957).
e. J. E. Griffiths and J. Owen, *Proc. Roy. Soc.* **A213**, 459 (1952).

atomic spectra of alkali metals.† He attributed the structures to the magnetic dipolar interaction between the nuclear and electron spins and found that if the electron is in the *ns* orbit the interaction is written in the form

$$\boldsymbol{H} = \frac{8\pi}{3} g\beta\gamma\beta_N \mathbf{I}\cdot\mathbf{s}|\psi_{ns}(0)|^2, \tag{4.11–6}$$

where γ is the nuclear magneton number of the nucleus, and β_N the nuclear magneton. The square $|\psi_{ns}(0)|^2$ is the density $\rho_{ns}(0)$ at the nucleus. The magnetic field component H_z^N which the nuclear magnetic moment $\gamma\beta_N I_z$ sees is given by

$$H_z^N = -\frac{\partial \boldsymbol{H}}{\partial(\gamma\beta_N I_z)} = -\frac{8\pi}{3} g\beta s_z \rho_{ns}(0). \tag{4.11–7}$$

When the hyperfine interaction, $A\mathbf{S}\cdot\mathbf{I}$, in the transition-element ions is isotropic, i. e., when A is a scalar, it appears that the dominant contribution comes from the contact-type interaction (4.11–6). It was suggested by several authors that the inner-core electrons, i. e., 1*s*, 2*s*, and 3*s* electrons, will have different wavefunctions according to whether the spin is parallel or antiparallel to that of the unbalanced *d* electrons.‡ Thus the density at

†E. Fermi, *Zeits. Phys.* **60**, 320 (1930).

‡V. Heine, *Phys. Rev.* **107**, 1002 (1957); J. H. Wood and G. W. Pratt, Jr., *Phys. Rev.* **107**, 995 (1957); A. J. Freeman and R. E. Watson, *Phys. Rev.* **123**, 2027 (1961).

the nucleus $\rho_{ns}(0)$ will differ and leave a net excess in one direction. We will obtain the magnetic field which the nucleus sees in two ways: (i) using the hyperfine term $A\mathbf{S}\cdot\mathbf{I}$, and (ii) applying the idea suggested above.

(i) The magnetic field component which acts on the nuclear magnetic moment $\gamma\beta_N I_z$ is obtained by taking the derivative of $A\mathbf{S}\cdot\mathbf{I}$ as

$$-\frac{\partial(A\mathbf{S}\cdot\mathbf{I})}{\partial(\gamma\beta_N I_z)} = -\frac{AS_z}{\gamma\beta_N}.$$

If the ion is in the state with $M_S = S$, the value of the magnetic field is

$$H_z^N = -\frac{AS}{\gamma\beta_N}. \tag{4.11-8}$$

(ii) The ion is to consist of ν electrons which completely fill the $1s$, $2s$, $\ldots$, $3p$ orbits and leave the $3d$ orbits partly filled. If the number of unpaired electrons in the $3d$ orbits is n, the maximum spin quantum number S equals $n/2$. Let us consider the many-electron state which has the maximum spin component $M_S = S$. The wavefunction of the state with $S = n/2$ and $M_S = S$ is given by the single determinant

$$\Psi(\mathbf{r}) = A\psi_{1s\uparrow}(\mathbf{r}_1 = \mathbf{r})\,\psi_{1s\downarrow}(\mathbf{r}_2 = \mathbf{r})\ldots\psi_{nlm_lm_s}(\mathbf{r}_i = \mathbf{r})\ldots, \tag{4.11-9}$$

where the operator A stands for taking the determinant as (3.2–1). The spin density, i. e., the difference between two electronic densities with opposite spin, at the position $\mathbf{r}$ is given by

$$S_z(\mathbf{r}) = \sum_{i-1}^{\nu} \int \underset{\nu-1}{\cdots} \int \Psi^*(\mathbf{r}) S_z \Psi(\mathbf{r})\, d\tau_1\, d\tau_2 \ldots d\tau_{i-1}\, d\tau_{i+1} \ldots\, d\tau_\nu,$$

where the summation is over ν electrons, and the integration over τ includes the spin summation. The spin operator S_z is $\sum_{i=1}^{\nu} s_{iz}$. We find the spin density in the form

$$S_z(\mathbf{r}) = \sum_k m_s \rho_{km_s}(\mathbf{r}) = \tfrac{1}{2} \sum_k \{\rho_{k\uparrow}(\mathbf{r}) - \rho_{k\downarrow}(\mathbf{r})\},$$

where k is the set of quantum numbers (nlm_l), being summed over all single-electron states involved in (4.11–9). The spin density at the nucleus, $\mathbf{r} = 0$, is

$$S_z(0) = \tfrac{1}{2} \sum_{n=1}^{3} \{\rho_{ns\uparrow}(0) - \rho_{ns\downarrow}(0)\}. \tag{4.11-10}$$

Replacing the spin density $s_z\rho_{ns}(0)$ in (4.11–7) by (4.11–10), we finally find the magnetic field at the nucleus as

$$H_z^N = -\frac{8\pi}{3} g\beta\,\tfrac{1}{2} \sum_{n=1}^{3} \{\rho_{ns\uparrow}(0) - \rho_{ns\downarrow}(0)\}. \tag{4.11-11}$$

A comparison of (4.11–8) and (4.11–11) leads to

$$A = \frac{2\pi}{3} g\beta\gamma\beta_N \frac{4}{2S} \sum_{n=1}^{3} \{\rho_{ns\uparrow}(0) - \rho_{ns\downarrow}(0)\}. \qquad (4.11\text{–}12)$$

In this formulation we assume that the single-electron wavefunctions in (4.11–9) are orthogonal. If this assumption were not the case, the single determinant (4.11–9) could not be the exact eigenfunction of the spin operator $\mathbf{S}^2$ with the eigenvalue $S(S+1)$.

The value of A has been measured in transition-metal ions incorporated into in various hosts by the electron paramagnetic resonance technique, the Mössbauer effect, and the measurement of nuclear specific heat at low temperatures. In Table 4.11–2, we list some of the A values observed by means of electron paramagnetic resonance. The values of A without plus or minus sign are the absolute magnitudes, the sign being undetermined. The magnitude of A of a given nuclear species differs from one host to another; however, it appears that the sign is insensitive to the surrounding ligands. We have available no free-ion values for A with which to compare the experimental values. Freeman and Watson, however, calculated the free-ion values of H^N for Mn^{++}, Fe^{++}, Fe^{+++}, and Ni^{++} ions by the unrestricted Hartree-Fock method.† These values are listed in Table 4.11–3. The values of A are calculated using the relation between A and H^N

$$A = -\frac{\gamma\beta_N H^N}{S} \quad \text{or} \quad H^N = -\frac{SA}{\gamma\beta_N}, \qquad (4.11\text{–}13)$$

where (4.11–11) and (4.11–12) are used, and the subscript z is omitted since H_z^N is independent of the spatial direction. We have converted the H^N values to the A values using the values of the nuclear magneton numbers, γ, which are listed in Table 4.11–4. Freeman and Watson found that the quantity

$$\sum_{n=1}^{3} \{\rho_{ns\uparrow}(0) - \rho_{ns\downarrow}(0)\}$$

is negative for these four ions. The magnetic field H^N, (4.11–11), becomes positive, and the A values are negative since the nuclear magnetic moments are positive.

One may note that the value of A for the Mn^{++} ion in $ZnSiF_6 \cdot 6H_2O$ is fairly close to the calculated one and reduces to about half of the latter when placed in Si and Ge. Other ions show more or less such a reduction of the magnitude of A, depending on the host.

Owen and Stevens first observed a complex hyperfine structure in the electron paramagnetic resonance spectra of the irridium ion Ir^{4+} diluted in a diamagnetic salt $(NH_4)_2(PtCl_6)$.‡ The hyperfine structure consists of sixteen equally spaced lines resolved in the most favorable direction

†A. J. Freeman and R. E. Watson, *Phys. Rev. Lett.* **5**, 498 (1960), and *Phys. Rev.* **123**, 2027 (1961).

‡J. Owen and K. W. H. Stevens, *Nature* **171**, 836 (1953).

TABLE 4.11–2

THE HYPERFINE CONSTANT A IN THE FIRST TRANSITION-ELEMENT IONS IN VARIOUS HOSTS (IN UNITS OF $10^{-4}cm^{-1}$)

Ion	Host	$A(10^{-4}cm^{-1})$	Reference
$^{51}V^{++}$	$ZnSiF_6 \cdot 6H_2O$	−83.9	a
	$KMgF_3$	86.2	b
	MgO	74.2	c
	$K_4Fe(CN)_6 \cdot 3H_2O$	−55.5	d
	Si	−42.1	e
$^{53}Cr^{3+}$	$KAl(SeO_4)_2 \cdot 12H_2O$	18.5	f
	MgO	16.2	g
	$K_3Mn(CN)_6$	14.7	h
	$K_3Co(CN)_6$	14.7	d
	NaF	14.0	i
	ZnS	13.4	j
	ZnSe	13.3	j
	ZnTe	12.4	j
	CdTe	12.78	k
	Si	+10.67	e
$^{57}Fe^{3+}$	MgO	10.1	l
	$AlCl_3 \cdot 6H_2O$	10.2	m
	ZnO	9.02	n
	ZnS	7.69	o
	ZnSe	6.6	p
	ZnTe	4.2	q
$^{59}Co^{2+}$	NaF	110	r
	$KMgF_3$	104	r
	MgO	97.8	s
$^{61}Ni^{2+}$	MgO	8.3	t
Cu^{2+}	MgO	19	u

a. J. M. Baker, unpublished.
b. T. P. P. Hall, W. Hayes, R. W. H. Stevenson, and J. Wilkens, *J. Chem. Phys.* **38**, 1977 (1963).
c. W. Low, *Phys. Rev.* **101**, 1827 (1956).
d. J. M. Baker, B. Bleaney, and K. D. Bowers, *Proc. Phys. Soc.* **B69**, 1205 (1956).
e. H. H. Woodbury and G. W. Ludwig, *Phys. Rev.* **117**, 102 (1960).
f. B. Bleaney, *Proc. Roy. Soc.* **A204**, 203 (1950).
g. W. Low, *Phys. Rev.* **105**, 801 (1957).
h. K. D. Bowers, *Proc. Phys. Soc.* **A65**, 860 (1952).
i. W. Hayes and D. A. Jones, *Proc. Phys. Soc.* **71**, 503 (1958).
j. R. S. Title, *Phys. Rev.* **133**, A1613 (1964).
k. G. W. Ludwig and M. R. Lorenz, *Phys. Rev.* **131**, 601 (1963).
l. E. S. Rosenvasser and G. Feher, *Bull. Am. Phys. Soc.* **6**, 117 (1960).
m. J. R. Chamberlain and C. H. A. Syms, *Proc. Phys. Soc.* **84**, 867 (1964).
n. W. M. Walsh, Jr., and L. W. Rupp, Jr., *Phys. Rev.* **126**, 1952 (1962).
o. R. S. Title, *Phys. Rev.* **131**, 623 (1963).
p. T. L. Estle, private communication.
q. J. C. Hensel, *Bull. Am. Phys. Soc.* **9**, 244 (1964).
r. T. P. P. Hall, W. Hayes, R. W. H. Stevenson, and J. Wilkens, *J. Chem. Phys.* **39**, 35 (1963).
s. W. Low, *Phys. Rev.* **109**, 256 (1958).
t. J. W. Orton, P. Auzins, and J. E. Wertz, *Phys. Rev.* **119**, 1691 (1960).
u. W. Hayes, unpublished.

TABLE 4.11–2 (cont.)

Ion	Host	$A(10^{-4}cm^{-1})$	Reference
$^{55}Mn^{2+}$	$NH_4ZnSO_4 \cdot 6H_2O$	−91	a′
	$ZnSiF_6 \cdot 6H_2O$	−95	a′
	$MgSiF_6$	−92	b′
	MgO	−86.82	c′
	CaO	−80.8	d′
	$BaTiO_3$	−81.6	e′
	$CaCO_3$	87.82	f′
	$ZnAl_2O_4$	74.9	g′
	ZnO	−75.0	h′
	CaF_2	97.8	i′
	ZnF_2	−96	j′
	CdF_2	−93	h′
	$KMgF_3$	−91.2	k′
	$KCdF_3$	−92.6	k′
	$KCaF_3$	−93.1	k′
	K_2MgF_4	−91.5	k′
	$NaMgF_3$	−92.5	k′
	NaF	88.6	l′
	LiF	87.7	l′
	KF	92.9	l′
	AgCl	81	m′
	AgBr	78	m′
	KCl	92	n′
	NaCl	81.2	o′
	LiCl	76	n′
	$CdCl_2$	−81.5	h′
	$MgCl_2$	−82	h′
	$SrCl_2$	81.2	p′
	ZnS	−63.73	q′
	ZnSe	−61.7	r′
	ZnTe	−56.2	r′
	CdS	−65.3	s′
	CdSe	61.5	t′
	CdTe	57.5	t′
	GaP	55	u′
	GaAs	52.4	v′
	Si	−53.47	w′
	Ge	−44.8	x′

a′ K. D. Bowers and J. Owen, *Repts. Progr. Phys.* **18**, 304 (1955).
b′ T. Arakawa, *J. Phys. Soc. Japan* **9**, 790 (1954).
c′ W. M. Walsh, Jr., *Phys. Rev.* **122**, 762 (1961).
d′ A. J. Shuskus, *Phys. Rev.* **127**, 1529 (1962).
e′ D. Shaltiel and W. Low, Note 1, Contract AF 61 (052)–59, A.R.D.C. (1958).
f′ F. K. Hurd, M. Sachs, and W. D. Hershberger, *Phys. Rev.* **93**, 373 (1954).
g′ D. Stahl-Brada and W. Low, *Phys. Rev.* **116**, 561 (1959).
h′ T. P. P. Hall, W. Hayes, and F. I. B. Williams, *Proc. Phys. Soc.* **78**, 883 (1961).
i′ J. M. Baker, B. Bleaney, and W. Hayes, *Proc. Roy. Soc.* A**247**, 141 (1958).
j′ M. Tinkham, *Proc. Roy. Soc.* A**236**, 535 (1956).

k′ S. Ogawa, *J. Phys. Soc. Japan* **15**, 1475 (1960).
l′ T. P. P. Hall, W. Hayes, R. W. H. Stevenson, and J. Wilkens, *J. Chem. Phys.* **38**, 1977 (1963).
m′ H. Abe, *J. Phys. Soc. Japan* **12**, 435 (1957).
n′ A. Fukuda, Y. Uchida, and H. Yoshimura, *J. Phys. Soc. Japan* **13**, 971 (1958).
o′ W. Low. *Proc. Phys. Soc.* **B69**, 837 (1956).
p′ W. Low and U. Rosenberger, *Phys. Rev.* **116**, 621 (1959).
q′ W. M. Walsh, Jr., *Phys Rev.* **122**, 762 (1961).
r′ R. S. Title, *Phys. Rev.* **130**, 17 (1963).
s′ B. P. Dorain, *Phys. Rev.* **112**, 1058 (1958).
t′ C. Kikuchi and G. H. Azarbayejani, *J. Phys. Soc. Japan* **17S**, B-I, 453 (1962).
u′ H. H. Woodbury and G. W. Ludwig, *Bull. Am. Phys. Soc.* **6**, 118 (1961).
v′ R. Bleekrode, J. Dielman, and H. J. Vegter, *Physics Letters* **2**, 355 (1962).
w′ H. H, Woodbury and G. W. Ludwig, *Phys. Rev.* **117**, 102 (1960).
x′ G. D. Watkins, *Bull. Am. Phys. Soc.* **2**, 345 (1959).

TABLE 4.11–3

CALCULATED VALUES OF H^N AND A FOR Mn^{++}, Fe^{++}, Fe^{+++}, AND Ni^{++} IN THE FREE IONIC STATE

	Mn^{++}	Fe^{++}	Fe^{+++}	Ni^{++}	Ni^{+++}
H^N (Kgauss)	700	550	630	330	270†
A $(10^{-4}cm^{-1})$	−99	−13	−12	−17	−14

†This value was calculated for the Ni^{2+} ion in a crude potential which arises from an octahedral array of six point charges of −2 atomic units each at a distance of 3.949 atomic units from the Ni nucleus.

TABLE 4.11–4

NUCLEAR MAGNETIC MOMENTS OF FIRST TRANSITION-ELEMENT NUCLEI

Isotope	Natural abundance per cent	Magnetic moment, μ, in β_N	Spin, I	Nuclear magneton number, $\gamma = \mu/I$
^{51}V	100	5.1392	$\frac{7}{2}$	1.4683
^{53}Cr	9.54	−0.4735	$\frac{3}{2}$	−0.3157
^{55}Mn	100	3.4610	$\frac{5}{2}$	1.3844
^{57}Fe	2.17	0.0903	$\frac{1}{2}$	0.1806
^{59}Co	100	4.6388	$\frac{7}{2}$	1.3252
^{61}Ni	1.25	0.30	$\frac{3}{2}$	0.20
^{63}Cu	69.09	2.2206	$\frac{3}{2}$	1.4804
^{65}Cu	30.91	2.3790	$\frac{3}{2}$	1.5860
^{67}Zn	4.12	0.8735	$\frac{5}{2}$	0.3495

instead of four lines that would be expected to correspond to the nuclear spin ($I = \frac{3}{2}$) of irridium–191 and 193. The magnetic moments of these two isotopes are approximately equal. They suggested that these additional lines would arise from two neighboring chlorine nuclei with $I = \frac{3}{2}$. This idea has been confirmed by Stevens† using the molecular orbital approximation. We will discuss the molecular orbital approximation in the next section. In the rest of this section we shall show direct evidence that the single-ion model is incapable of explaining such a superhyperfine interaction.

We take an example of CaF_2: Mn in which the manganous ion Mn^{2+} is surrounded by eight fluorine ions F^- in a cube coordination. Baker, Bleaney, and Hayes observed the superhyperfine structure in the paramagnetic resonance spectra of the Mn^{2+} ion.‡ If the structure were arising only from the magnetic dipolar interaction between the manganese $3d$ electrons and the fluorine nuclei, this interaction would disappear in the spectrum when the magnetic field was applied along one of the cube edges. We may approximate the manganese magnetic moment by a point dipole situated at the manganese site, since the Mn^{2+} ion is in a rather spherical state ^6S. The dipolar interaction then is written in the form

$$H_{dd} = g\beta\gamma\beta_N R^{-3} \sum_{n=1}^{8} \{3S_{zn} I^n_{zn} - (\mathbf{S}\cdot\mathbf{I}^n)\} \qquad (4.11\text{–}14)$$

where n is summed over eight fluorine nuclei, R is the Mn-F distance, and zn is the direction connecting the nth fluorine toward the central manganese ion. If the magnetic field H is applied in the direction making angles θ_n with zn, the dipolar interaction (4.11–4) takes the form to a first approximation

$$H_{dd} = g\beta\gamma\beta_N R^{-3} \sum_{n=1}^{8} \{S_z I^n_z (3\cos^2\theta_n - 1)\}, \qquad (4.11\text{–}15)$$

where z is the direction of the magnetic field, and the terms $S_x I^n_x$ and $S_y I^n_y$ are averaged out. If the magnetic field is applied along one of the cube edges, the dipolar interaction vanishes since $\cos^2\theta_n = \frac{1}{3}$ for each n; however, Baker, Bleaney, and Hayes actually observed the superhyperfine structure which appears to consist of nine lines with intensities in the ratio 1:8:28:56:70:56:28:8:1. This observation clearly contradicts the expectation based on (4.11–15).

4.12 MOLECULAR ORBITAL APPROXIMATION

We have seen in Sec. 4.10 that Racah's parameters B and C determined from optical transitions in transition-element ions in crystal potential

†K. W. H. Stevens, *Proc. Roy. Soc.* A**219**, 542 (1953).
‡J. M. Baker, B. Bleaney, and W. Hayes, *Proc. Roy. Soc.* A**247**, 141 (1958).

differ from those for the free-ion state, and in Sec. 4.11 that the spin-orbit coupling constant in a crystal potential also differs from that for free-ion. The magnitude of the hyperfine interaction constant of a given transition-element ion depends on the surrounding ligands in a given host. In order to explain these differences, it is suggested that we need to go to further approximations beyond the single-ion approximation. This suggestion may be put forward by the observation of the superhyperfine structure in the electron paramagnetic resonance spectra, the origin of which could not be explained by the single-ion approximation.

The single-ion approximation of a transition-element ion in a crystal potential does not explicitly take into account the role of ligand electrons. For example, it assumes that the charge cloud of the ligand electrons does not overlap that of the transition-element ion, i. e., $\Delta V(\mathbf{r}) = 0$, where $\mathbf{r}$ is a position vector within the charge cloud of the transition-element ion. This assumption can hardly be true in actual cases. The electrons of ligands may migrate into the charge cloud of the transition-element ion and spend some time in that ion's incomplete $3d$ orbit. Such a migration may occur since the positive charge of the core of the transition-element ion attracts the electron more than the ligand ion cores when the electron approaches the transition-element ion core. For example, we consider a complex or cluster, $(MF_6)^{n-}$, in a host crystal, where M is an iron-group ion surrounded by six fluorine ions octahedrally. The cluster itself interacts with the rest of the host; however, we assume for simplicity that the interaction may be replaced by a constant potential over the whole cluster.† This constant potential then simply shifts the energy levels of the cluster as a whole. Thus we need to consider interaction within the cluster. The $2s$ or $2p$ electrons of the six F^- ions may migrate to the incomplete $3d$ orbit of the M ion, the $3d$ electron to the $2s$ or $2p$ orbit which is emptied for some time. We may ignore the migration of the inner-core electrons compared with the outer-shell electrons. Let us formulate this idea as follows. The seven core charges are regarded as point positive charges, forming six vertices and center of a regular octahedron. Every outer-shell electron moves in the potential of these positive charges. The single-electron wavefunctions may be approximated by linear combinations of the $3d$, $2s$, and $2p$ wavefunctions to a first order. The wavefunctions must be classified by the irreducible representations of the point group $\mathbf{O}_h$, since the potential is unaltered by the transformations. In what follows, we simply regard the coefficients of the linear combinations to be parameters.

†This assumption should be carefully examined in actual cases. For example, the fluorine ion may actually be placed in a crystal potential of certain symmetry. If the symmetry is lower than the cubic symmetry, the fluorine $2p$ level may be split into two or more sublevels by the crystal potential and the spin-orbit coupling in the fluorine ion.

The model based on this idea may be called the *ligand complex* or *cluster model.*

Determination of the magnitudes of the coefficients of the symmetry-classified linear combinations may require elaborate calculations; however, the relative magnitudes of the coefficients of the ligand orbitals that are transformed among themselves can be easily determined by symmetry requirements. The six $2s$ orbitals transform among themselves. The six $2p$ orbitals that are directed toward the central M ion transform among themselves, being symmetric about the line connecting the M ion and the respective ligand. Such orbitals are called *σ orbital.* The other twelve $2p$ orbitals that have the probability maximum in the plane perpendicular to the line also transform among themselves, being called *π orbital.* These three groups of orbitals are never mixed by the transformations of the group $\mathbf{O}_h$. The eighteen $2p$ orbitals are illustrated in Fig. 4.12–1. The plus

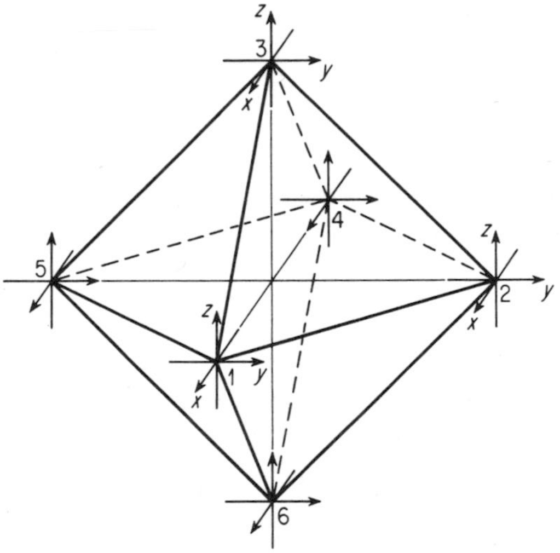

Figure 4.12-1

and minus signs must be kept in mind in constructing the proper linear combinations; the direction of arrows indicates the plus-sign part of the p orbitals.

We show, for example, a procedure of finding the proper linear combinations of six $p\sigma$ orbitals. First we list the transformation properties of these $p\sigma$ orbitals for certain transformations in Table 4.12–1. One may easily find the reducible characters with respect to these six orbitals:

	E	C_3	C_2	C_2'	C_4	I	IC_3	IC_2	IC_2'	IC_4
$\chi =$	6	0	2	0	2	0	0	4	2	0.

TABLE 4.12–1

TRANSFORMATION PROPERTIES OF SIX $p\sigma$ ORBITALS UNDER CERTAIN TRANSFORMATIONS OF $\mathbf{O}_h$

Orbitals†	$C_3^{[111]}$	$C_2^{[001]}$	$C_2^{[110]}$	$C_4^{[001]}$	I	$IC_4^{[001]}$
$1x$	$2y$	$-4x$	$2y$	$2y$	$-4x$	$-5y$
$2y$	$3z$	$-5y$	$1x$	$-4x$	$-5x$	$1x$
$3z$	$1x$	$3z$	$-6z$	$3z$	$-6z$	$-6z$
$4x$	$5y$	$-1x$	$5x$	$5y$	$-1x$	$-2y$
$5y$	$6z$	$-2y$	$4x$	$-1x$	$-2y$	$4x$
$6z$	$4x$	$6z$	$-3z$	$6z$	$-3z$	$-3z$

†The numerals 1, 2, . . . , 6 refer to the ligands.

With reference to Table 2.18–4, we decompose the reducible characters into:

$$A_{1g} + E_g + T_{1u}.$$

The six $p\sigma$ orbitals are therefore classified in three sets of linear combinations: A_{1g}, E_g, and T_{1u}. Every linear combination must have the common form:

$$c_1(1x) + c_2(2y) + c_3(3z) + c_4(4x) + c_5(5y) + c_6(6z).$$

The six coefficients can be determined, apart from the absolute phase and normalization, with the use of the symmetry properties of irreducible bases listed in Table 2.17–5. The six symmetry-classified linear combinations are given in Table 4.12–2. For example, three relations $C_2^{[001]} t_{1u} z = t_{1u} z$, $C_2^{[110]} t_{1u} z = -t_{1u} z$, and $C_4^{[001]} t_{1u} z = t_{1u} z$ are sufficient to determine the linear combination $t_{1u} z$. The other two components $t_{1u} x$ and $t_{1u} y$ are obtained by applying $C_3^{[111]}$ on the $t_{1u} z$.

TABLE 4.12–2

SYMMETRY-CLASSIFIED SIX $p\sigma$ ORBITALS FOR OCTAHEDRAL COORDINATION

Symmetry	Linear combination
a_{1g}	$\left(\frac{1}{6}\right)^{1/2}\{-(1x) - (2y) - (3z) + (4x) + (5y) + (6z)\}$
$e_g u$	$\left(\frac{1}{12}\right)^{1/2}\{(1x) + (2y) - (4x) - (5y) - 2(3z) + 2(6z)\}$
$e_g v$	$\left(\frac{1}{2}\right)\{-(1x) + (2y) + (4x) - (5y)\}$
$t_{1u} x$	$\left(\frac{1}{2}\right)^{1/2}\{-(1x) - 4(x)\}$
$t_{1u} y$	$\left(\frac{1}{2}\right)^{1/2}\{-(2y) - (5y)$
$t_{1u} z$	$\left(\frac{1}{2}\right)^{1/2}\{-(3z) - (6z)\}$

Symmetry-classified linear combinations of six $2s$ orbitals are obtained in a similar way. Twelve $p\pi$ orbitals are also classified in four sets of linear combinations that transform according to the irreducible representations T_{1g}, T_{1u}, T_{2g}, and T_{2u} of the octahedral group $\mathbf{O}_h$. These are presented in Appendix 4.4, where symmetry-classified ligand orbitals for tetrahedral and cube coordinations are also listed.

We may justify the linear combinations listed in Table 4.12–2 by illustrative pictures. For example, the linear combination $t_{1u}z$ is illustrated together with the $pt_{1u}z$ located at the center of the octahedral coordination, Fig. 4.12–2(a). The plus part of the central $pt_{1u}z$ is directed toward the

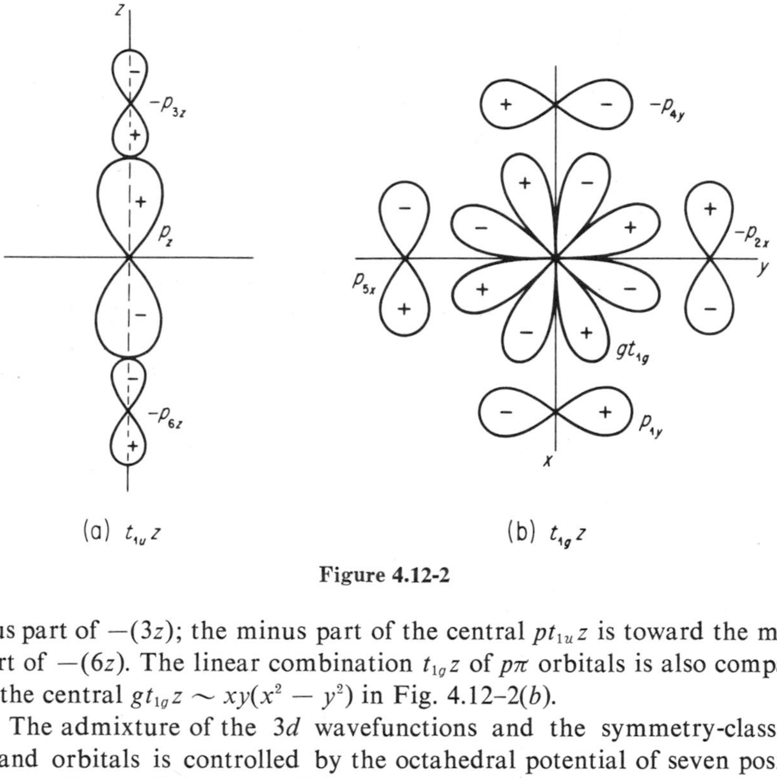

Figure 4.12-2

plus part of $-(3z)$; the minus part of the central $pt_{1u}z$ is toward the minus part of $-(6z)$. The linear combination $t_{1g}z$ of $p\pi$ orbitals is also compared to the central $gt_{1g}z \sim xy(x^2 - y^2)$ in Fig. 4.12–2(*b*).

The admixture of the 3*d* wavefunctions and the symmetry-classified ligand orbitals is controlled by the octahedral potential of seven positive charges. In principle, the coefficients of the admixture should be determined by solving the secular determinant. The secular determinant involves nonvanishing elements only between the 3*d* and symmetry-classified ligand orbitals that belong to the same label of the same irreducible representation. This is easily established by Theorem 2.20–3. The $3dt_{2g}\zeta$ orbital is, for example, admixed only with the $p\pi t_{2g}\zeta$ orbital, since the eigenfunctions of the secular matrix are linear combinations of the 3*d* and symmetry-classified ligand orbitals that have nonvanishing matrix element of the potential. Such a linear combination of atomic orbitals is called a *linear combination of atomic orbital molecular orbital* (LCAO MO). The secular matrix for the $3dt_{2g}\zeta$ and $p\pi t_{2g}\zeta$ orbitals may be written in the form

$$\begin{matrix} 3dt_{2g}\zeta & p\pi t_{2g}\zeta \end{matrix}$$
$$\begin{bmatrix} E_{3d} - V_d & V_{dp} \\ V_{pd} & E_{2p} - V_p \end{bmatrix}, \tag{4.12–1}$$

where E_{3d} is the energy eigenvalue of the single $3d$ electron in the free state of the M ion, and E_{2p} is the energy eigenvalue of the single $2p$ electron in the free state of the F^- ion. The Hamiltonian operator H is

$$H = -\frac{\hbar^2}{2m}\nabla^2 - \frac{Z_0 e^2}{r_0} - \sum_{i=1}^{6} \frac{Ze^2}{r_i},$$

where Z_0 is the effective charge of the M-ion core, and Z is the effective charge of the F^--ion core. The distance of the electron from the M ion is r_0; that from the ith F^- ion is r_i. We have the equations

$$\begin{aligned}
\langle 3dt_{2g}\zeta|H|3dt_{2g}\zeta\rangle &= E_{3d} - \left\langle 3dt_{2g}\zeta\right| \sum_i \frac{Ze^2}{r_i} \left|3dt_{2g}\zeta\right\rangle \\
&= E_{3d} - V_d, \\
\langle p\pi t_{2g}\zeta|H|p\pi t_{2g}\zeta\rangle &= E_{2p} - \left\langle p\pi t_{2g}\zeta\right| \frac{Z_0 e^2}{r_0} \left|p\pi t_{2g}\zeta\right\rangle \\
&\quad - \left\langle 1y\right| \sum_{i(\neq 1)} \frac{Ze^2}{r_i} \left|1y\right\rangle \\
&= E_{2p} - V_p,
\end{aligned}$$

and

$$\begin{aligned}
\langle 3dt_{2g}\zeta|H|p\pi t_{2g}\zeta\rangle &= E_{2p} S_\pi - \left\langle 3dt_{2g}\zeta\right| \sum_{i(\neq 1)} \frac{Ze^2}{r_i} \left|1y\right\rangle \\
&\quad - \left\langle 3dt_{2g}\zeta\right| \frac{Z_0 e^2}{r_0} \left|p\pi t_{2g}\zeta\right\rangle = V_{dp} \\
&= \langle p\pi t_{2g}\zeta|H|3dt_{2g}\zeta\rangle \\
&= E_{3d} S_\pi - \left\langle p\pi t_{2g}\zeta\right| \sum_i \frac{Ze^2}{r_i} \left|3dt_{2g}\zeta\right\rangle \\
&= V_{pd},
\end{aligned}$$

where in the second equation overlap-type integrals between different ligands are ignored, and S_π is the *group overlap integral* $\langle p\pi t_{2g}\zeta|3dt_{2g}\zeta\rangle$. We do not go into the details of these matrix elements but formally obtain the eigenvalues of the secular matrix (4.12–1). The eigenvalues are

$$\mathcal{E} = \tfrac{1}{2}[(\mathcal{E}_d + \mathcal{E}_p) \pm \{(\mathcal{E}_d - \mathcal{E}_p)^2 + 4V_{dp}^2\}^{1/2}],$$

where $\mathcal{E}_d = E_{3d} - V_d$, and $\mathcal{E}_p = E_{2p} - V_p$. If $\mathcal{E}_d$ is greater than $\mathcal{E}_p$, we have

$$\mathcal{E}_> > \mathcal{E}_d > \mathcal{E}_p > \mathcal{E}_<,$$

where $\mathcal{E}_>$ is the greater and $\mathcal{E}_<$ the lesser of the two eigenvalues. The lower level of the two eigenstates becomes lower than the $\mathcal{E}_p$ level, and the higher one higher than $\mathcal{E}_d$. If the electron goes into the lower level, the system is more stabilized than the original two levels. If the electron goes into the higher level, the system is less stabilized. The stabilized orbital may be called the *bonding orbital*, and the less stabilized one the *antibonding orbital*. In a similar way we find that the $3de_gu$ orbital is linearly combined with the $2se_gu$ and $2p\sigma e_gu$ orbitals. We may write the antibonding orbitals in the form

$$\begin{aligned} \Psi_e^a &= N_e(\phi_e - \lambda_s\chi_s - \lambda_\sigma\chi_\sigma), \\ \Psi_t^a &= N_t(\phi_t - \lambda_\pi\chi_\pi), \end{aligned} \tag{4.12–2}$$

where the ϕ's are atomic d functions, the subscripts e and t refer to the symmetry E_g and T_{2g}, and the χ's are symmetry-classified ligand orbitals. We omit the labels of the components of the irreducible bases in (4.12–2). The normalization constants N_e and N_t are

$$\begin{aligned} N_e^{-2} &= 1 - 2\lambda_s S_s - 2\lambda_\sigma S_\sigma + \lambda_s^2 + \lambda_\sigma^2, \\ N_t^{-2} &= 1 - 2\lambda_\pi S_\pi + \lambda_\pi^2, \end{aligned} \tag{4.12–3}$$

where the S's are the group overlap integrals between ϕ's and χ's.

There are also other symmetry-classified ligand orbitals that are not combined with the $3de_g$ or $3dt_{2g}$ orbitals. These orbitals are indicated in parentheses in Fig. 4.12–3. We assume that these orbitals lie below the

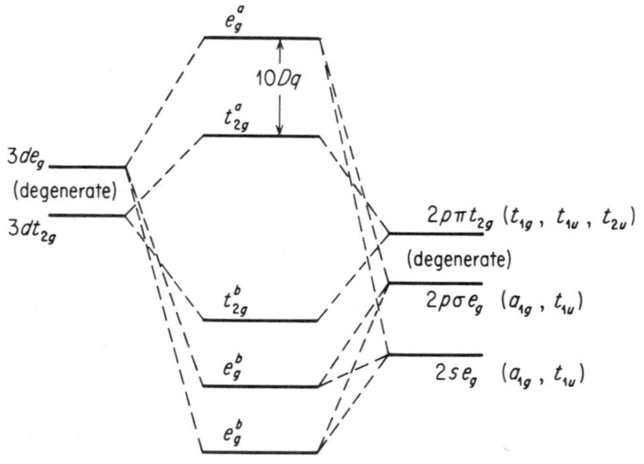

Figure 4.12-3

antibonding orbitals. The energy-level diagram assumed is schematically illustrated in Fig. 4.12–3.

If the cluster is $(CrF_6)^{3-}$, there are 51 electrons in the outer-shell orbitals. If we fill these with electrons from the lowest orbitals, three electrons are left in the antibonding orbitals. If the cluster is $(NiF_6)^{4-}$, we have eight electrons in the antibonding orbitals for the ground state configuration. For the case of $(MnF_6)^{4-}$, there are five electrons among the antibonding orbitals.

The antibonding orbitals are classified in two types (4.12–2); the one belonging to E_g symmetry can accommodate four electrons, the other belonging to T_{2g} six electrons. In Appendix 4.3 we have given the many-electron statevectors that are classified according to the irreducible representations of the point group $\mathbf{O}_h$. If the exchange interaction between the electrons favors the greater spin of all the electrons, the ground state has the maximum spin quantum number. For example, the ground state of the cluster $(MnF_6)^{4-}$ then has the spin quantum number $S = \frac{5}{2}$, being ${}^6A_{1g}$. The ground state of two clusters $(VF_6)^{4-}$ and $(CrF_6)^{3-}$ may be ${}^4A_{2g}$ if the antibonding orbital t_{2g} is lower in energy than the e_g antibonding orbital.† The cluster $(NiF_6)^{4-}$ is complementary to the cluster $(VF_6)^{3-}$ if we are concerned only with the antibonding orbitals t_{2g} and e_g.

We are now in a position to calculate the g-factor again, using the modified orbitals (4.12–2). For example, the complex $(CrF_6)^{3-}$ has the ground state ${}^4A_{2g}$, the excited spin quartet states ${}^4T_{1g}$ and ${}^4T_{2g}$ arising from the electron configuration t_{2g}^2e, and ${}^4T_{1g}$ from $t_{2g}e^2$. We may confine the calculation of g-factor within these spin quartet states to a first approximation. The Hamiltonian operator $\boldsymbol{H}$ is written in the form, in place of (4.11–2),

$$\boldsymbol{H} = \zeta_d \sum_{i=1}^{3} \mathbf{l}_i \cdot \mathbf{s}_i + \beta H \sum_{i=1}^{3} (l_{iz} + g_f s_{iz}) \tag{4.12–4}$$

where ζ_d is the single-electron spin-orbit coupling constant, and g_f is the free-spin g-factor, 2.0023. The z direction is taken along the applied magnetic field. Within the spin quartets, the single-electron spin operator $\mathbf{s}_i$ may be replaced by $c\mathbf{S}$ using the replacement theorem in Sec. 1.13. The factor c is easily determined to be $\frac{1}{3}$ since

$$\langle S = \tfrac{3}{2}\, M_S = \tfrac{3}{2} | s_{iz} | S = \tfrac{3}{2}\, M_S = \tfrac{3}{2} \rangle = \tfrac{1}{2} = c \cdot (\tfrac{3}{2}).$$

We perform the perturbation calculation similar to (4.11–3), using the many-electron wavefunctions in terms of the antibonding orbitals

$$|{}^4A_{2g}\, M_S = \tfrac{3}{2}\rangle = |\xi\eta\zeta\rangle$$

and

$$|{}^4T_{2g}\, M_S = \tfrac{3}{2}\rangle = |\xi\eta v\rangle,$$

where

$$\zeta = N_t[dt_{2g}\zeta - \lambda_\pi \tfrac{1}{2}\{(1y) + (2x) - (4y) - (5x)\}] \tag{4.12–5}$$

and

$$v = N_e[de_g v - \lambda_s \tfrac{1}{2}\{(s_1 - s_2 + s_4 - s_5)\} - \lambda_\sigma \tfrac{1}{2}\{-(1x) + (2y) + (4x) - (5y)\}]. \tag{4.12–6}$$

†Capital letters A_{1g}, A_{2g}, E_g, . . . are used for many-electron states; small letters a_{1g}, a_{2g}, e_g, . . . for single-electron states.

We do not need the explicit expressions for ξ and η orbitals. The second-order energy correction is

$$\Delta E(S_z, H) = -2\frac{S_z}{3}\zeta_d\beta H\langle v|l_z|\zeta\rangle\langle\zeta|l_z|v\rangle/10Dq,$$

where $10Dq$ is to be the energy separation between two antibonding orbitals t_{2g} and e_g. The matrix element $\langle\zeta|l_z|v\rangle$ is calculated as follows.

$$\begin{aligned} l_z|v\rangle = N_e\Big[&(2i)\, dt_{2g}\zeta \\ &-\frac{\lambda_s}{2}\{ap_y(s_1) + ap_x(s_2) - ap_y(s_4) - ap_x(s_5)\} \\ &-\frac{\lambda_\sigma}{2}(-i)\{(1y) + (2x) - (4y) - (5x)\} \\ &-\frac{\lambda_\sigma}{2}\{-ap_y(1x) - ap_x(2y) - ap_y(4x) - ap_x(5y)\}\Big], \end{aligned}$$

where a is the distance between the Cr and F nuclei, p_x and p_y are linear momentum operators. We have used the matrix elements of (4.5–6) and (4.5–8). The angular momentum operator l_z is referred to the Cr nucleus and is transformed to the angular momentum operator referred to the ligand nuclei when it operates on the ligand orbitals. For example,

$$l_z = l_{1z} + ap_y \qquad \text{for the ligand 1.}$$

The matrix element is found to be

$$\begin{aligned} \langle\zeta|l_z|v\rangle = N_e N_t(2i)\Big\{1 &- \lambda_s S_s - \lambda_\sigma S_\sigma - \lambda_\pi S_\pi + \tfrac{1}{2}\lambda_\sigma S_\pi \\ &- \tfrac{1}{2}\lambda_\sigma\lambda_\pi - \frac{ia}{2}\lambda_s\lambda_\pi\langle 1y|p_y|s_1\rangle\Big\}, \end{aligned} \qquad (4.12\text{–}7)$$

where the S's are the group overlap integrals:

$$S_s = \langle de_g v|\tfrac{1}{2}(s_1 - s_2 + s_4 - s_5)\rangle,$$

$$S_\sigma = \langle de_g v|\tfrac{1}{2}\{-(1x) + (2y) + (4x) - (5y)\}\rangle,$$

and

$$S_\pi = \langle dt_{2g}\zeta|\tfrac{1}{2}\{(1y) + (2x) - (4y) - (5x)\}\rangle.$$

In this calculation we have ignored the overlap-type integrals between different ligands and assumed, for example, that the quantity $\langle dt_{2g}\zeta|ap_y|1x\rangle$ is approximately equal to $\langle dt_{2g}\zeta|l_z|1x\rangle = 2i\langle de_g v|1x\rangle$ since $l_z = xp_y - yp_x$ may be approximated by ap_y in the vicinity of the ligand 1. If we take the ratio between (4.12–7) and $\langle 3dt_{2g}\zeta|l_z|3de_g v\rangle = 2i$, the angular momentum is effectively reduced by the ratio,

$$k_{\sigma\pi} = \frac{\langle\zeta|l_z|v\rangle}{\langle 3dt_{2g}\zeta|l_z|3de_g v\rangle}. \qquad (4.12\text{–}8)$$

Such a factor $k_{\sigma\pi}$ is called the *effective orbital g-factor* or *orbital reduction factor*. The matrix element $\langle v|l_z|\zeta\rangle$ is obtained in a similar way, being given by replacing the fifth term in (4.12–7) by $\lambda_\pi S_\sigma$ and taking the complex conjugate to this approximation. These two matrix elements are exactly complex conjugate.

The g-shift is now given by

$$\Delta g = -\frac{8k_{\sigma\pi}^2\lambda}{10Dq}, \tag{4.12–9}$$

where the following relation is used

$$\zeta_d \sum \mathbf{l}_i\cdot\mathbf{s}_i = \zeta_d c\mathbf{S}\cdot\mathbf{L} = \lambda\mathbf{S}\cdot\mathbf{L}.$$

For the case of $(NiF_6)^{4-}$, the g-shift may be found to be given by (4.12–9). The reduction of the spin-orbit constant observed in the previous section is now partly attributed to the orbital reduction factor which is introduced by the molecular orbital approximation. The spin-orbit constant in a crystal may be altered from the free-ion value, depending on the ligand field effects. If the crystal spin-orbit constant were not far from the free-ion value, we could equate the square of the orbital reduction factor $k_{\sigma\pi}^2$ to the ratio λ_{eff}/λ_f listed in Table 4.11–1. In the case of Ni^{2+} in the octahedral $(NiF_6)^{4-}$ cluster, Sugano and Shulman estimated the orbital reduction factor $k_{\sigma\pi}$ to be about 0.88 and obtained a crystal spin-orbit constant of -320cm^{-1}, very close to the free-ion value -324cm^{-1}.†

The hyperfine interaction has not been established by the molecular orbital approximation up till now. We cannot compare the observed reduction of the hyperfine constant with the degree of admixture of the ligand orbitals in the antibonding orbitals (Table 4.11–2).

We now come to the interpretation of the superhyperfine interaction by the molecular orbital approximation. The octahedral cluster $(MnF_6)^{4-}$ is considered. The ground state is $^6A_{1g}$ whose statevectors are available in Appendix 4.3. The magnetic dipolar interaction between the electrons and the ligand nuclei is

$$\begin{aligned} H_{dd} &= \sum_{n=1}^{6}\sum_{i=1}^{5} g\beta\gamma\beta_N r_{in}^{-3}\{3(\mathbf{e}_{in}\cdot\mathbf{s}_i)(\mathbf{e}_{in}\cdot\mathbf{I}^n) - (\mathbf{s}_i\cdot\mathbf{I}^n)\} \\ &= \sum_{n=1}^{6} H_{dd}^n, \end{aligned}$$

where n sums over six fluorine nuclei, and i over the five electrons in the antibonding orbitals. The distance r_{in} is between the ith electron and the nth nucleus, and $\mathbf{e}_{in}$ is the unit vector connecting the nth nucleus toward the ith electron. The matrix element $\langle {}^6A_{1g}M_S = \frac{5}{2}|H_{dd}|{}^6A_{1g}M_S = \frac{5}{2}\rangle$ is calculated replacing the spin operator $\mathbf{s}_i$ by $c\mathbf{S}$ with $c = \frac{1}{5} = 1/2S$. The state $|{}^6A_{1g}M_S = \frac{5}{2}\rangle$ is given in Appendix 4.3, being

$$|{}^6A_{1g}M_S = \tfrac{5}{2}\rangle = |\xi\eta\zeta uv\rangle,$$

where

†S. Sugano and R. G. Shulman, *Phys. Rev.* **130**, 517 (1963).

$$\xi = N_t[dt_{2g}\xi - \lambda_\pi \tfrac{1}{2}\{(2z) + (3y) - (5z) - (6y)\}], \tag{4.12–5a}$$

$$\eta = N_t[dt_{2g}\eta - \lambda_\pi \tfrac{1}{2}\{(1z) + (3x) - (4z) - (6x)\}], \tag{4.12–5b}$$

$$u = N_e[de_g u - \lambda_s(\tfrac{1}{12})^{1/2}(-s_1 - s_2 - s_4 - s_5 + 2s_3 + 2s_6) - \lambda_\sigma(\tfrac{1}{12})^{1/2}\{(1x) + (2y) - (4x) - (5y) - 2(3z) + 2(6z)\}], \tag{4.12–6b}$$

ζ and v are given by (4.12–5) and (4.12–6) respectively. For simplicity, only the fluorine nucleus 3 is considered, being located at the distance a from the origin along the z axis. The dipolar interaction H_{dd}^3 is then written in detail:

$$H_{dd}^3 = \frac{g\beta\gamma\beta_N}{2S} r_3^{-3} \times \{3(S_\xi I_\xi \sin^2\theta\cos^2\varphi + S_\xi I_\eta \sin^2\theta \sin\varphi\cos\varphi + S_\xi I_\zeta \sin\theta\cos\theta\cos\varphi + S_\eta I_\xi \sin^2\theta\sin\varphi\cos\varphi + S_\eta I_\eta \sin^2\theta\sin^2\varphi + S_\eta I_\zeta \sin\theta\cos\theta\sin\varphi + S_\zeta I_\xi \sin\theta\cos\theta\cos\varphi + S_\zeta I_\eta \sin\theta\cos\theta\sin\varphi + S_\zeta I_\zeta\cos^2\theta) - \mathbf{S}\cdot\mathbf{I}\},$$

where the angles θ and φ are referred to the polar coordinates with the origin at the nucleus 3. The superscript 3 on the spin operator $\mathbf{I}$ is omitted. The ξ, η, and ζ components are referred to the Cartesian coordinates with the ζ axis along the line joining the Mn and the fluorine nucleus 3 which is to be the new origin. The matrix element of H_{dd}^3 with respect to the state $|{}^6A_{1g}M_S = \tfrac{5}{2}\rangle$ is

$$\begin{aligned} &N_t^2\{\langle dt_{2g}\xi|H_{dd}^3|dt_{2g}\xi\rangle + \langle dt_{2g}\eta|H_{dd}^3|dt_{2g}\eta\rangle + \langle dt_{2g}\zeta|H_{dd}^3|dt_{2g}\zeta\rangle\} \\ &+ N_e^2\{\langle de_g u|H_{dd}^3|de_g u\rangle + \langle de_g v|H_{dd}^3|de_g v\rangle\} \\ &+ N_t^2\lambda_\pi\{-\langle dt_{2g}\xi|H_{dd}^3|(3y)\rangle - \langle dt_{2g}\eta|H_{dd}^3|(3x)\rangle\} \\ &- 2N_e^2\left(\frac{1}{3}\right)^{1/2}\{\lambda_s\langle de_g u|H_{dd}^3|s_3\rangle + \lambda_\sigma\langle de_g u|H_{dd}^3|(3z)\rangle\} \\ &+ \frac{N_t^2\lambda_\pi^2}{4}\{\langle(3y)|H_{dd}^3|(3y)\rangle + \langle(3x)|H_{dd}^3|(3x)\rangle\} \\ &+ \frac{N_e^2\lambda_s^2}{3}\langle s_3|H_{dd}^3|s_3\rangle + \frac{N_e^2\lambda_\sigma^2}{3}\langle(3z)|H_{dd}^3|(3z)\rangle, \end{aligned} \tag{4.12–10}$$

where all terms are neglected if the integral involves at least one fluorine atomic orbital other than that of the fluorine 3. The integration of the terms other than the last three terms in (4.12–10) requires elaborate numerical calculation; the last three terms are calculated to be

$$\frac{g\beta\gamma\beta_N}{2S}\left[\frac{N_e^2\lambda_s^2}{3}\frac{8\pi}{3}|\psi_{2s}(0)|^2\mathbf{S}\cdot\mathbf{I}^3 + \frac{2}{5}\left(\frac{N_e^2\lambda_\sigma^2}{3} - \frac{N_t^2\lambda_\pi^2}{4}\right)\langle r^{-3}\rangle_{2p}(3S_\zeta I_\zeta^3 - \mathbf{S}\cdot\mathbf{I}^3)\right] \tag{4.12–11}$$

where $|\psi_{2s}(0)|^2$ is the fluorine $2s$ density at the nucleus, $\langle r^{-3}\rangle_{2p}$ is the average over the fluorine $2p$ radial function. The interaction (4.12–11) may be called the *transferred hyperfine interaction*. The contributions of other fluorine nuclei can be obtained by replacing the superscript 3 by the respective superscript and the ζ direction by the respective ζ direction. One obtains the whole transferred hyperfine interaction in the form

$$\sum_n \{A_s \mathbf{S}\cdot\mathbf{I}^n + (A_\sigma - A_\pi)(3S_z I_z^n \cos^2\theta_n - \mathbf{S}\cdot\mathbf{I}^n)\}, \tag{4.12–12}$$

where θ_n is the angle between the ζ axis of the nth nucleus and the applied magnetic field, and n sums over six fluorine nuclei. The parameters A_s, A_σ, and A_π are

$$A_s = \frac{g\beta\gamma\beta_N}{2S}\frac{N_e^2\lambda_s^2}{3}\frac{8\pi}{3}|\psi_{2s}(0)|^2, \tag{4.12–13}$$

$$A_\sigma = \frac{g\beta\gamma\beta_N}{2S}\frac{2}{5}\frac{N_e^2\lambda_\sigma^2}{3}\langle r^{-3}\rangle_{2p}, \tag{4.12–14}$$

and

$$A_\pi = \frac{g\beta\gamma\beta_N}{2S}\frac{2}{5}\frac{N_t^2\lambda_\pi^2}{4}\langle r^{-3}\rangle_{2p}. \tag{4.12–15}$$

By a similar method one can calculate the transferred hyperfine interaction for the tetrahedral cluster $(MnF_4)^{2-}$ and cube cluster $(MnF_8)^{6-}$. The antibonding orbitals are easily constructed with the use of Appendix 4.4. One obtains the transferred hyperfine interaction in a form similar to (4.12–12), except that n sums over four fluorine nuclei for the $(MnF_4)^{2-}$ cluster and eight fluorine nuclei for the $(MnF_8)^{6-}$ cluster and that the parameters are, for $(MnF_4)^{2-}$,

$$A_s = \frac{g\beta\gamma\beta_N}{2S}\frac{3N_t^2\lambda_s^2}{4}\frac{8\pi}{3}|\psi_{2s}(0)|^2,$$

$$A_\sigma = \frac{g\beta\gamma\beta_N}{2S}\frac{2}{5}\frac{3N_t^2\lambda_\sigma^2}{4}\langle r^{-3}\rangle_{2p},$$

$$A_\pi = \frac{g\beta\gamma\beta_N}{2S}\frac{2}{5}\left\{\frac{3N_t^2\lambda_\pi^2}{8} + \frac{N_e^2\lambda_\pi^2}{4}\right\}\langle r^{-3}\rangle_{2p},$$

and, for $(MnF_8)^{6-}$,

$$A_s = \frac{g\beta\gamma\beta_N}{2S}\frac{3N_t^2\lambda_s^2}{8}\frac{8\pi}{3}|\psi_{2s}(0)|^2,$$

$$A_\sigma = \frac{g\beta\gamma\beta_N}{2S}\frac{2}{5}\frac{3N_t^2\lambda_\sigma^2}{8}\langle r^{-3}\rangle_{2p},$$

$$A_\pi = \frac{g\beta\gamma\beta_N}{2S}\frac{2}{5}\left\{\frac{3N_t^2\lambda_\pi^2}{16} + \frac{N_e^2\lambda_\pi^2}{8}\right\}\langle r^{-3}\rangle_{2p}.$$

The terms other than the last three in (4.12–10) may also be reduced to the form

$$\sum_n A_d(3S_z I_z^n \cos^2\theta_n - \mathbf{S}\cdot\mathbf{I}^n). \tag{4.12–16}$$

The factor A_d may be written as

$$A_d = (g\beta\gamma\beta_N)\frac{f}{R^3}, \tag{4.12–17}$$

where R is the distance between the central ion and the fluorine ligands. The magnitude of the factor f should be determined numerically or is unity if the manganese electronic magnetic moment is assumed to be a point dipole located at the Mn nucleus.

The superhyperfine interaction term in (4.11–1) is now written as

$$\sum_n A_s\mathbf{S}\cdot\mathbf{I}^n + \sum_n (A_d + A_\sigma - A_\pi)(3S_z I_z^n \cos^2\theta_n - \mathbf{S}\cdot\mathbf{I}^n). \tag{4.12–18}$$

If the magnetic field is applied along one of the cube edges for case of the cube cluster $(MnF_8)^{6-}$, the second term in (4.12–18) vanishes to first order, yet the first term remains to show superhyperfine structure in the electron paramagnetic resonance spectra. This was observed by Baker, Bleaney, and Hayes, as mentioned in the previous section. The fluorine nucleus has the spin $I = \frac{1}{2}$. The first term in (4.12–18) gives rise to an additional magnetic field on the electron magnetic moment; the additional field is given to the first order by

$$\left(\frac{A_s}{g\beta}\right)\sum_{n=1}^{8} I_z^n.$$

One expects in this case nine superhyperfine lines with equal spacing $(A_s/g\beta)$ and with intensities in the ratio 1:8:28:56:70:56:28:8:1. From this spacing one can determine the magnitude of A_s. The magnitude of the additional field due to A_s is independent of the direction of the applied field; however, that due to the second term in (4.12–18) depends on the direction. One can determine the magnitude of the sum $A_d + A_\sigma - A_\pi$ from the angular dependence of the superhyperfine separation. The value of A_d may be calculated if the factor f is put to be unity and the distance R is known. Thus the value $A_\sigma - A_\pi$ may be determined. If the magnitudes of the hyperfine interaction constants for the free fluorine ion A_{2s} and A_{2p} are known, one can estimate the magnitudes of admixtures of the fluorine $2s$ and $2p$ orbitals in the antibonding orbitals. These constants are given by

$$A_{2s} = (g\beta\gamma\beta_N)\left(\frac{8\pi}{3}\right)|\psi_{2s}(0)|^2,$$

and

$$A_{2p} = (g\beta\gamma\beta_N)\langle r^{-3}\rangle_{2p}.$$

These quantities are referred to the single $2s$ and $2p$ electron respectively. One should compare the single-electron quantities $2SA_s$ and $2S(A_\sigma - A_\pi)$ with the free-ion quantities. The factor $2S$ must be multiplied, since if one is concerned with the single spin **s** the replacement $\mathbf{s} = c\mathbf{S}$ is not needed. The magnitudes of $2s$ and $2p$ admixture are expressed in the form

$$f_s = \frac{2SA_s}{A_{2s}} = \frac{N_e^2\lambda_s^2}{3}$$

and

$$f_\sigma - f_\pi = \frac{2S(A_\sigma - A_\pi)}{A_{2p}} = \frac{2}{5}\left\{\frac{N_e^2\lambda_\sigma^2}{3} - \frac{N_t^2\lambda_\pi^2}{4}\right\},$$

for the octahedral cluster. The constants A_{2s} and A_{2p} have been estimated to be

$A_{2s} = 1.57\ \text{cm}^{-1}$	(Moriya)†	$A_{2s} = 1.503\ \text{cm}^{-1}$	(Shulman and Sugano)‡
$A_{2p} = 0.044\ \text{cm}^{-1}$		$A_{2p} = 0.0429\ \text{cm}^{-1}$	

In other octahedral clusters, e. g., $(VF_6)^{4-}$, $(CrF_6)^{3-}$, $(CrF_6)^{5-}$, $(FeF_6)^{3-}$, and $(NiF_6)^{4-}$, in which the ground state is an orbital singlet with maximum spin, one obtains for the superhyperfine interaction the same expression as (4.12–18), except for S being given by one-half of the number of the unpaired electrons.

The superhyperfine interaction has been observed also in the nuclear magnetic resonance spectra of the fluorine nuclei in antiferromagnetic crystals, $KMnF_3$ and $KNiF_3$.§ The resonance of the free nuclear spin of ^{19}F should be observed at 60,000 Mc/sec when ^{19}F is placed in the magnetic field of 14,979.4 gauss. The unpaired electrons in the antibonding orbitals of the $(MnF_6)^{4-}$ and $(NiF_6)^{4-}$ clusters produce an additional magnetic field at the position of the fluorine nuclei. The resonance field of ^{19}F has been observed to be shifted a few per cent in these crystals. From the magnitude of the shift one can estimate the parameters for the transferred hyperfine interaction A_s and $A_\sigma - A_\pi$.

Table 4.12–3 gives the magnitudes of the superhyperfine constants of some octahedral fluoride clusters, together with estimates of the magnitudes of $2s$ and $2p$ admixture in the antibonding orbitals. The values for A_d are estimated assuming f to be unity in (4.12–17). Hall *et al* corrected the values A_s and $A_\sigma - A_\pi$ for Ni^{2+} in NaF and $KMgF_3$, taking account the corrections pointed out by Marshall.* Shulman and Sugano also took account of Marshall's corrections to estimate the parameters for Ni^{2+} in $KNiF_3$. The values for A_{2s} and A_{2p} estimated by Moriya were used to evaluate the magnitudes of f_s and $f_\sigma - f_\pi$ except for Ni^{2+} in $KNiF_3$ in the last row of Table 4.12–3

†T. Moriya, *Progr. Theoret. Phys. (Kyoto)* **16**, 23 (1956).
‡R. G. Shulman and S. Sugano, *Phys. Rev.* **130**, 506 (1963).
§R. G. Shulman and K. Knox, *Phys. Rev. Lett.* **4**, 603 (1960).
*W. Marshall, *Paramagnetic Resonance*, vol. 1, ed. W. Low (New York: Academic Press, 1963), p. 347.

Watson and Freeman pointed out the possibility that the bonding orbitals will have different wavefunctions according to whether the spin is parallel or antiparallel to that of the unpaired electrons in the antibonding orbitals.† They estimated the effects of the difference on the transferred hyperfine interaction in $KNiF_3$ and suggested that admixture parameters in the antibonding orbital with spin antiparallel to the antibonding electron should be compared with experimental results. The reader is referred to the original paper.

TABLE 4.12–3

MAGNITUDES OF OBSERVED SUPERHYPERFINE CONSTANTS AND ESTIMATES OF $2s$ AND $2p$ ADMIXTURE IN THE ANTIBONDING ORBITALS IN SOME OCTAHEDRAL FLUORIDE CLUSTERS

Ion	Host	A_d 10^{-4} cm^{-1}	A_s 10^{-4} cm^{-1}	$A_\sigma - A_\pi$ 10^{-4} cm^{-1}	f_s %	$f_\sigma - f_\pi$ %	Reference
V^{2+}	$KMgF_3$	3.1	(−)1.0	(−)6.1	(−)0.019	(−)4.15	a
Cr^{3+}	$KMgF_3$	3.1	(−)1.6	(−)7.0	(−)0.031	(−)4.76	a
Cr^{+}	NaF	2.0	12.5	0.5 ±0.5	0.40	−0.6 ±0.6	a
	$KMgF_3$	3.1	19.3	−1.2	0.61	−1.3	a
Mn^{2+}	LiF	3.0	14.9	0.7	0.47	0.8	a
	NaF	2.0	12.9	1.2	0.41	1.3	a
	KF	1.3	12.6	2.1	0.40	2.3	a
	$KMgF_3$	3.1	17.2	0.3 ±0.5	0.55	0.3 ±0.5	a, b
	$KMnF_3$	..	16.26	0.17	0.52	0.19	c
Fe^{3+}	$KMgF_3$	3.1	24.0	2.9	0.763	3.3	a
	$KCdF_3$	2.4	22.7	3.3	0.722	3.7	a
Ni^{2+}	NaF	3.3	35.4	7.5	0.488	3.4	a
	$KMgF_3$	3.5	42.0	6.9	0.526	3.13	a
	$KNiF_3$	..	33.9	8.10†	0.538	3.78†	d

†These values are for A_σ and f_σ.
[a]T. P. P. Hall, W. Hayes, R. W. H. Stevenson, and J. Wilkens, *J. Chem. Phys.* **38**, 1977 (1963).
[b]S. Ogawa, *J. Phys. Soc. Japan* **15**, 1475 (1960).
[c]R. G. Shulman and K. Knox, *Phys. Rev. Lett.* **4**, 603 (1960).
[d]R. G. Shulman and S. Sugano, *Phys. Rev.* **130**, 506 (1963).

The electrostatic interactions between the electrons in antibonding orbitals are also calculated by the molecular orbital approximation. Koide and Pryce discussed the splitting of the crystal terms $^4A_{1g}$ and ^4E_g from ^4G of the Mn^{2+} ion in some hydrated salts by the molecular orbital approximation.‡ These two terms are accidentally degenerate in a cubic crystal potential, as shown in Fig. 4.7–2; however, experiment has shown that they

†R. E. Watson and A. J. Freeman, *Phys. Rev.* **134**, A1521 (1964).
‡S. Koide and M. H. L. Pryce, *Phil. Mag.* **3**, 607 (1958).

actually split. The electrostatic interaction is calculated using the antibonding orbitals (4.12–5, 5a, 5b) and (4.12–6, 6a). The five-electron wavefunctions are available in Appendix 4.3, and the matrix elements in Table 4.8–1. The electrostatic energy of $t_2^3(^4A_2)e^2(^3A_2)^4A_{1g}$ is calculated to be

$$E(^4A_{1g}) = 3d - 3j + 2(3)^{1/2}c + e - 3f - g - (3)^{-1/2}h$$
$$= (3A - 15B)N_t^4 + (6A - 2B + 5C)N_t^2N_e^2 + (A - 8B)N_e^4,$$

where we have ignored the integrals involving the ligand orbitals. There are two ^4E_g crystal terms, which have the following secular matrix for the electrostatic interaction:

$$\begin{array}{cc} t_2^3(^4A_2)e^2(^1E)^4E_g & t_2^3(^2E)e^2(^3A_2)^4E_g \end{array}$$
$$\begin{bmatrix} (3A-15B)N_t^4+(6A-2B+5C)N_t^2N_e^2 \\ \quad +(A-8B)N_e^4 & 2(3)^{1/2}BN_t^2N_e^2 \\ 2(3)^{1/2}BN_t^2N_e^2 & (3A-15B)N_t^4+(6A-6B+3C)N_t^2N_e^2 \\ & \quad +(A+2C)N_e^4 \end{bmatrix}$$

Koide and Pryce took into account the ligand σ orbitals in the antibonding orbitals and ignored the π orbitals. This is equivalent to taking the value of N_t^2 to be unity. They estimated the value of $(1 - N_e^2)$ to be 0.08 so that the splitting of $^4A_{1g}$ and ^4E_g from ^4G observed by experiment could be fitted. They called the quantity $(1 - N_e^2) = \mathcal{E}$ the *covalency parameter.* Some of the values of the covalency parameter are listed in Table 4.12–4.

TABLE 4.12–4

COVALENCY PARAMETERS FOR IRON-GROUP IONS

Ion	Host	Covalency parameter	Reference
Cr^{3+}	Al_2O_3	0.19	a
Mn^{2+}	hydrated salts	0.08	b
	MnF_2	0.06	c
	$MnCl_2$	0.13	d
		0.03	e
		$\leqslant$0.04	f
	$MnBr_2$	0.15	d
		0.05	e
		$\leqslant$0.04	f
Ni^{2+}	$KNiF_3$	0.039	g

a. S. Sugano and M. Peter, *Phys. Rev.* **122**, 381 (1961).
b. S. Koide and M. H. L. Pryce, *Phil. Mag.* **3**, 607 (1958).
c. J. W. Stout, *J.Chem. Phys.* **31**, 707 (1959).
d. J. W. Stout, *J. Chem. Phys.* **33**, 303 (1960).
e. R. Pappalardo, *J. Chem. Phys.* **31**, 1050 (1959), **33**, 613 (1960).
f. J. C. Zahner and G. Drickamer, *J. Chem. Phys.* **35**, 1483 (1961).
g. S. Sugano and R. G. Shulman, *Phys. Rev.* **130**, 517 (1963).

The values of $\mathcal{E}$ referred to as *a*, *b*, *c*, and *d* are determined by using fixed values for Racah's parameters *B* and *C*, e. g., the free-ion values. Pappalardo obtained the values of $\mathcal{E}$ referred to as *e* by choosing the values of *B*, *C*, and $\mathcal{E}$ in a self-consistent way, ignoring the free-ion values. In this context Pappalardo's estimate appears more likely. The covalency parameter should be replaced by $1 - (N_e^2/N_t^2)$ when the ligand π orbitals are also taken into account, and the factor N_t^4 is absorbed in Racah's parameters. The value of $\mathcal{E}$ referred to as *g* is obtained by estimating $1 - (N_e^2/N_t^2)$ from first principles, with the values of N_e and N_t being 0.968 and 0.988 respectively.

We have seen that many results on transition-element ion complexes are more satisfactorily explained by the molecular orbital approximation based on LCAO MO. Several authors have tried calculations from first principles using LCAO MO, which we have not touched upon. The reader is referred to the articles listed at the end of the Bibliography.

Appendix 1.1

EULERIAN ANGLES

Two definitions of Eulerian angles are currently used. The relation between the two is presented below.

1. *Whittaker:* In the text, we use Whittaker's definition. The first rotation is performed around the z-axis by an angle α; the second rotation

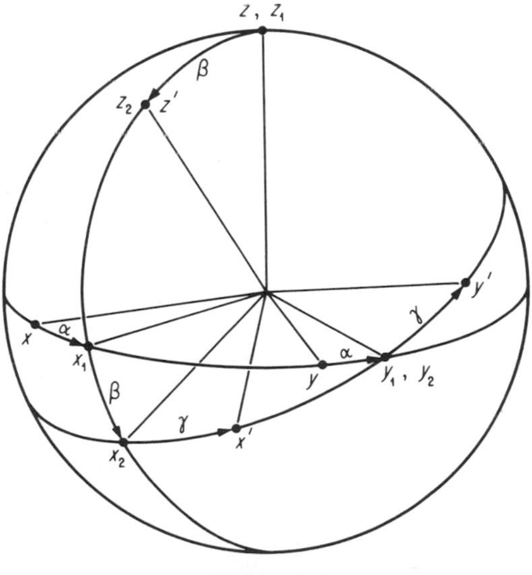

Figure A-1

around the new y'-axis by β; and, the third rotation around the new z''-axis by γ. The operator for these rotations is written either in the form (1.3–9) or (1.3–10). These rotations are illustrated in Fig. A–1.

The coordinates x, y, and z referred to the original frame are related to the coordinates x', y', and z' referred to the final frame through

$$\begin{bmatrix} x' \\ y' \\ z' \end{bmatrix} = \begin{bmatrix} \cos\alpha\cos\beta\cos\gamma - \sin\alpha\sin\gamma, & \sin\alpha\cos\beta\cos\gamma + \cos\alpha\sin\gamma, & -\sin\beta\cos\gamma \\ -\cos\alpha\cos\beta\sin\gamma - \sin\alpha\cos\gamma, & -\sin\alpha\cos\beta\sin\gamma + \cos\alpha\cos\gamma, & \sin\beta\sin\gamma \\ \cos\alpha\sin\beta, & \sin\alpha\sin\beta, & \cos\beta \end{bmatrix} \begin{bmatrix} x \\ y \\ z \end{bmatrix} \tag{A–1}$$

or in terms of irreducible forms $-(x + iy)/\sqrt{2}$, z, and $(x - iy)/\sqrt{2}$

$$\left[-\frac{x' + iy'}{\sqrt{2}},\ z',\ \frac{x' - iy'}{\sqrt{2}}\right] = \left[-\frac{x + iy}{\sqrt{2}},\ z,\ \frac{x - iy}{\sqrt{2}}\right] \times \begin{bmatrix} e^{-i(\alpha+\gamma)}\cos^2\frac{\beta}{2}, & -e^{-i\alpha}\frac{\sin\beta}{\sqrt{2}}, & e^{-i(\alpha-\gamma)}\sin^2\frac{\beta}{2} \\ e^{-i\gamma}\frac{\sin\beta}{\sqrt{2}}, & \cos\beta, & -e^{i\gamma}\frac{\sin\beta}{\sqrt{2}} \\ e^{i(\alpha-\gamma)}\sin^2\frac{\beta}{2}, & e^{i\alpha}\frac{\sin\beta}{\sqrt{2}}, & e^{i(\alpha+\gamma)}\cos^2\frac{\beta}{2} \end{bmatrix}. \tag{A–2}$$

2. *Goldstein:* The second rotation in Goldstein's definition differs from the second rotation of Whittaker's, being a rotation by an angle β around the new x'-axis. These two sets of angles are related through

$$\alpha_G = \alpha_W + \frac{\pi}{2}, \quad \beta_G = \beta_W, \quad \text{and} \quad \gamma_G = \frac{\pi}{2} - \gamma_W.$$

Appendix 1.2

SPHERICAL HARMONICS TO SIXTH ORDER

$$Y_{00} = \left(\frac{1}{4\pi}\right)^{1/2}$$

$$Y_{10} = \left(\frac{3}{4\pi}\right)^{1/2} \cos\theta$$

$$Y_{1\pm1} = \mp\left(\frac{3}{4\pi}\right)^{1/2}\left(\frac{1}{2}\right)^{1/2} \sin\theta\, e^{\pm i\phi}$$

$$Y_{20} = \left(\frac{5}{4\pi}\right)^{1/2}\frac{1}{2}\,(3\cos^2\theta - 1)$$

$$Y_{2\pm1} = \mp\left(\frac{5}{4\pi}\right)^{1/2}\left(\frac{3}{2}\right)^{1/2} \sin\theta\cos\theta\, e^{\pm i\phi}$$

$$Y_{2\pm2} = \left(\frac{5}{4\pi}\right)^{1/2}\left(\frac{3}{8}\right)^{1/2} \sin^2\theta\, e^{\pm 2i\phi}$$

$$Y_{30} = \left(\frac{7}{4\pi}\right)^{1/2}\frac{1}{2}\,(5\cos^3\theta - 3\cos\theta)$$

$$Y_{3\pm1} = \mp\left(\frac{7}{4\pi}\right)^{1/2}\left(\frac{3}{16}\right)^{1/2} \sin\theta\,(5\cos^2\theta - 1)e^{\pm i\phi}$$

$$Y_{3\pm2} = \left(\frac{7}{4\pi}\right)^{1/2}\left(\frac{15}{8}\right)^{1/2} \sin^2\theta\cos\theta\, e^{\pm 2i\phi}$$

$$Y_{3\pm3} = \mp\left(\frac{7}{4\pi}\right)^{1/2}\left(\frac{5}{16}\right)^{1/2} \sin^3\theta\, e^{\pm 3i\phi}$$

$$Y_{40} = \left(\frac{9}{4\pi}\right)^{1/2}\frac{1}{8}\,(35\cos^4\theta - 30\cos^2\theta + 3)$$

$$Y_{4\pm1} = \mp\left(\frac{9}{4\pi}\right)^{1/2}\left(\frac{5}{16}\right)^{1/2} \sin\theta\,(7\cos^3\theta - 3\cos\theta)e^{\pm i\phi}$$

$$Y_{4\pm2} = \left(\frac{9}{4\pi}\right)^{1/2}\left(\frac{5}{32}\right)^{1/2}\sin^2\theta\,(7\cos^2\theta - 1)e^{\pm 2i\phi}$$

$$Y_{4\pm3} = \mp\left(\frac{9}{4\pi}\right)^{1/2}\left(\frac{35}{16}\right)^{1/2}\sin^3\theta\cos\theta\, e^{\pm 3i\phi}$$

$$Y_{4\pm4} = \left(\frac{9}{4\pi}\right)^{1/2}\left(\frac{35}{2}\right)^{1/2}\frac{1}{8}\sin^4\theta\, e^{\pm 4i\phi}$$

$$Y_{50} = \left(\frac{11}{4\pi}\right)^{1/2}\frac{1}{8}(63\cos^5\theta - 70\cos^3\theta + 15\cos\theta)$$

$$Y_{5\pm1} = \mp\left(\frac{11}{4\pi}\right)^{1/2}\left(\frac{15}{2}\right)^{1/2}\frac{1}{8}\sin\theta(21\cos^4\theta - 14\cos^2\theta + 1)e^{\pm i\phi}$$

$$Y_{5\pm2} = \left(\frac{11}{4\pi}\right)^{1/2}\left(\frac{105}{32}\right)^{1/2}\sin^2\theta(3\cos^3\theta - \cos\theta)e^{\pm 2i\phi}$$

$$Y_{5\pm3} = \mp\left(\frac{11}{4\pi}\right)^{1/2}(35)^{1/2}\frac{1}{16}\sin^3\theta(9\cos^2\theta - 1)e^{\pm 3i\phi}$$

$$Y_{5\pm4} = \left(\frac{11}{4\pi}\right)^{1/2}\left(\frac{315}{2}\right)^{1/2}\frac{1}{8}\sin^4\theta\cos\theta\, e^{\pm 4i\phi}$$

$$Y_{5\pm5} = \mp\left(\frac{11}{4\pi}\right)^{1/2}(7)^{1/2}\frac{3}{16}\sin^5\theta\, e^{\pm 5i\phi}$$

$$Y_{60} = \left(\frac{13}{4\pi}\right)^{1/2}\frac{1}{16}(231\cos^6\theta - 315\cos^4\theta + 105\cos^2\theta - 5)$$

$$Y_{6\pm1} = \mp\left(\frac{13}{4\pi}\right)^{1/2}\left(\frac{21}{2}\right)^{1/2}\frac{1}{8}\sin\theta \times (33\cos^5\theta - 30\cos^3\theta + 5\cos\theta)e^{\pm i\phi}$$

$$Y_{6\pm2} = \left(\frac{13}{4\pi}\right)^{1/2}(105)^{1/2}\frac{1}{32}\sin^2\theta \times (33\cos^4\theta - 18\cos^2\theta + 1)e^{\pm 2i\phi}$$

$$Y_{6\pm3} = \mp\left(\frac{13}{4\pi}\right)^{1/2}(105)^{1/2}\frac{1}{16}\sin^3\theta(11\cos^3\theta - 3\cos\theta)e^{\pm 3i\phi}$$

$$Y_{6\pm4} = \left(\frac{13}{4\pi}\right)^{1/2}\left(\frac{7}{2}\right)^{1/2}\frac{3}{16}\sin^4\theta(11\cos^2\theta - 1)e^{\pm 4i\phi}$$

$$Y_{6\pm5} = \mp\left(\frac{13}{4\pi}\right)^{1/2}(77)^{1/3}\frac{3}{16}\sin^5\theta\cos\theta\, e^{\pm 5i\phi}$$

$$Y_{6\pm6} = \left(\frac{13}{4\pi}\right)^{1/2}(231)^{1/2}\frac{1}{32}\sin^6\theta\, e^{\pm 6i\phi}$$

Appendix 1.3

IRREDUCIBLE TENSOR OPERATORS TO RANK SIX IN TERMS OF j_z, j_+, AND j_-

k	p	
1	± 1	$\mp j_{\pm}$
	0	$(2)^{1/2} j_z$
2	± 2	$j_{\pm}^2$
	± 1	$\mp j_{\pm}(2j_z \pm 1)$
	0	$\left(\frac{2}{3}\right)^{1/2} \{3j_z^2 - j(j+1)\}$
3	± 3	$\mp j_{\pm}^3$
	± 2	$(6)^{1/2} j_{\pm}^2(j_z \pm 1)$
	± 1	$\mp \left(\frac{1}{15}\right)^{1/2} j_{\pm}\{15j_z^2 \pm 15j_z - 3j(j+1) + 6\}$
	0	$\left(\frac{4}{5}\right)^{1/2} \{5j_z^3 - 3j(j+1)j_z + j_z\}$
4	± 4	$j_{\pm}^4$
	± 3	$\mp(2)^{1/2} j_{\pm}^3(2j_z \pm 3)$
	± 2	$\frac{2}{(7)^{1/2}} j_{\pm}^2\{7j_z^2 \pm 14j_z - j(j+1) + 9\}$
	± 1	$\mp \left(\frac{2}{7}\right)^{1/2} j_{\pm}\{14j_z^3 \pm 21j_z^2 + 19j_z - 6j(j+1)j_z \mp 3j(j+1) \pm 6\}$
	0	$\left(\frac{2}{35}\right)^{1/2} \{35j_z^4 - 30j(j+1)j_z^2 + 25j_z^2 + 3j^2(j+1)^2 - 6j(j+1)\}$

k	p	
5	± 5	$\mp j_\pm^5$
	± 4	$\left(\frac{2}{5}\right)^{1/2} j_\pm^4(5j_z \pm 10)$
	± 3	$\mp \frac{(5)^{1/2}}{3} j_\pm^3\{9j_z^2 \pm 27j_z - j(j+1) + 24\}$
	± 2	$\left(\frac{40}{3}\right)^{1/2} j_\pm^2\{3j_z^3 \pm 9j_z^2 + 12j_z - j(j+1)j_z \mp j(j+1) \pm 6\}$
	± 1	$\mp \left(\frac{10}{21}\right)^{1/2} j_\pm\{21j_z^4 \pm 42j_z^3 - 14j(j+1)j_z^2 + 63j_z^2 \mp 14j(j+1)j_z \pm 42j_z$ $+ j^2(j+1)^2 - 8j(j+1) + 12\}$
	0	$\frac{2}{3(7)^{1/2}}\{63j_z^5 - 70j(j+1)j_z^3 + 105j_z^3 + 15j^2(j+1)^2 j_z - 50j(j+1)j_z$ $+ 12j_z\}$
6	± 6	$j_\pm^6$
	± 5	$\mp(3)^{1/2} j_\pm^5(2j_z \pm 5)$
	± 4	$\left(\frac{6}{11}\right)^{1/2} j_\pm^4\{11j_z^2 \pm 44j_z - j(j+1) + 50\}$
	± 3	$\mp \left(\frac{10}{11}\right)^{1/2} j_\pm^3\{22j_z^3 \pm 99j_z^2 - 6j(j+1)j_z + 179j_z \mp 9j(j+1) \pm 120\}$
	± 2	$\left(\frac{10}{11}\right)^{1/2} j_\pm^2\{33j_z^4 \pm 132j_z^3 - 18j(j+1)j_z^2 + 273j_z^2 \mp 36j(j+1)j_z \pm 282j_z$ $+ j^2(j+1)^2 - 26j(j+1) + 120\}$
	± 1	$\mp \left(\frac{4}{11}\right)^{1/2} j_\pm\{66j_z^5 \pm 165j_z^4 - 60j(j+1)j_z^3 + 360j_z^3 \mp 90j(j+1)j_z^2 \pm 375j_z^2$ $+ 10j^2(j+1)^2 j_z - 110j(j+1)j_z + 2340j_z \pm 5j^2(j+1)^2 \mp 40j(j+1)$ $\pm 60\}$
	0	$\frac{4}{(11)^{1/2}}\{231j_z^6 - 315j(j+1)j_z^4 + 735j_z^4 + 105j^2(j+1)^2 j_z^2 - 525j(j+1)j_z^2$ $+ 294j_z^2 - 5j^3(j+1)^3 + 40j^2(j+1)^2 - 60j(j+1)\}$

Appendix 2.1

BASIS FUNCTIONS FOR OCTAHEDRAL GROUP

Octahedral basis functions are listed in terms of spherical harmonics Y_{nm}, up to $n = 6$, and in terms of Cartesian coordinates x, y, and z. The Cartesian coordinate expressions are normalized to $[4\pi/(2n+1)]$; x, y, and z are written for x/y, y/r, z/r.

n	Name	Octahedral basis function in terms of spherical harmonics	in terms of Cartesian coordinates
0	a_1	Y_{00}	1
1	t_1x	$\left(\frac{1}{2}\right)^{1/2}(-Y_{11}+Y_{1-1})$	x
	t_1y	$i\left(\frac{1}{2}\right)^{1/2}(Y_{11}+Y_{1-1})$	y
	t_1z	Y_{10}	z
2	eu	Y_{20}	$(3z^2-r^2)/2$
	ev	$\left(\frac{1}{2}\right)^{1/2}(Y_{22}+Y_{2-2})$	$(3)^{1/2}\frac{x^2-y^2}{2}$
	$t_2\xi$	$i\left(\frac{1}{2}\right)^{1/2}(Y_{21}+Y_{2-1})$	$(3)^{1/2}yz$
	$t_2\eta$	$\left(\frac{1}{2}\right)^{1/2}(-Y_{21}+Y_{2-1})$	$(3)^{1/2}zx$
	$t_2\zeta$	$i\left(\frac{1}{2}\right)^{1/2}(-Y_{22}+Y_{2-2})$	$(3)^{1/2}xy$

n	Name	Octahedral basis function in terms of spherical harmonics	in terms of Cartesian coordinates
3	a_2	$i\left(\frac{1}{2}\right)^{1/2}(-Y_{32}+Y_{3-2})$	$(15)^{1/2}xyz$
	t_1x	$\left(\frac{1}{4}\right)\{(5)^{1/2}(-Y_{33}+Y_{3-3})$ $+(3)^{1/2}(Y_{31}-Y_{3-1})\}$	$\frac{5}{2}\left(x^3-\frac{3xr^2}{5}\right)$
	t_1y	$-i\left(\frac{1}{4}\right)\{(5)^{1/2}(Y_{33}+Y_{3-3})$ $+(3)^{1/2}(Y_{31}+Y_{3-1})\}$	$\frac{5}{2}\left(y^3-\frac{3yr^2}{5}\right)$
	t_1z	Y_{30}	$\frac{5}{2}\left(z^3-\frac{3zr^2}{5}\right)$
	$t_2\xi$	$-\frac{1}{4}\{(5)^{1/2}(-Y_{31}+Y_{3-1})$ $+(3)^{1/2}(-Y_{33}+Y_{3-3})\}$	$\left(\frac{15}{4}\right)^{1/2}x(y^2-z^2)$
	$t_2\eta$	$i\left(\frac{1}{4}\right)\{(5)^{1/2}(Y_{31}+Y_{3-1})$ $-(3)^{1/2}(Y_{33}+Y_{3-3})\}$	$\left(\frac{15}{4}\right)^{1/2}y(z^2-x^2)$
	$t_2\zeta$	$\left(\frac{1}{2}\right)^{1/2}(Y_{32}+Y_{3-2})$	$\left(\frac{15}{4}\right)^{1/2}z(x^2-y^2)$
4	a_1	$\left(\frac{1}{24}\right)^{1/2}\{(14)^{1/2}Y_{40}$ $+(5)^{1/2}(Y_{44}+Y_{4-4})\}$	$\left(\frac{7}{3}\right)^{1/2}\frac{5}{4}\left(x^4+y^4+z^4-\frac{3r^4}{5}\right)$
	eu	$\left(\frac{1}{24}\right)^{1/2}\{(10)^{1/2}Y_{40}$ $-(7)^{1/2}(Y_{44}+Y_{4-4})\}$	$7(5)^{1/2}\left[z^4-\frac{x^4+y^4}{2}-\frac{6}{7}\left\{z^2-\frac{1}{2}(x^2+y^2)\right\}r^2\right]$
	ev	$\left(\frac{1}{2}\right)^{1/2}(-Y_{42}-Y_{4-2})$	$\frac{7(5)^{1/2}}{4}\left\{(x^4-y^4)-\frac{6}{7}z^2(x^2-y^2)\right\}$
	t_1x	$-i\frac{1}{4}\{(7)^{1/2}(Y_{41}+Y_{4-1})$ $+(Y_{43}+Y_{4-3})\}$	$\frac{(35)^{1/2}}{2}yz(y^2-z^2)$
	t_1y	$\frac{1}{4}\{(7)^{1/2}(-Y_{41}+Y_{4-1})$ $+(Y_{43}-Y_{4-3})\}$	$\frac{(35)^{1/2}}{2}zx(z^2-x^2)$
	t_1z	$-i\left(\frac{1}{2}\right)^{1/2}(Y_{44}-Y_{4-4})$	$\frac{(35)^{1/2}}{2}xy(x^2-y^2)$
	$t_2\xi$	$-\frac{i}{4}\{(7)^{1/2}(Y_{43}+Y_{4-3})$ $-(Y_{41}+Y_{4-1})\}$	$\frac{7(5)^{1/2}}{2}yz\left(x^2-\frac{r^2}{7}\right)$
	$t_2\eta$	$\frac{1}{4}\{(7)^{1/2}(Y_{43}-Y_{4-3})$ $+(Y_{41}-Y_{4-1})\}$	$\frac{7(5)^{1/2}}{2}zx\left(y^2-\frac{r^2}{7}\right)$
	$t_2\zeta$	$-i\left(\frac{1}{2}\right)^{1/2}(Y_{42}-Y_{4-2})$	$\frac{7(5)^{1/2}}{2}xy\left(z^2-\frac{r^2}{7}\right)$
5	eu	$-i\left(\frac{1}{2}\right)^{1/2}(Y_{54}-Y_{5-4})$	$(105)^{1/2}xyz\left(z^2-\frac{x^2+y^2}{2}\right)$
	ev	$i\left(\frac{1}{2}\right)^{1/2}(Y_{52}-Y_{5-2})$	$\frac{3}{2}(35)^{1/2}xyz(x^2-y^2)$
	t_1x	$\frac{1}{16}\{3(7)^{1/2}(-Y_{55}+Y_{5-5})$ $+(35)^{1/2}(Y_{53}-Y_{5-3})\}$	$\frac{1}{8}x\{8x^4-40x^2(y^2+z^2)$ $+15(y^2+z^2)^2\}$

n	Name	Octahedral basis function in terms of spherical harmonics	Octahedral basis function in terms of Cartesian coordinates
	t_1y	$\frac{i}{16}\{3(7)^{1/2}(Y_{55}+Y_{5-5})$ $+(35)^{1/2}(Y_{53}+Y_{5-3})\}$	$\frac{1}{8}y\{8y^4-40y^2(z^2+x^2)$ $+15(z^2+x^2)^2\}$
	t_1z	Y_{50}	$\frac{1}{8}z\{8z^4-40z^2(x^2+y^2)$ $+15(x^2+y^2)^2\}$
	$t_1'x$	$(2)^{-1/2}\left(\frac{1}{16}\right)$ $\times\{(10)^{1/2}(-Y_{55}+Y_{5-5})$ $+9(2)^{1/2}(-Y_{53}+Y_{5-3})$ $+2(21)^{1/2}(-Y_{51}+Y_{5-1})\}$	$(35)^{1/2}\frac{3}{2}$ $\times x\left\{y^4+z^4-\frac{3(y^2+z^2)^2}{4}\right\}$
	$t_1'y$	$i(2)^{-1/2}\frac{1}{16}$ $\times\{(10)^{1/2}(Y_{55}+Y_{5-5})$ $-9(2)^{1/2}(Y_{53}+Y_{5-3})$ $+2(21)^{1/2}(Y_{51}+Y_{5-1})\}$	$(35)^{1/2}\frac{3}{2}$ $\times y\left\{z^4+x^4-\frac{3(z^2+x^2)^2}{4}\right\}$
	$t_1'z$	$\left(\frac{1}{2}\right)^{1/2}(Y_{54}+Y_{5-4})$	$(35)^{1/3}\frac{3}{2}$ $\times z\left\{x^4+y^4-\frac{3(x^2+y^2)^2}{4}\right\}$
	$t_2\xi$	$\frac{1}{8}\{(15)^{1/2}(Y_{55}-Y_{5-5})$ $+(3)^{1/2}(Y_{53}-Y_{5-3})$ $-(14)^{1/2}(Y_{51}-Y_{5-1})\}$	$(105)^{1/2}\frac{3}{4}$ $\times x(y^2-z^2)\left(x^2-\frac{r^2}{3}\right)$
	$t_2\eta$	$\frac{i}{8}\{(15)^{1/2}(Y_{55}+Y_{5-5})$ $-(3)^{1/2}(Y_{53}+Y_{5-3})$ $-(14)^{1/2}(Y_{51}+Y_{5-1})$	$(105)^{1/2}\frac{3}{4}$ $\times y(z^2-x^2)\left(y^2-\frac{r^2}{3}\right)$
	$t_2\zeta$	$\left(\frac{1}{2}\right)^{1/2}(Y_{52}+Y_{5-2})$	$(105)^{1/2}\frac{3}{4}$ $\times z(x^2-y^2)\left(z^2-\frac{r^2}{3}\right)$
6	a_1	$\frac{1}{4}\{(2)^{1/2}Y_{60}$ $-(7)^{1/2}(Y_{64}+Y_{6-4})\}$	$(2)^{1/2}\frac{231}{8}$ $\times\left\{x^2y^2z^2+\left(x^4+y^4+z^4-\frac{3r^4}{5}\right)\frac{r^2}{22}\right.$ $\left.-\frac{r^6}{105}\right\}$
	a_2	$(2)^{-1/2}\frac{1}{4}$ $\times\{(11)^{1/2}(Y_{62}+Y_{6-2})$ $-(5)^{1/2}(Y_{66}+Y_{6-6})\}$	$\frac{(2310)^{1/2}}{8}$ $\times\{x^4(y^2-z^2)+y^4(z^2-x^2)$ $+z^4(x^2-y^2)\}$

n	Name	Octahedral basis function in terms of spherical harmonics	in terms of Cartesian coordinates
	eu	$\frac{1}{4}\{(14)^{1/2} Y_{60} + (Y_{64} + Y_{6-4})\}$	$(14)^{1/2}\frac{11}{4} \times \left[z^6 - \frac{(x^6 + y^6)}{2} - \frac{15}{11}\left\{z^4 - \frac{x^4 + y^4}{2} - \frac{6}{7}\left(z^2 - \frac{x^2 + y^2}{2}\right)r^2\right\}r^2 - \frac{5}{7}\left(z^2 - \frac{x^2 + y^2}{2}\right)r^4\right]$
	ev	$(2)^{-1/2}\frac{1}{4} \times \{(5)^{1/2}(Y_{62} + Y_{6-2}) + (11)^{1/2}(Y_{66} + Y_{6-6})\}$	$(42)^{1/2}\frac{11}{8}\left[x^6 - y^6 - \frac{15}{11}\left\{x^4 - y^4 - \frac{6}{7}(x^2 - y^2)r^2\right\}r^2 - \frac{5}{7}(x^2 - y^2)r^4\right]$
	t_1x	$i(2)^{-1/2}\frac{1}{8} \times \{2(3)^{1/2}(Y_{61} + Y_{6-1}) - (30)^{1/2}(Y_{63} + Y_{6-3}) - (22)^{1/2}(Y_{65} + Y_{6-5})\}$	$(7)^{1/2}\frac{33}{4} \times \left\{yz(y^2 - z^2)\left(x^2 - \frac{r^2}{11}\right)\right\}$
	t_1y	$(2)^{-1/2}\frac{1}{8} \times \{2(3)^{1/2}(Y_{61} - Y_{6-1}) + (30)^{1/2}(Y_{63} - Y_{6-3}) - (22)^{1/2}(Y_{65} - Y_{6-5})\}$	$(7)^{1/2}\frac{33}{4} \times \left\{zx(z^2 - x^2)\left(y^2 - \frac{r^2}{11}\right)\right\}$
	t_1z	$-i(2)^{-1/2}(Y_{64} - Y_{6-4})$	$(7)^{1/2}\frac{33}{4} \times \left\{xy(x^2 - y^2)\left(z^2 - \frac{r^2}{11}\right)\right\}$
	$t_2\xi$	$i(2)^{-1/2}\frac{1}{16} \times \{3(22)^{1/2}(Y_{61} + Y_{6-1}) + (55)^{1/2}(Y_{63} + Y_{6-3}) + (3)^{1/2}(Y_{65} + Y_{6-5})\}$	$\left(\frac{231}{2}\right)^{1/2} yz\left\{y^4 + z^4 - \frac{5(y^2 + z^2)^2}{8}\right\}$
	$t_2\eta$	$(2)^{-1/2}\frac{1}{16} \times \{3(22)^{1/2}(-Y_{61} + Y_{6-1}) + (55)^{1/2}(Y_{63} - Y_{6-3}) - (3)^{1/2}(Y_{65} - Y_{6-5})\}$	$\left(\frac{231}{2}\right)^{1/2} zx\left\{z^4 + x^4 - \frac{5(z^2 + x^2)^2}{8}\right\}$
	$t_2\zeta$	$-i(2)^{-1/2}(Y_{66} - Y_{6-6})$	$\left(\frac{231}{2}\right)^{1/2} xy\left\{x^4 + y^4 - \frac{5(x^2 + y^2)^2}{8}\right\}$

n	Name	Octahedral basis function in terms of spherical harmonics	in terms of Cartesian coordinates
	$t_2\xi$	$i(2)^{-1/2}\frac{1}{16}$ $\times\{(10)^{1/2}(Y_{61}+Y_{6-1})$ $+9(Y_{63}+Y_{6-3})$ $-(165)^{1/2}(Y_{65}+Y_{6-5})\}$	$(210)^{1/2}\frac{33}{16}$ $\times\left\{yz\left(x^4-\frac{6x^2r^2}{11}+\frac{r^4}{33}\right)\right\}$
	$t_2\eta$	$(2)^{-1/2}\frac{1}{16}$ $\times\{-(10)^{1/2}(Y_{61}-Y_{6-1})$ $-9(Y_{63}-Y_{6-3})$ $+(165)^{1/2}(-Y_{65}+Y_{6-5})\}$	$(210)^{1/2}\frac{33}{16}$ $\times\left\{zx\left(y^4-\frac{6y^2r^2}{11}+\frac{r^4}{33}\right)\right\}$
	$t_2\zeta$	$-i(2)^{-1/2}(Y_{62}-Y_{6-2})$	$(210)^{1/2}\frac{33}{16}$ $\times\left\{xy\left(z^4-\frac{6z^2r^2}{11}+\frac{r^4}{33}\right)\right\}$

Appendix 2.2

CHARACTER TABLES FOR POINT GROUPS IN THE FIRST AND SECOND COLUMNS OF TABLE 2.181

$\mathbf{C}_1$	E
A	1

$\mathbf{C}_2$			E	C_2
	$\mathbf{C}_i$		E	I
		$\mathbf{C}_s$	E	σ
A: z	A_g	A	1	1
B: x, y	A_u	B	1	-1

$\mathbf{C}_3$		E	C_3	C_3^2
A: z		1	1	1
E:	$x + iy$	1	ϵ	ϵ^2
	$x - iy$	1	ϵ^2	ϵ

†$\epsilon = e^{2i\pi/3}$

$\mathbf{C}_4$			E	C_4	C_2	C_4^3
		$\mathbf{S}_4$	E	S_4	C_2	S_4^3
A: z		A	1	1	1	1
B		B: z	1	-1	1	-1
E:	$x + iy$	E	1	i	-1	$-i$
	$x - iy$		1	$-i$	-1	i

$\mathbf{C}_6$		E	C_6	C_3	C_2	C_3^2	C_6^5
A: z		1	1	1	1	1	1
B		1	-1	1	-1	1	-1
E_1		1	ω^2	$-\omega$	1	ω^2	$-\omega$
		1	$-\omega$	ω^2	1	$-\omega$	ω^2
E_2:	$x + iy$	1	ω	ω^2	-1	$-\omega$	$-\omega^2$
	$x - iy$	1	$-\omega^2$	$-\omega$	-1	ω^2	ω

†$\omega = e^{i\pi/3}$

$\mathbf{D}_2$			E	C_2^x	C_2^y	C_2^z
	$\mathbf{C}_{2h}$		E	C_2^z	σ_h	I
		$\mathbf{C}_{2v}$	E	C_2^z	σ_v	σ_v'
A	A_g	$A_1: z$	1	1	1	1
$B_1: x$	$A_u: z$	A_2	1	1	-1	-1
$B_2: y$	$B_u: x, y$	$B_1: x$	1	-1	1	-1
$B_3: z$	B_g	$B_2: y$	1	-1	-1	1

$\mathbf{D}_3$		E	$2C_3$	$3C_2'$†
	$\mathbf{C}_{3v}$	E	$2C_3$	$3\sigma_v$
A_1	$A_1: z$	1	1	1
$A_2: z$	A_2	1	1	-1
$E: x, y$	$E: x, y$	2	-1	0

†The class C_2' is primed to indicate that the axes are in the plane perpendicular to the threefold axis.

$\mathbf{D}_4$			E	C_2	$2C_4$	$2C_2'$	$2C_2''$
	$\mathbf{C}_{4v}$		E	C_2	$2C_4$	$2\sigma_v$	$2\sigma_v'$
		$\mathbf{D}_{2d}$	E	C_2	$2S_4$	$2C_2'$	$2\sigma_d$
$A_1: 3z^2 - r^2$	$A_1: z$	A_1	1	1	1	1	1
$A_2: z$	A_2	A_2	1	1	1	-1	-1
$B_1: x^2 - y^2$	B_1	B_1	1	1	-1	1	-1
$B_2: xy$	B_2	$B_2\ z$	1	1	-1	-1	1
$E: x, y$	$E: x, y$	$E: x, y$	2	-2	0	0	0
yz, zx							

$\mathbf{D}_6$			E	C_2	$2C_3$	$2C_6$	$3C_2'$	$3C_2''$
	$\mathbf{C}_{6v}$		E	C_2	$2C_3$	$2C_6$	$3\sigma_v$	$3\sigma_v'$
		$\mathbf{D}_{3h}$	E	σ_h	$2C_3$	$2S_3$	$3C'$	$3\sigma_v$
A_1	$A_1: z$	A_1	1	1	1	1	1	1
$A_2: z$	A_2	A_2	1	1	1	1	-1	-1
B_1	B_1	B_1	1	-1	1	-1	1	-1
B_2	B_2	$B_2: z$	1	-1	1	-1	-1	1
E_1	E_1	$E_1: x, y$	2	2	-1	-1	0	0
$E_2: x, y$	$E_2: x, y$	E_2	2	-2	-1	1	0	0

$\mathbf{T}$	E	$3C_2$	$4C_3$	$4C_3^2$
A	1	1	1	1
E	1	1	ϵ	ϵ^2
	1	1	ϵ^2	ϵ
$T_1: x, y, z$	3	-1	0	0

$\epsilon = e^{2i\pi/3}$

$\mathbf{O}$		E	$8C_3$	$3C_2$	$6C_2'$	$6C_4$
	$\mathbf{T}_d$	E	$8C_3$	$3C_2$	$6\sigma_d$	$6S_4$
A_1	A_1	1	1	1	1	1
A_2	A_2	1	1	1	-1	-1
E	E	2	-1	2	0	0
$T_1: x, y, z$	T_1	3	0	-1	-1	1
T_2	$T_2: x, y, z$	3	0	-1	1	-1

Appendix 2.3

CHARACTER TABLES FOR DOUBLE POINT GROUPS

C_1'	E	Q
A_1'	1	-1

C_2'	E	Q	C_2	QC_2
E'	$\begin{cases}1\\1\end{cases}$	$\begin{matrix}-1\\-1\end{matrix}$	$\begin{matrix}-i\\i\end{matrix}$	$\begin{matrix}i\\-i\end{matrix}$

C_3'	E	Q	C_3	QC_3	C_3^2	QC_3^2
A'	1	-1	-1	1	1	-1
E'	$\begin{cases}1\\1\end{cases}$	$\begin{matrix}-1\\-1\end{matrix}$	$\begin{matrix}\epsilon\\\epsilon^5\end{matrix}$	$\begin{matrix}\epsilon^4\\\epsilon^2\end{matrix}$	$\begin{matrix}\epsilon^2\\\epsilon^4\end{matrix}$	$\begin{matrix}\epsilon^5\\\epsilon\end{matrix}$

$\epsilon = e^{i\pi/3}$

C_4'	E	Q	C_4	QC_4	C_2	QC_2	C_4^3	QC_4^3
E_1'	$\begin{cases}1\\1\end{cases}$	$\begin{matrix}-1\\-1\end{matrix}$	$\begin{matrix}\gamma\\\gamma^7\end{matrix}$	$\begin{matrix}\gamma^5\\\gamma^3\end{matrix}$	$\begin{matrix}\gamma^2\\\gamma^6\end{matrix}$	$\begin{matrix}\gamma^6\\\gamma^2\end{matrix}$	$\begin{matrix}\gamma^3\\\gamma^5\end{matrix}$	$\begin{matrix}\gamma^7\\\gamma\end{matrix}$
E_2'	$\begin{cases}1\\1\end{cases}$	$\begin{matrix}-1\\-1\end{matrix}$	$\begin{matrix}\gamma^3\\\gamma^5\end{matrix}$	$\begin{matrix}\gamma^7\\\gamma\end{matrix}$	$\begin{matrix}\gamma^6\\\gamma^2\end{matrix}$	$\begin{matrix}\gamma^2\\\gamma^6\end{matrix}$	$\begin{matrix}\gamma\\\gamma^7\end{matrix}$	$\begin{matrix}\gamma^5\\\gamma^3\end{matrix}$

$\gamma = e^{i\pi/4}$

C_6'	E	Q	C_6	QC_6	C_3	QC_3	C_2	QC_2	C_3^2	QC_3^2	C_6^5	QC_6^5
E_1'	1	-1	δ	δ^7	δ^2	δ^8	δ^3	δ^9	δ^4	δ^{10}	δ^5	δ^{11}
	1	-1	δ^{11}	δ^5	δ^{10}	δ^4	δ^9	δ^3	δ^8	δ^2	δ^7	δ
E_2'	1	-1	δ^3	δ^9	-1	1	δ^9	δ^3	1	-1	δ^3	δ^9
	1	-1	δ^9	δ^3	-1	1	δ^3	δ^9	1	-1	δ^9	δ^3
E_3'	1	-1	δ^5	δ^{11}	δ^{10}	δ^4	δ^3	δ^9	δ^8	δ^2	δ	δ^7
	1	-1	δ^7	δ	δ^2	δ^8	δ^9	δ^3	δ^4	δ^{10}	δ^{11}	δ^5

$\delta = e^{i\pi/6}$

D_2'	E	Q	C_2^x QC_2^x	C_2^y QC_2^y	C_2^z QC_2^z
$E' = D^{1/2}$	2	-2	0	0	0

D_3'	E	Q	$3C_2$	$3C_2'$	C_3 QC_3^2	C_3^2 QC_3
E_1'	1	-1	i	$-i$	-1	1
	1	-1	$-i$	i	-1	1
$E_2' = D^{1/2}$	2	-2	0	0	1	-1

D_4'	E	Q	C_2 QC_2	C_4 QC_4^3	C_4^3 QC_4	$2QC_2'$ $2C_2'$	$2QC_2''$ $2C_2''$
$E_1' = D^{1/2}$	2	-2	0	$2^{1/2}$	$-2^{1/2}$	0	0
E_2'	2	-2	0	$-2^{1/2}$	$2^{1/2}$	0	0

D_6'	E	Q	C_2 QC_2	C_3 QC_3^2	C_3^2 QC_3	C_6 QC_6^5	C_6^5 QC_6	$3C_2'$ $3QC_2'$	$3C_2''$ $3QC_2''$
$E_1' = D^{1/2}$	2	-2	0	1	-1	$3^{1/2}$	$-3^{1/2}$	0	0
E_2'	2	-2	0	1	-1	$-3^{1/2}$	$3^{1/2}$	0	0
E_3'	2	-2	0	-2	2	0	0	0	0

T'	E	Q	$4C_3$	$4C_3^2$	$4QC_3$	$4QC_3^2$	$3C_2$ $3QC_2$
$E' = D^{1/2}$	2	-2	1	-1	-1	1	0
G'	2	-2	ϵ	$-\epsilon^2$	$-\epsilon$	ϵ^2	0
	2	-2	ϵ^2	$-\epsilon$	$-\epsilon^2$	ϵ	0

$\epsilon = e^{2i\pi/3}$

O'	E	Q	$4C_3$ $4QC_3^2$	$4C_3^2$ $4QC_3$	$3C_2$ $3QC_2$	$6C_2'$ $6QC_2'$	$3C_4$ $3QC_4^3$	$3C_4^3$ $3QC_4$
$E_1' = D^{1/2}$	2	-2	1	-1	0	0	$2^{1/2}$	$-2^{1/2}$
E_2'	2	-2	1	-1	0	0	$-2^{1/2}$	$2^{1/2}$
$G' = D^{3/2}$	4	-4	-1	1	0	0	0	0

Appendix 2.4

CLEBSCH-GORDAN COEFFICIENTS FOR CUBIC GROUPS

Clebsch-Gordan coefficients for cubic groups are listed with respect to bases which transform according to Table 2.17–5.

$A_2 \times E$		E	
		u	v
a_2	u	0	1
a_2	v	-1	0

$A_2 \times T_1$		T_2		
		ξ	η	ζ
a_2	x	1	0	0
a_2	y	0	1	0
a_2	z	0	0	1

$A_2 \times T_2$		T_1		
		x	y	z
a_2	ξ	1	0	0
a_2	η	0	1	0
a_2	ζ	0	0	1

$E \times E$		A_1	A_2	E	
		a_1	a_2	u	v
u	u	$2^{-1/2}$	0	$-2^{-1/2}$	0
u	v	0	$2^{-1/2}$	0	$2^{-1/2}$
v	u	0	$-2^{-1/2}$	0	$2^{-1/2}$
v	v	$2^{-1/2}$	0	$2^{-1/2}$	0

$E \times T_1$		T_1 x	y	z	T_2 ξ	η	ζ
u	x	$\frac{1}{2}$	0	0	$-\frac{(3)^{1/2}}{2}$	0	0
u	y	0	$\frac{1}{2}$	0	0	$\frac{(3)^{1/2}}{2}$	0
u	z	0	0	-1	0	0	0
v	x	$-\frac{(3)^{1/2}}{2}$	0	0	$-\frac{1}{2}$	0	0
v	y	0	$\frac{(3)^{1/2}}{2}$	0	0	$-\frac{1}{2}$	0
v	z	0	0	0	0	0	1

$E \times T_2$		T_1 x	y	z	T_2 ξ	η	ζ
u	ξ	$\frac{(3)^{1/2}}{2}$	0	0	$\frac{1}{2}$	0	0
u	η	0	$-\frac{(3)^{1/2}}{2}$	0	0	$\frac{1}{2}$	0
u	ζ	0	0	0	0	0	-1
v	ξ	$\frac{1}{2}$	0	0	$-\frac{(3)^{1/2}}{2}$	0	0
v	η	0	$\frac{1}{2}$	0	0	$\frac{(3)^{1/2}}{2}$	0
v	ζ	0	0	-1	0	0	0

$T_1 \times T_1$		$T_2 \times T_2$		A_1 a_1	E u	v
x	x	ξ	ξ	$(3)^{-1/2}$	$(6)^{-1/2}$	$-(2)^{-1/2}$
y	y	η	η	$(3)^{-1/2}$	$(6)^{-1/2}$	$(2)^{-1/2}$
z	z	ζ	ζ	$(3)^{-1/2}$	$-2(6)^{-1/2}$	0

$T_1 \times T_2$		$T_2 \times T_2$		T_1 x	y	z	T_2 ξ	η	ζ
x	y	ξ	η	0	0	$-(2)^{-1/2}$	0	0	$-(2)^{-1/2}$
x	z	ξ	ζ	0	$(2)^{-1/2}$	0	0	$-(2)^{-1/2}$	0
y	x	η	ξ	0	0	$2^{-1/2}$	0	0	$-2^{-1/2}$
y	z	η	ζ	$-2^{-1/2}$	0	0	$-2^{-1/2}$	0	0
z	x	ζ	ξ	0	$-2^{-1/2}$	0	0	$-2^{-1/2}$	0
z	y	ζ	η	$2^{-1/2}$	0	0	$-2^{-1/2}$	0	0

$T_1 \times T_2$		A_2 a_2	E u	v
x	ξ	$3^{-1/2}$	$-2^{-1/2}$	$-6^{-1/2}$
y	η	$3^{-1/2}$	$2^{-1/2}$	$-6^{-1/2}$
z	ζ	$3^{-1/2}$	0	$2(6)^{-1/2}$

$T_1 \times T_2$		T_1			T_2		
		x	y	z	ξ	η	η
x	η	0	0	$-2^{-1/2}$	0	0	$-2^{-1/2}$
x	ζ	0	$-2^{-1/2}$	0	0	$2^{-1/2}$	0
y	ξ	0	0	$-2^{-1/2}$	0	0	$2^{-1/2}$
y	ζ	$-2^{-1/2}$	0	0	$-2^{-1/2}$	0	0
z	ξ	0	$-2^{-1/2}$	0	0	$-2^{-1/2}$	0
	ζ	$-2^{-1/2}$	0	0	$2^{-1/2}$	0	0

Appendix 3.1

SENIORITY-SCHEME STATEVECTORS FOR d^n CONFIGURATIONS, $n = 1$ TO 5†

n		
0	vacuum	
2	$\lvert {}^{1}_{0}\mathrm{S}\rangle$	$= 5^{-1/2}(\lvert 2, -\bar{2}\rangle - \lvert 1, -\bar{1}\rangle + \lvert 0, \bar{0}\rangle - \lvert -1, \bar{1}\rangle + \lvert 2, -\bar{2}\rangle)$
	$\lvert {}^{1}_{2}\mathrm{D}\ 2\ 0\rangle$	$= 7^{-1/2}(2^{1/2}\lvert 2, \bar{0}\rangle - 3^{1/2}\lvert 1, \bar{1}\rangle + 2^{1/2}\lvert 0, \bar{2}\rangle)$
	$\lvert {}^{1}_{2}\mathrm{G}\ 4\ 0\rangle$	$= \lvert 2, \bar{2}\rangle$
	$\lvert {}^{3}_{2}\mathrm{P}\ 1\ 1\rangle$	$= 5^{-1/2}(3^{1/2}\lvert 1, 0\rangle - 2^{1/2}\lvert 2, -1\rangle)$
	$\lvert {}^{3}_{2}\mathrm{F}\ 3\ 1\rangle$	$= \lvert 2, 1\rangle$
4	$\lvert {}^{1}_{0}\mathrm{S}\rangle$	$= 10^{-1/2}(\lvert 2, 1, -\bar{1}, -\bar{2}\rangle - \lvert 2, 0, \bar{0}, -\bar{2}\rangle + \lvert 2, -1, \bar{1}, \bar{2}\rangle$ $-\lvert 2, -2, \bar{2}, -\bar{2}\rangle + \lvert 1, 0, \bar{0}, -\bar{1}\rangle - \lvert 1, -1, \bar{1}, -\bar{1}\rangle$ $+\lvert 1, -2, \bar{2}, -\bar{1}\rangle + \lvert 0, -1, \bar{1}, \bar{0}\rangle - \lvert 0, -2, \bar{2}, \bar{0}\rangle$ $+\lvert -1, -2, \bar{2}, \bar{1}\rangle)$
	$\lvert {}^{1}_{2}\mathrm{D}\ 2\ 0\rangle$	$= 21^{-1/2}(2^{1/2}\lvert 2, 1, \bar{0}, -\bar{1}\rangle - 2^{1/2}\lvert 2, -1, \bar{1}, \bar{0}\rangle$ $+ 2^{1/2}\lvert 2, -2, \bar{2}, \bar{0}\rangle - 3^{1/2}\lvert 2, 1, \bar{1}, -\bar{2}\rangle + 3^{1/2}\lvert 1, 0, \bar{1}, \bar{0}\rangle$ $-3^{1/2}\lvert 1, -2, \bar{2}, \bar{1}\rangle + 2^{1/2}\lvert 2, 0, \bar{2}, -\bar{2}\rangle - 2^{1/2}\lvert 1, 0, \bar{2}, -\bar{1}\rangle$ $+2^{1/2}\lvert 0, -1, \bar{2}, \bar{1}\rangle)$
	$\lvert {}^{1}_{2}\mathrm{G}\ 4\ 0\rangle$	$= 3^{-1/2}(-\lvert 2, 1, \bar{2}, -\bar{1}\rangle + \lvert 2, 0, \bar{2}, \bar{0}\rangle - \lvert 2, -1, \bar{2}, \bar{1}\rangle)$
	$\lvert {}^{3}_{2}\mathrm{P}\ 1\ 1\rangle$	$= 15^{-1/2}(3^{1/2}\lvert 2, 1, 0, -\bar{2}\rangle - 3^{1/2}\lvert 1, 0, -1, \bar{1}\rangle$

†Many-electron statevectors are denoted as $\lvert {}^{2S+1}_{v}L\ M_L\ M_S\rangle$.

n	
	$+3^{1/2}\|1,0,-2,\bar{2}\rangle - 2^{1/2}\|2,1,-1,-\bar{1}\rangle + 2^{1/2}\|2,0,-1,\bar{0}\rangle - 2^{1/2}\|2,-1,-2,\bar{2}\rangle)$
	$\|{}^{3}_{2}F\,3\,1\rangle = 3^{-1/2}(\|2,1,0,\bar{0}\rangle - \|2,1,-1,\bar{1}\rangle + \|2,1,-2,\bar{2}\rangle)$
	$\|{}^{1}_{4}S\,0\,0\rangle = 210^{-1/2}(3\|2,1,-\bar{1},-\bar{2}\rangle - 3\|2,0,\bar{0},-\bar{2}\rangle - \|2,-1,\bar{1},-\bar{2}\rangle + 5\|2,-2,\bar{2},-\bar{2}\rangle - 3\|1,0,\bar{0},-\bar{1}\rangle - \|1,-1,\bar{1},-\bar{1}\rangle - \|1,-2,\bar{2},-\bar{1}\rangle - 3\|0,-1,\bar{1},\bar{0}\rangle - 3\|0,-2,\bar{2},\bar{0}\rangle + 3\|-1,-2,\bar{2},\bar{1}\rangle - 4\|2,-2,\bar{1},-\bar{1}\rangle + 2(6)^{1/2}\|2,-1,\bar{0},-\bar{1}\rangle - 4\|1,-1,\bar{2},-\bar{2}\rangle + 2(6)^{1/2}\|0,-1,\bar{2},-\bar{1}\rangle + 2(6)^{1/2}\|1,0,\bar{1},-\bar{2}\rangle + 2(6)^{1/2}\|1,-2,\bar{1},\bar{0}\rangle)$
	$\|{}^{1}_{4}D\,2\,0\rangle = 42^{-1/2}(2^{1/2}\|2,-1,\bar{1},\bar{0}\rangle + 2^{1/2}\|2,-2,\bar{2},\bar{0}\rangle - 3^{1/2}\|2,1,\bar{1},-\bar{2}\rangle - 2(3)^{1/2}\|1,0,\bar{1},\bar{0}\rangle - 3^{1/2}\|1,-2,\bar{2},\bar{1}\rangle + 2^{1/2}\|2,0,\bar{2},-\bar{2}\rangle + 2^{1/2}\|1,0,\bar{2},-\bar{1}\rangle + 2^{1/2}\|2,0,\bar{1},-\bar{1}\rangle - 2(3)^{1/2}\|2,-1,\bar{2},-\bar{1}\rangle + 2^{1/2}\|1,-1,\bar{2},\bar{0}\rangle)$
	$\|{}^{1}_{4}F\,3\,0\rangle = 120^{-1/2}(3\|2,1,\bar{1},-\bar{1}\rangle + 6^{1/2}\|2,0,\bar{2},-\bar{1}\rangle - 3\|2,0,\bar{1},\bar{0}\rangle + 6^{1/2}\|2,-1,\bar{2},\bar{0}\rangle - 3\|1,0,\bar{2},\bar{0}\rangle + 3\|1,-1,\bar{2},\bar{1}\rangle - 6\|2,1,\bar{2},-\bar{2}\rangle - 6\|2,-2,\bar{2},\bar{1}\rangle)$
	$\|{}^{1}_{4}G\,4\,0\rangle = 66^{-1/2}(2^{1/2}\|2,1,\bar{2},-\bar{1}\rangle + 2(2)^{1/2}\|2,0,\bar{2},\bar{0}\rangle + 2^{1/2}\|2,-1,\bar{2},\bar{1}\rangle - 3(3)^{1/2}\|2,1,\bar{1},\bar{0}\rangle - 3(3)^{1/2}\|1,0,\bar{2},\bar{1}\rangle)$
	$\|{}^{1}_{4}I\,6\,0\rangle = \|2,1,\bar{2},\bar{1}\rangle$
	$\|{}^{3}_{4}P\,1\,1\rangle = 210^{-1/2}\{4(3)^{1/2}\|2,1,0,-\bar{2}\rangle + 2(3)^{1/2}\|1,0,-1,\bar{1}\rangle - 2(3)^{1/2}\|1,0,-2,\bar{2}\rangle - 4(2)^{1/2}\|2,1,-1,-\bar{1}\rangle + 2^{1/2}\|2,0,-1,\bar{0}\rangle + 5(2)^{1/2}\|2,-1,-2,\bar{2}\rangle + 3(3)^{1/2}\|2,1,-2,\bar{0}\rangle - 3(3)^{1/2}\|2,0,-2,\bar{1}\rangle\}$
	$\|{}^{3}_{4}D\,2\,1\rangle = 84^{-1/2}\{3\|2,1,0,-\bar{1}\rangle - 3\|2,1,-1,\bar{0}\rangle + 2(6)^{1/2}\|2,1,-2,\bar{1}\rangle - \|2,0,-1,\bar{1}\rangle - 4\|2,0,-2,\bar{2}\rangle + 5\|1,0,-1,\bar{2}\rangle\}$
	$\|{}^{3}_{4}F\,3\,1\rangle = 12^{-1/2}(\|2,1,0,\bar{0}\rangle - \|2,1,-1,\bar{1}\rangle - 2\|2,1,-2,\bar{2}\rangle + 6^{1/2}\|2,0,-1,\bar{2}\rangle)$
	$\|{}^{3}_{4}G\,4\,1\rangle = 5^{-1/2}(3^{1/2}\|2,1,0,\bar{1}\rangle - 2^{1/2}\|2,1,-1,\bar{2}\rangle)$
	$\|{}^{3}_{4}H\,5\,1\rangle = \|2,1,0,\bar{2}\rangle$
	$\|{}^{5}_{4}D\,2\,2\rangle = \|2,1,0,-1\rangle$
1	$\left\|{}^{2}_{1}D\,2\,\tfrac{1}{2}\right\rangle = \|2\rangle$
3	$\left\|{}^{2}_{1}D\,2\,\tfrac{1}{2}\right\rangle = \tfrac{1}{2}(-\|2,1,-\bar{1}\rangle + \|2,0,\bar{0}\rangle - \|2,-1,\bar{1}\rangle + \|2,-2,\bar{2}\rangle)$
	$\left\|{}^{2}_{3}P\,1\,\tfrac{1}{2}\right\rangle = 210^{-1/2}\{4(3)^{1/2}\|2,1,-\bar{2}\rangle - 4(2)^{1/2}\|2,0,-\bar{1}\rangle + 2^{1/2}\|2,-1,\bar{0}\rangle + 2(3)^{1/2}\|2,-2,\bar{1}\rangle + 3(3)^{1/2}\|1,0,\bar{0}\rangle - 3(3)^{1/2}\|1,-1,\bar{1}\rangle - 2(3)^{1/2}\|1,-2,\bar{2}\rangle + 5(2)^{1/2}\|0,-1,\bar{2}\rangle\}$
	$\left\|{}^{2}_{3}D\,2\,\tfrac{1}{2}\right\rangle = 84^{-1/2}(3\|2,1,-\bar{1}\rangle - 3\|2,0,\bar{0}\rangle - \|2,-1,\bar{1}\rangle + 5\|2,-2,\bar{2}\rangle + 2(6)^{1/2}\|1,0,\bar{1}\rangle - 4\|1,-1,\bar{2}\rangle)$
	$\left\|{}^{2}_{3}F\,3\,\tfrac{1}{2}\right\rangle = 12^{-1/2}(\|2,1,\bar{0}\rangle - \|2,0,\bar{1}\rangle + 6^{1/2}\|2,-1,\bar{2}\rangle - 2\|1,0,\bar{2}\rangle)$
	$\left\|{}^{2}_{3}G\,4\,\tfrac{1}{2}\right\rangle = 5^{-1/2}(3^{1/2}\|2,1,\bar{1}\rangle - 2^{1/2}\|2,0,\bar{2}\rangle)$
	$\left\|{}^{2}_{3}H\,5\,\tfrac{1}{2}\right\rangle = \|2,1,\bar{2}\rangle$
	$\left\|{}^{4}_{3}P\,1\,\tfrac{3}{2}\right\rangle = 5^{-1/2}(3^{1/2}\|2,1,-2\rangle - 2^{1/2}\|2,0,-1\rangle)$

n

$$\left|{}^{4}_{3}F\,3\,\tfrac{3}{2}\right\rangle = |2, 1, 0\rangle$$

5

$$\begin{aligned}
\left|{}^{2}_{1}D\,2\,\tfrac{1}{2}\right\rangle &= 6^{-1/2}(|2, 1, 0, \bar{0}, -\bar{1}\rangle - |2, 1, -1, \bar{1}, -\bar{1}\rangle \\
&\quad + |2, 1, -2, \bar{2}, -\bar{1}\rangle + |2, 0, -1, \bar{1}, \bar{0}\rangle - |2, 0, -2, \bar{2}, \bar{0}\rangle \\
&\quad + |2, -1, -2, \bar{2}, \bar{1}\rangle)
\end{aligned}$$

$$\begin{aligned}
\left|{}^{2}_{3}P\,1\,\tfrac{1}{2}\right\rangle &= 420^{-1/2}\{3^{1/2}|2, 1, 0, \bar{0}, -\bar{2}\rangle - 3^{1/2}|2, 1, -1, \bar{1}, -\bar{2}\rangle \\
&\quad + 6(3)^{1/2}|2, 1, -2, \bar{2}, -\bar{2},\rangle + 4(2)^{1/2}|2, 0, -1, \bar{1}, -\bar{1}\rangle \\
&\quad - 4(2)^{1/2}|2, 0, -2, \bar{2}, -\bar{1}\rangle - 2^{1/2}|2, 1, -1, \bar{0}, -\bar{1}\rangle \\
&\quad + 2^{1/2}|2, -1, -2, \bar{2}, \bar{0}\rangle - 2(3)^{1/2}|2, 1, -2, \bar{1}, -\bar{1}\rangle \\
&\quad + 2(3)^{1/2}|2, 0, -2, \bar{1}, \bar{0}\rangle - 6(3)^{1/2}|1, 0, -1, \bar{1}, \bar{0}\rangle \\
&\quad + 3^{1/2}|1, 0, -2, \bar{2}, \bar{0}\rangle - 3^{1/2}|1, -1, -2, \bar{2}, \bar{1}\rangle \\
&\quad - 5(2)^{1/2}|2, 0, -1, \bar{2}, -\bar{2}\rangle\}
\end{aligned}$$

$$\begin{aligned}
\left|{}^{2}_{3}D\,2\,\tfrac{1}{2}\right\rangle &= 42^{-1/2}(3|2, 1, 0, 0, -\bar{1}\rangle - |2, 1, -1, \bar{1}, -\bar{1}\rangle \\
&\quad - |2, 1, -2, \bar{2}, -\bar{1}\rangle + |2, 0, -1, \bar{1}, \bar{0}\rangle + |2, 0, -2, \bar{2}, \bar{0}\rangle \\
&\quad - 3|2, -1, -2, \bar{2}, \bar{1}\rangle - 6^{1/2}|2, 1, 0, \bar{1}, -\bar{2}\rangle \\
&\quad + 6^{1/2}|1, 0, -2, \bar{2}, \bar{1}\rangle + 2|2, 1, -1, \bar{2}, -\bar{2}\rangle \\
&\quad - 2|1, 0, -1, \bar{2}, \bar{0}\rangle)
\end{aligned}$$

$$\begin{aligned}
\left|{}^{2}_{3}F\,3\,\tfrac{1}{2}\right\rangle &= 24^{-1/2}(-|2, 1, -1, \bar{1}, \bar{0}\rangle + |2, 1, -2, \bar{2}, \bar{0}\rangle \\
&\quad + |2, 1, 0, \bar{1}, -\bar{1}\rangle - |2, 0, -2, \bar{2}, \bar{1}\rangle - 6^{1/2}|2, 1, -1, \bar{2}, -\bar{1}\rangle \\
&\quad + 6^{1/2}|2, 0, -1, \bar{2}, \bar{0}\rangle + 2|2, 1, 0, \bar{2}, -\bar{2}\rangle \\
&\quad -2|1, 0, -1, \bar{2}, \bar{1}\rangle)
\end{aligned}$$

$$\begin{aligned}
\left|{}^{2}_{3}G\,4\,\tfrac{1}{2}\right\rangle &= 10^{-1/2}(-3^{1/2}|2, 1, 0, \bar{1}, \bar{0}\rangle + 3^{1/2}|2, 1, -2, \bar{2}, \bar{1}\rangle \\
&\quad + 2^{1/2}|2, 1, 0, \bar{2}, -\bar{1}\rangle - 2^{1/2}|2, 0, -1, \bar{2}, \bar{1}\rangle)
\end{aligned}$$

$$\left|{}^{2}_{3}H\,5\,\tfrac{1}{2}\right\rangle = 2^{-1/2}(-|2, 1, 0, \bar{2}, \bar{0}\rangle + |2, 1, -1, \bar{2}, \bar{1}\rangle)$$

$$\begin{aligned}
\left|{}^{4}_{3}P\,1\,\tfrac{3}{2}\right\rangle &= 10^{-1/2}(-3^{1/2}|2, 1, 0, -2, \bar{0}\rangle + 3^{1/2}|2, 1, -1, -2, \bar{1}\rangle \\
&\quad + 2^{1/2}|2, 1, 0, -1, -\bar{1}\rangle - 2^{1/2}|2, 0, -1, -2, \bar{2}\rangle)
\end{aligned}$$

$$\left|{}^{4}_{3}F\,3\,\tfrac{3}{2}\right\rangle = 2^{-1/2}(-|2, 1, 0, -1, \bar{1}\rangle + |2, 1, 0, -2, \bar{2}\rangle)$$

$$\begin{aligned}
\left|{}^{2}_{5}S\,0\,\tfrac{1}{2}\right\rangle &= 210^{-1/2}\{3|2, 1, 0, -\bar{1}, -\bar{2}\rangle - 3|2, 1, -1, \bar{0}, -\bar{2}\rangle \\
&\quad + 2(6)^{1/2}|2, -1, -2, \bar{2}, -\bar{1}\rangle + 2(6)^{1/2}|2, 1, -2, \bar{1}, -\bar{2}\rangle \\
&\quad - 3|2, 1, -2, \bar{0}, -\bar{1}\rangle - |2, 0, -1, \bar{1}, -\bar{2}\rangle + 2(6)^{1/2}|2, 0, -1, \bar{0}, -\bar{1}\rangle \\
&\quad - 4|2, 0, -2, \bar{2}, -\bar{2}\rangle - |2, 0, -2, \bar{1}, -\bar{1}\rangle - 3|2, -1, -2, \bar{1}, \bar{0}\rangle \\
&\quad + 5|1, 0, -1, \bar{2}, -\bar{2}\rangle - 4|1, 0, -1, \bar{1}, -\bar{1}\rangle - |1, 0, -2, \bar{2}, -\bar{1}\rangle \\
&\quad + 2(6)^{1/2}|1, 0, -2, \bar{1}, \bar{0}\rangle - 3|1, -1, -2, \bar{2}, \bar{0}\rangle + 3|0, -1, -2, \bar{2}, \bar{1}\rangle\}
\end{aligned}$$

$$\begin{aligned}
\left|{}^{2}_{5}D\,2\,\tfrac{1}{2}\right\rangle &= 84^{-1/2}\{6^{1/2}|2, 1, 0, \bar{1}, -\bar{2}\rangle - 2|2, 1, -1, \bar{2}, -\bar{2}\rangle \\
&\quad - 2|2, 1, -1, \bar{1}, -\bar{1}\rangle - 2|2, 1, -2, \bar{2}, -\bar{1}\rangle + 2(6)^{1/2}|2, 1, -2, \bar{1}, \bar{0}\rangle \\
&\quad + 2(6)^{1/2}|2, 0, -1, \bar{2}, -\bar{1}\rangle - 2|2, 0, -1, \bar{1}, \bar{0}\rangle \\
&\quad - 2|2, 0, -2, \bar{2}, \bar{0}\rangle - 2|1, 0, -1, \bar{2}, \bar{0}\rangle + 6^{1/2}|1, 0, -2, \bar{2}, \bar{1}\rangle\}
\end{aligned}$$

$$\begin{aligned}
\left|{}^{2}_{5}F\,3\,\tfrac{1}{2}\right\rangle &= 40^{-1/2}\{2(3)^{1/2}|2, 1, 0, \bar{2}, -\bar{2}\rangle - 3^{1/2}|2, 1, 0, \bar{1}, -\bar{1}\rangle \\
&\quad - 2^{1/2}|2, 1, -1, \bar{2}, -\bar{1}\rangle + 3^{1/2}|2, 1, -1, \bar{1}, \bar{0}\rangle \\
&\quad + 3^{1/2}|2, 1, -2, \bar{2}, \bar{0}\rangle - 2^{1/2}|2, 0, -1, \bar{2}, \bar{0}\rangle
\end{aligned}$$

n	
	$-\ 3^{1/2}\|2, 0, -2, \bar{2}, \bar{1}\rangle + 2(3)^{1/2}\|1, 0, -1, \bar{2}, \bar{1}\rangle\}$
	$\left\|{}^{2}_{5}G\ 4\ \frac{1}{2}\right\rangle = 132^{-1/2}\{2\|2, 1, 0, \bar{2}, -\bar{1}\rangle - 3(6)^{1/2}\|2, 1, 0, \bar{1}, \bar{0}\rangle$
	$+\ 4\|2, 1, -1, \bar{2}, \bar{0}\rangle - 3(6)^{1/2}\|2, 1, -2, \bar{2}, \bar{1}\rangle + 2\|2, 0, -1, \bar{2}, \bar{1}\rangle\}$
	$\left\|{}^{2}_{5}I\ 6\ \frac{1}{2}\right\rangle = \|2, 1, 0, \bar{2}, \bar{1}\rangle$
	$\left\|{}^{4}_{5}D\ 2\ \frac{3}{2}\right\rangle = 7^{-1/2}(2^{1/2}\|2, 1, 0, -1, \bar{0}\rangle - 3^{1/3}\|2, 1, 0, -2, \bar{1}\rangle$
	$+2^{1/2}\|2, 1, -1, -2, \bar{2}\rangle)$
	$\left\|{}^{4}_{5}G\ 4\ \frac{3}{2}\right\rangle = \|2, 1, 0, -1, \bar{2}\rangle$
	$\left\|{}^{6}_{5}S\ 0\ \frac{5}{2}\right\rangle = \|2, 1, 0, -1, -2\rangle$

Appendix 4.1

MATRIX ELEMENTS OF EQUIVALENT OPERATORS†

1. $3L_z^2 - L(L+1)$.

L	F							
$L_z =$		0	±1	±2	±3	±4	±5	±6
0	0	0						
1	1	−2	1					
2	3	−2	−1	2				
3	3	−4	−3	0	5			
4	1	−20	−17	−8	7	28		
5	3	−10	−9	−6	−1	6	15	
6	3	−14	−13	−10	−5	2	11	22

The numbers in column F are multiplying factors common to all the elements in the row.

2. $\frac{1}{2}(L_+^2 + L_-^2)$.

†Tables 1 and 3 are reproduced from K. W. H. Stevens, *Proc. Phys. Soc.* **A65**, 209 (1952); tables 2 and 4 from D. A. Jones, J. M. Baker, and D. F. Pope, *Proc. Phys. Soc.* **74**, 249 (1959); table 5 from B. R. Judd, *Proc. Roy. Soc.* **A227**, 552 (1955); table 6 from J. M. Baker, B. Bleaney, and W. Hayes, *Proc. Roy. Soc.* **A247**, 141 (1958). Permission for reproduction is greatly appreciated.

L	$\langle \pm 1 \Vert \mp 1 \rangle$	$\langle \pm 2 \Vert 0 \rangle$	$\langle \pm 3 \Vert \pm 1 \rangle$	$\langle \pm 4 \Vert \pm 2 \rangle$	$\langle \pm 5 \Vert \pm 3 \rangle$	$\langle \pm 6 \Vert \pm 4 \rangle$
1	1					
2	3	$6^{1/2}$				
3	6	$30^{1/2}$	$15^{1/2}$			
4	10	$3(10)^{1/2}$	$3(7)^{1/2}$	$2(7)^{1/2}$		
5	15	$210^{1/2}$	$2(42)^{1/2}$	$6(3)^{1/2}$	$3(5)^{1/2}$	
6	21	$2(105)^{1/2}$	$6(10)^{1/2}$	$3(30)^{1/2}$	$165^{1/2}$	$66^{1/2}$

3. $35L_z^4 - 30L(L+1)L_z^2 + 25L_z^2 - 6L(L+1) + 3L^2(L+1)^2$.

L	F							
$L_z =$		0	± 1	± 2	± 3	± 4	± 5	± 6
0	0	0						
1	0	0	0					
2	12	6	−4	1				
3	60	6	1	−7	3			
4	60	18	9	−11	−21	14		
5	420	6	4	−1	−6	−6	6	
6	60	84	64	11	−54	−96	−66	99

4. $\frac{1}{4}[\{7L_z^2 - L(L+1) - 5\}(L_+^2 + L_-^2) + (L_+^2 + L_-^2)$
$\times \{7L_z^2 - L(L+1) - 5\}]$.

L	F	$\langle \pm 1 \Vert \mp 1 \rangle$	$\langle \pm 2 \Vert 0 \rangle$	$\langle \pm 3 \Vert \pm 1 \rangle$	$\langle \pm 4 \Vert \pm 2 \rangle$	$\langle \pm 5 \Vert \pm 3 \rangle$	$\langle \pm 6 \Vert \pm 4 \rangle$
2	3	−4	$6^{1/2}$				
3	3	−20	$-30^{1/2}$	$6(15)^{1/2}$			
4	3	−60	$-11(10)^{1/2}$	$10(7)^{1/2}$	$30(7)^{1/2}$		
5	21	−20	$-210^{1/2}$	0	$10(3)^{1/2}$	$12(5)^{1/2}$	
6	3	−280	$-22(105)^{1/2}$	$-24(10)^{1/2}$	$23(30)^{1/2}$	$24(165)^{1/2}$	$45(66)^{1/2}$

5. $\frac{1}{4}\{L_z(L_+^3 + L_-^3) + (L_+^3 + L_-^3)L_z\}$.

L	F	$\langle \pm 2 \Vert \mp 1 \rangle$	$\langle \pm 3 \Vert 0 \rangle$	$\langle \pm 4 \Vert \pm 1 \rangle$	$\langle \pm 5 \Vert \pm 2 \rangle$	$\langle \pm 6 \Vert \pm 3 \rangle$
2	3	1				
3	3	$(10)^{1/2}$	$3(5)^{1/2}$			
4	3	$5(2)^{1/2}$	$3(35)^{1/2}$	$5(14)^{1/2}$		
5	3	$5(7)^{1/2}$	$6(35)^{1/2}$	$10(21)^{1/2}$	$7(30)^{1/2}$	
6	3	$7(10)^{1/2}$	$6(105)^{1/2}$	$50(3)^{1/2}$	$7(165)^{1/2}$	$9(55)^{1/2}$

6. $\frac{1}{2}(L_+^4 + L_-^4)$.

L	F	$\langle \pm 2 \Vert \mp 2 \rangle$	$\langle \pm 3 \Vert \mp 1 \rangle$	$\langle \pm 4 \Vert 0 \rangle$	$\langle \pm 5 \Vert \pm 1 \rangle$	$\langle \pm 6 \Vert \pm 2 \rangle$
2	12	1				
3	12	5	$(15)^{1/2}$			
4	12	15	$5(7)^{1/2}$	$(70)^{1/2}$		
5	12	35	$5(42)^{1/2}$	$3(70)^{1/2}$	$210^{1/2}$	
6	12	70	$21(10)^{1/2}$	$15(14)^{1/2}$	$5(66)^{1/2}$	$3(55)^{1/2}$

Appendix 4.2

EIGENVALUES AND EIGENVECTORS FOR OCTAHEDRAL POTENTIAL[†]

Equivalent operator

$$V = \frac{B_4}{60}\{35L_z^4 - 30L(L+1)L_z^2 + 25L_z^2 + 3L^2(L+1)^2 - 6L(L+1) + \frac{5}{2}(L_+^4 + L_-^4)\}$$

is used; eigenvectors are presented in terms of $|LM_L\rangle$.

L	Term	Energy	Eigenvector
0	A_1	0	$A_1 = \|00\rangle$
1	T_1	0	$T_11 = \|11\rangle$
			$T_10 = \|10\rangle$
			$T_1\text{-}1 = \|1\text{-}1\rangle$

$$\dagger T_11 = -\frac{T_1x + iT_1y}{\sqrt{2}}, \qquad T_10 = T_1z, \qquad T_1\text{-}1 = \frac{T_1x - iT_1y}{\sqrt{2}},$$

$$T_21 = -\frac{T_2\xi + iT_2\eta}{\sqrt{2}}, \qquad T_20 = T_2\zeta, \qquad T_2\text{-}1 = \frac{T_2\xi - iT_2\eta}{\sqrt{2}}.$$

L	Term	Energy	Eigenvector
2	E	$\frac{6}{5}B_4$	$Eu = \|20\rangle$
			$Ev = \left(\frac{1}{2}\right)^{1/2}(\|22\rangle + \|2\text{-}2\rangle)$
	T_2	$-\frac{4}{5}B_4$	$T_21 = \|2\text{-}1\rangle$
			$T_20 = \left(\frac{1}{2}\right)^{1/2}(\|22\rangle - \|2\text{-}2\rangle)$
			$T_2\text{-}1 = -\|21\rangle$
3	A_2	$-12B_4$	$A_2 = \left(\frac{1}{2}\right)^{1/2}(\|32\rangle - \|3\text{-}2\rangle)$
	T_1	$6B_4$	$T_11 = \left(\frac{1}{8}\right)^{1/2}(-5^{1/2}\|3\text{-}3\rangle - 3^{1/2}\|31\rangle)$
			$T_10 = \|30\rangle$
			$T_1\text{-}1 = \left(\frac{1}{8}\right)^{1/2}(-5^{1/2}\|33\rangle - 3^{1/2}\|3\text{-}1\rangle)$
	T_2	$-2B_4$	$T_21 = \left(\frac{1}{8}\right)^{1/2}(5^{1/2}\|3\text{-}1\rangle - 3^{1/2}\|33\rangle)$
			$T_20 = \left(\frac{1}{2}\right)^{1/2}(\|32\rangle + \|3\text{-}2\rangle)$
			$T_2\text{-}1 = \left(\frac{1}{8}\right)^{1/2}(5^{1/2}\|31\rangle - 3^{1/2}\|3\text{-}3\rangle)$
4	A_1	$28B_4$	$A_1 = \left(\frac{1}{24}\right)^{1/2}(14^{1/2}\|40\rangle + 5^{1/2}\|44\rangle + 5^{1/2}\|4\text{-}4\rangle)$
	E	$4B_4$	$Eu = \left(\frac{1}{24}\right)^{1/2}(10^{1/2}\|40\rangle - 7^{1/2}\|44\rangle - 7^{1/2}\|4\text{-}4\rangle)$
			$Ev = \left(\frac{1}{2}\right)^{1/2}(-\|42\rangle - \|4\text{-}2\rangle)$
	T_1	$14B_4$	$T_11 = \left(\frac{1}{8}\right)^{1/2}(7^{1/2}\|41\rangle + \|4\text{-}3\rangle)$
			$T_10 = \left(\frac{1}{2}\right)^{1/2}(-\|44\rangle + \|4\text{-}4\rangle)$
			$T_1\text{-}1 = \left(\frac{1}{8}\right)^{1/2}(-7^{1/2}\|4\text{-}1\rangle - \|43\rangle)$
	T_2	$-26B_4$	$T_21 = \left(\frac{1}{8}\right)^{1/2}(7^{1/2}\|43\rangle - \|4\text{-}1\rangle)$
			$T_20 = \left(\frac{1}{2}\right)^{1/2}(\|42\rangle - \|4\text{-}2\rangle)$
			$T_2\text{-}1 = \left(\frac{1}{8}\right)^{1/2}(-7^{1/2}\|4\text{-}3\rangle + \|41\rangle)$
5	E	$-42B_4$	$Eu = \left(\frac{1}{2}\right)^{1/2}(\|54\rangle - \|5\text{-}4\rangle)$
			$Ev = \left(\frac{1}{2}\right)^{1/2}(-\|52\rangle + \|5\text{-}2\rangle)$
	T_1	$42B_4$	$T_11 = \left(\frac{1}{128}\right)^{1/2}\{3(7)^{1/2}\|55\rangle + 35^{1/2}\|5\text{-}3\rangle + 30^{1/2}\|51\rangle\}$
			$T_10 = \|50\rangle$
			$T_1\text{-}1 = \left(\frac{1}{128}\right)^{1/2}\{3(7)^{1/2}\|5\text{-}5\rangle + 35^{1/2}\|53\rangle + 30^{1/2}\|5\text{-}1\rangle\}$
	T_1'	$-42B_4$	$T_11 = \left(\frac{1}{16}\right)\{10^{1/2}\|55\rangle - 9(2)^{1/2}\|5\text{-}3\rangle + 2(21)^{1/2}\|51\rangle\}$

L	Term	Energy	Eigenvector
			$T_1 0 = \left(\frac{1}{2}\right)^{1/2}(\|54\rangle + \|5{-}4\rangle)$
			$T_1{-}1 = \left(\frac{1}{16}\right)\{10^{1/2}\|5{-}5\rangle - 9(2)^{1/2}\|53\rangle + 2(21)^{1/2}\|5{-}1\rangle\}$
	T_2	$28B_4$	$T_2 1 = \left(\frac{1}{32}\right)^{1/2}(15^{1/2}\|5{-}5\rangle - 3^{1/2}\|53\rangle - 14^{1/2}\|5{-}1\rangle)$
			$T_2 0 = \left(\frac{1}{2}\right)^{1/2}(\|52\rangle + \|5{-}2\rangle)$
			$T_2{-}1 = \left(\frac{1}{32}\right)^{1/2}(15^{1/2}\|55\rangle - 3^{1/2}\|5{-}3\rangle - 14^{1/2}\|51\rangle)$
6	A_1	$-126B_4$	$A_1 = \left(\frac{1}{4}\right)(2^{1/2}\|60\rangle - 7^{1/2}\|64\rangle - 7^{1/2}\|6{-}4\rangle)$
	A_2	$66B_4$	$A_2 = \left(\frac{1}{32}\right)^{1/2}(11^{1/2}\|62\rangle + 11^{1/2}\|6{-}2\rangle - 5^{1/2}\|66\rangle - 5^{1/2}\|6{-}6\rangle)$
	E	$114B_4$	$Eu = \left(\frac{1}{4}\right)(14^{1/2}\|60\rangle + \|64\rangle + \|6{-}4\rangle)$
			$Ev = \left(\frac{1}{32}\right)^{1/2}(5^{1/2}\|62\rangle + 5^{1/2}\|6{-}2\rangle + 11^{1/2}\|66\rangle + 11^{1/2}\|6{-}6\rangle)$
	T_1	$-96B_4$	$T_1 1 = \left(\frac{1}{8}\right)\{2(3)^{1/2}\|61\rangle - 30^{1/2}\|6{-}2\rangle - 22^{1/2}\|65\rangle\}$
			$T_1 0 = \left(\frac{1}{2}\right)^{1/2}(\|64\rangle - \|6{-}4\rangle)$
			$T_1{-}1 = \left(\frac{1}{8}\right)\{2(3)^{1/2}\|6{-}1\rangle + 30^{1/2}\|63\rangle + 22^{1/2}\|6{-}5\rangle\}$
	T_2	$-59B_4$	$T_2 1 = \left(\frac{1}{16}\right)(10^{1/2}\|6{-}1\rangle - 9\|63\rangle + 165^{1/2}\|6{-}5\rangle)$
			$T_2 0 = \left(\frac{1}{2}\right)^{1/2}(\|62\rangle - \|6{-}2\rangle)$
			$T_2{-}1 = \left(\frac{1}{16}\right)(-10^{1/2}\|61\rangle + 9\|6{-}3\rangle - 165^{1/2}\|65\rangle)$
	T_2'	$99B_4$	$T_2 1 = \left(\frac{1}{16}\right)\{3(22)^{1/2}\|6{-}1\rangle + 55^{1/2}\|63\rangle + 3^{1/2}\|6{-}5\rangle\}$
			$T_2 0 = \left(\frac{1}{2}\right)^{1/2}(\|66\rangle - \|6{-}6\rangle)$
			$T_2{-}1 = \left(\frac{1}{16}\right)\{-3(22)^{1/2}\|61\rangle - 55^{1/2}\|6{-}3\rangle - 3^{1/2}\|65\rangle\}$

Appendix 4.3

STATEVECTORS IN STRONG-FIELD SCHEME†

Configuration	Crystal term	Statevector
t_2	${}^2T_2\,\zeta\,\frac{1}{2}$	$\vert\zeta\rangle$
e	${}^2E\,u\,\frac{1}{2}$	$\vert u\rangle$
t_2^2	${}^3T_1\,z\,1$	$\vert\xi\eta\rangle$
	${}^1T_2\,\zeta$	$\left(\frac{1}{2}\right)^{1/2}(\vert\xi\bar{\eta}\rangle - \vert\bar{\xi}\eta\rangle)$
	${}^1E\ u$	$\left(\frac{1}{6}\right)^{1/2}(\vert\xi\bar{\xi}\rangle + \vert\eta\bar{\eta}\rangle - 2\vert\zeta\bar{\zeta}\rangle)$
	v	$\left(\frac{1}{2}\right)^{1/2}(-\vert\xi\bar{\xi}\rangle + \vert\eta\bar{\eta}\vert\rangle)$
	${}^1A_1$	$\left(\frac{1}{3}\right)^{1/2}(\vert\xi\bar{\xi}\rangle + \vert\eta\bar{\eta}\rangle + \vert\zeta\bar{\zeta}\rangle)$
t_2e	${}^3T_1\,z\,1$	$\vert\zeta v\rangle$
	${}^3T_2\,\zeta\,1$	$\vert\zeta u\rangle$
	${}^1T_1\,z$	$\left(\frac{1}{2}\right)^{1/2}(\vert\zeta\bar{v}\rangle - \vert\bar{\zeta}v\rangle)$
	${}^1T_2\,\zeta$	$\left(\frac{1}{2}\right)^{1/2}(\vert\zeta\bar{u}\rangle - \vert\bar{\zeta}u\rangle)$

†Statevectors are presented in a form ${}^{2S+1}\Gamma M_S$ for $t_2^m e^n$ configurations, with $m + n = 1$ to 5.

Configuration	Crystal term	Statevector
e^2	$^3A_2 \quad 1$	$\lvert uv\rangle$
	$^1E \quad u$	$\left(\frac{1}{2}\right)^{1/2}(-\lvert u\bar{u}\rangle + \lvert v\bar{v}\rangle)$
	v	$\left(\frac{1}{2}\right)^{1/2}(\lvert u\bar{v}\rangle - \lvert \bar{u}v\rangle)$
	$^1A_1$	$\left(\frac{1}{2}\right)^{1/2}(\lvert u\bar{u}\rangle + \lvert v\bar{v}\rangle)$
t_2^3	$^4A_2 \quad \frac{3}{2}$	$\lvert \xi\eta\zeta\rangle$
	$^2E \; u \, \frac{1}{2}$	$\left(\frac{1}{2}\right)^{1/2}(\lvert \xi\bar{\eta}\zeta\rangle - \lvert \bar{\xi}\eta\zeta\rangle)$
	$v \, \frac{1}{2}$	$\left(\frac{1}{6}\right)^{1/2}(-\lvert \xi\bar{\eta}\zeta\rangle - \lvert \bar{\xi}\eta\zeta\rangle + 2\lvert \xi\eta\bar{\zeta}\rangle)$
	$^2T_1 z \, \frac{1}{2}$	$\left(\frac{1}{2}\right)^{1/2}(\lvert \xi\bar{\xi}\zeta\rangle - \lvert \eta\bar{\eta}\zeta\rangle)$
	$^2T_2 \zeta \, \frac{1}{2}$	$\left(\frac{1}{2}\right)^{1/2}(\lvert \xi\bar{\xi}\zeta\rangle + \lvert \eta\bar{\eta}\zeta\rangle)$
$t_2^2(^1T_2)e$	$^2T_1 z \, \frac{1}{2}$	$\left(\frac{1}{2}\right)^{1/2}(-\lvert \xi\bar{\eta}v\rangle + \lvert \bar{\xi}\eta v\rangle)$
$(^3T_1)$	$^2T_2 \zeta \, \frac{1}{2}$	$\left(\frac{1}{6}\right)^{1/2}(-2\lvert \xi\eta\bar{v}\rangle + \lvert \xi\bar{\eta}v\rangle + \lvert \bar{\xi}\eta v\rangle)$
$(^1T_2)$	$^2T_2 \zeta \, \frac{1}{2}$	$\left(\frac{1}{2}\right)^{1/2}(-\lvert \xi\bar{\eta}u\rangle + \lvert \bar{\xi}\eta u\rangle)$
$(^3T_1)$	$^2T_1 z \, \frac{1}{2}$	$\left(\frac{1}{6}\right)^{1/2}(-2\lvert \xi\eta\bar{u}\rangle + \lvert \xi\bar{\eta}u\rangle + \lvert \bar{\xi}\eta u\rangle)$
$(^3T_1)$	$^4T_1 z \, \frac{3}{2}$	$\lvert \xi\eta u\rangle$
$(^3T_1)$	$^4T_2 \zeta \, \frac{3}{2}$	$\lvert \xi\eta v\rangle$
$t_2^2(^1E)e$	$^2A_1 \quad \frac{1}{2}$	$\left(\frac{1}{12}\right)^{1/2}\{(1) + (2) - 2(3) - 3^{1/2}(4) + 3^{1/2}(5)\}$
(^1E)	$^2A_2 \quad \frac{1}{2}$	$\left(\frac{1}{12}\right)^{1/2}\{3^{1/2}(1) - 3^{1/2}(2) + (4) + (5) - 2(6)\}$
(^1E)	$^2E \; u \, \frac{1}{2}$	$\left(\frac{1}{12}\right)^{1/2}\{(1) + (2) - 2(3) + 3^{1/2}(4) - 3^{1/2}(5)\}$
	$v \, \frac{1}{2}$	$\left(\frac{1}{2}\right)^{1/2}\{3^{1/2}(1) - 3^{1/2}(2) - (4) - (5) + 2(6)\}$
$(^1A_1)$	$^2E \; u \, \frac{1}{2}$	$\left(\frac{1}{3}\right)^{1/2}\{(1) + (2) + (3)\}$
	$v \, \frac{1}{2}$	$\left(\frac{1}{3}\right)^{1/2}\{(4) + (5) + (6)\}$
where		$(1) = \lvert \xi\bar{\xi}u\rangle$, $(2) = \lvert \eta\bar{\eta}u\rangle$, $(3) = \lvert \zeta\bar{\zeta}u\rangle$, $(4) = \lvert \xi\bar{\xi}v\rangle$, $(5) = \lvert \eta\bar{\eta}v\rangle$, $(6) = \lvert \zeta\bar{\zeta}v\rangle$.
$t_2(^2T_2)e^2(^3A_2)$	$^4T_1 z \, \frac{3}{2}$	$\lvert \zeta uv\rangle$
	$^2T_1 z \, \frac{1}{2}$	$\left(\frac{1}{6}\right)^{1/2}(\lvert \zeta u\bar{v}\rangle + \lvert \zeta\bar{u}v\rangle - 2\lvert \bar{\zeta}uv\rangle)$
(^1E)	$^2T_1 z \, \frac{1}{2}$	$\left(\frac{1}{2}\right)^{1/2}(\lvert \zeta u\bar{v}\rangle - \lvert \zeta\bar{u}v\rangle)$

Configuration	Crystal term	Statevector
$(^1A_1)$	$^2T_2\,\zeta\,\frac{1}{2}$	$\left(\frac{1}{2}\right)^{1/2}(\lvert\zeta u\bar{u}\rangle + \lvert\zeta v\bar{v}\rangle)$
(^1E)	$^2T_2\,\zeta\,\frac{1}{2}$	$\left(\frac{1}{2}\right)^{1/2}(\lvert\zeta u\bar{u}\rangle - \lvert\zeta v\bar{v}\rangle)$
e^3	$^2E\ u\,\frac{1}{2}$	$\lvert uv\bar{v}\rangle$
	$v\,\frac{1}{2}$	$\lvert u\bar{u}v\rangle$
t_2^4	$^3T_1\,z\,1$	$\lvert\xi\eta\zeta\bar{\zeta}\rangle$
	$^1T_2\,\zeta$	$\left(\frac{1}{2}\right)^{1/2}(\lvert\xi\bar{\eta}\zeta\bar{\zeta}\rangle - \lvert\bar{\xi}\eta\zeta\bar{\zeta}\rangle)$
	$^1A_1$	$\left(\frac{1}{3}\right)^{1/2}\{(1) + (2) + (3)\}$
	$^1E\ u$	$\left(\frac{1}{6}\right)^{1/2}\{-2(1) + (2) + (3)\}$
	v	$\left(\frac{1}{2}\right)^{1/2}\{-(2) + (3)\}$
where		$(1) = \lvert\xi\bar{\xi}\eta\bar{\eta}\rangle$, $(2) = \lvert\eta\bar{\eta}\zeta\bar{\zeta}\rangle$, $(3) = \lvert\xi\bar{\xi}\zeta\bar{\zeta}\rangle$.
$t_2^3(^4A_2)e$	$^5E\ u\,2$	$\lvert\xi\eta\zeta v\rangle$
	$v\,2$	$-\lvert\xi\eta\zeta u\rangle$
$t_2^3(^2E)e$	$^3A_1\ \ 1$	$\left(\frac{1}{12}\right)^{1/2}\{3^{1/2}(2) - 3^{1/2}(3) + 2(4) - (5) - (6)\}$
	$^3A_2\ \ 1$	$\left(\frac{1}{12}\right)^{1/2}\{2(1) - (2) - (3) - 3^{1/2}(5) + 3^{1/2}(6)\}$
	$^3E\ u\,1$	$\left(\frac{1}{12}\right)^{1/2}\{-3^{1/2}(2) + 3^{1/2}(3) + 2(4) - (5) - (6)\}$
	$v\,1$	$\left(\frac{1}{12}\right)^{1/2}\{2(1) - (2) - (3) + 3^{1/2}(5) - 3^{1/2}(6)\}$
$(^4A_2)$	$^3E\ u\,1$	$\left(\frac{1}{12}\right)^{1/2}\{(4) + (5) + (6) - 3\lvert\xi\eta\zeta\bar{v}\rangle\}$
	$v\,1$	$\left(\frac{1}{12}\right)^{1/2}\{-(1) - (2) - (3) + 3\lvert\xi\eta\zeta\bar{u}\rangle\}$
where		$(1) = \lvert\xi\eta\bar{\zeta}u\rangle$, $(2) = \lvert\xi\bar{\eta}\zeta u\rangle$, $(3) = \lvert\bar{\xi}\eta\zeta u\rangle$, $(4) = \lvert\xi\eta\bar{\zeta}v\rangle$, $(5) = \lvert\xi\bar{\eta}\zeta v\rangle$, $(6) = \lvert\bar{\xi}\eta\zeta v\rangle$.
$t_2^3(^2E)e$	$^1A_1$	$\left(\frac{1}{24}\right)^{1/2}\{3^{1/2}(1) - 3^{1/2}(2) + (4) + (5) - 2(6)$ $- 3^{1/2}(8) + 3^{1/2}(9) - 2(10) + (11) + (12)\}$
	$^1A_2$	$\left(\frac{1}{24}\right)^{1/2}\{(1) + (2) - 2(3) - 3^{1/2}(4) + 3^{1/2}(5)$ $- 2(7) + (8) + (9) + 3^{1/2}(11) - 3^{1/2}(12)\}$
	$^1E\ u$	$\left(\frac{1}{24}\right)^{1/2}\{-3^{1/2}(1) + 3^{1/2}(2) + (4) + (5) - 2(6)$ $+ 3^{1/2}(8) - 3^{1/2}(9) - 2(10) + (11) + (12)\}$
	v	$\left(\frac{1}{24}\right)^{1/2}\{(1) + (2) - 2(3) + 3^{1/2}(4) - 3^{1/2}(5)$ $- 2(7) + (8) + (9) - 3^{1/2}(11) + 3^{1/2}(12)\}$
where		$(1) = \lvert\xi\bar{\eta}\bar{\zeta}u\rangle$, $(2) = \lvert\bar{\xi}\eta\bar{\zeta}u\rangle$, $(3) = \lvert\bar{\xi}\bar{\eta}\zeta u\rangle$, $(4) = \lvert\xi\bar{\eta}\bar{\zeta}v\rangle$, $(5) = \lvert\bar{\xi}\eta\bar{\zeta}v\rangle$, $(6) = \lvert\bar{\xi}\bar{\eta}\zeta v\rangle$,

Configuration	Crystal term	Statevector
		$(7) = \|\xi\eta\bar{\zeta}\bar{u}\rangle$, $(8) = \|\xi\bar{\eta}\zeta\bar{u}\rangle$, $(9) = \|\bar{\xi}\eta\zeta\bar{u}\rangle$, $(10) = \|\xi\eta\bar{\zeta}\bar{v}\rangle$, $(11) = \|\xi\bar{\eta}\zeta\bar{v}\rangle$, $(12) = \|\bar{\xi}\eta\zeta\bar{v}\rangle$.
$t_2^3(^2T_1)e$	$^3T_1\ z\ 1$	$\left(\frac{1}{2}\right)^{1/2}(\|\xi\bar{\xi}\zeta u\rangle - \|\eta\bar{\eta}\zeta u\rangle)$
$(^2T_2)$	$^3T_2\ \zeta\ 1$	$\left(\frac{1}{2}\right)^{1/2}(\|\xi\bar{\xi}\zeta u\rangle + \|\eta\bar{\eta}\zeta u\rangle)$
$(^2T_1)$	$^3T_2\ \zeta\ 1$	$\left(\frac{1}{2}\right)^{1/2}(\|\xi\bar{\xi}\zeta v\rangle - \|\eta\bar{\eta}\zeta v\rangle)$
$(^2T_2)$	$^3T_1\ z\ 1$	$\left(\frac{1}{2}\right)^{1/2}(\|\xi\bar{\xi}\zeta v\rangle + \|\eta\bar{\eta}\zeta v\rangle)$
$(^2T_1)$	$^1T_1\ z$	$\left(\frac{1}{2}\right)(\|\xi\bar{\xi}\bar{\zeta}u\rangle - \|\eta\bar{\eta}\bar{\zeta}u\rangle - \|\xi\bar{\xi}\zeta\bar{u}\rangle + \|\eta\bar{\eta}\zeta\bar{u}\rangle)$
$(^2T_2)$	$^1T_2\ \zeta$	$\left(\frac{1}{2}\right)(\|\xi\bar{\xi}\bar{\zeta}u\rangle + \|\eta\bar{\eta}\bar{\zeta}u\rangle - \|\xi\bar{\xi}\zeta\bar{u}\rangle - \|\eta\bar{\eta}\zeta\bar{u}\rangle)$
$(^2T_1)$	$^1T_2\ \zeta$	$\left(\frac{1}{2}\right)(\|\xi\bar{\xi}\bar{\zeta}v\rangle - \|\eta\bar{\eta}\bar{\zeta}v\rangle - \|\xi\bar{\xi}\zeta\bar{v}\rangle + \|\eta\bar{\eta}\zeta\bar{v}\rangle)$
$(^2T_2)$	$^1T_1\ z$	$\left(\frac{1}{2}\right)(\|\xi\bar{\xi}\bar{\zeta}v\rangle + \|\eta\bar{\eta}\bar{\zeta}v\rangle - \|\xi\bar{\xi}\zeta\bar{v}\rangle - \|\eta\bar{\eta}\zeta\bar{v}\rangle)$
$t_2^2(^3T_1)e^2(^3A_2)$	$^5T_2\ \zeta\ 2$	$\|\xi\eta uv\rangle$
$(^1A_1)$	$^3A_2\ \ 1$	$\left(\frac{1}{3}\right)^{1/2}(\|\xi\bar{\xi}uv\rangle + \|\eta\bar{\eta}uv\rangle + \|\zeta\bar{\zeta}uv\rangle)$
(^1E)	$^3E\ \ u\ 1$	$\left(\frac{1}{2}\right)^{1/2}(\|\xi\bar{\xi}uv\rangle - \|\eta\bar{\eta}uv\rangle)$
	$v\ 1$	$\left(\frac{1}{6}\right)^{1/2}(\|\xi\bar{\xi}uv\rangle + \|\eta\bar{\eta}uv\rangle - 2\|\zeta\bar{\zeta}uv\rangle)$
$(^3T_1)e^2(^1E)$	$^3T_1\ z\ 1$	$\left(\frac{1}{2}\right)^{1/2}(-\|\xi\eta u\bar{u}\rangle + \|\xi\eta v\bar{v}\rangle)$
$(^3T_1)e^2(^1A_1)$	$^3T_1\ z\ 1$	$\left(\frac{1}{2}\right)^{1/2}(\|\xi\eta u\bar{u}\rangle + \|\xi\eta v\bar{v}\rangle)$
$(^1T_2)e^2(^3A_2)$	$^3T_1\ z\ 1$	$\left(\frac{1}{2}\right)^{1/2}(\|\xi\bar{\eta}uv\rangle - \|\bar{\xi}\eta uv\rangle)$
$(^3T_1)e^2(^1E)$	$^3T_2\ \zeta\ 1$	$\left(\frac{1}{2}\right)^{1/2}(-\|\xi\eta u\bar{v}\rangle + \|\xi\eta\bar{u}v\rangle)$
$(^3T_1)e^2(^3A_2)$	$^3T_2\ \zeta\ 1$	$\left(\frac{1}{2}\right)(\|\xi\bar{\eta}uv\rangle + \|\bar{\xi}\eta uv\rangle - \|\xi\eta u\bar{v}\rangle - \|\xi\eta\bar{u}v\rangle)$
$t_2^2(^1A_1)e^2(^1A_1)$	$^1A_1$	$\left(\frac{1}{6}\right)^{1/2}\{(1) + (2) + (3) + (4) + (5) + (6)\}$
$t_2^2(^1E)e^2(^1E)$	$^1A_1$	$\left(\frac{1}{24}\right)^{1/2}\{(1) + (2) - 2(3) - (4) - (5) + 2(6) + 3^{1/2}(7) - 3^{1/2}(8) - 3^{1/2}(10) + 3^{1/2}(11)\}$
	$^1A_2$	$\left(\frac{1}{24}\right)^{1/2}\{3^{1/2}(1) - 3^{1/3}(2) - 3^{1/2}(4) + 3^{1/2}(5) - (7) - (8) + 2(9) + (10) + (11) - 2(12)\}$
$e^2(^1A_1)$	$^1E\ \ u$	$\left(\frac{1}{12}\right)^{1/2}\{(1) + (2) - 2(3) + (4) + (5) - 2(6)\}$
	v	$\left(\frac{1}{2}\right)\{-(1) + (2) - (4) + (5)\}$
$t_2^2(^1A_1)e^2(^1E)$	$^1E\ \ u$	$\left(\frac{1}{6}\right)^{1/2}\{-(1) - (2) - (3) + (4) + (5) + (6)\}$
	v	$\left(\frac{1}{6}\right)^{1/2}\{(7) + (8) + (9) - (10) - (11) - (12)\}$

Configuration	Crystal term	Statevector
$t_2^2(^1E)\,e^2(^1E)$	$^1E\ u$	$\left(\frac{1}{24}\right)^{1/2}\{(1) + (2) - 2(3) - (4) - (5) + 2(6) - 3^{1/2}(7) + 3^{1/2}(8) + 3^{1/2}(10) - 3^{1/2}(11)\}$
	v	$\left(\frac{1}{24}\right)^{1/2}\{3^{1/2}(1) - 3^{1/2}(2) - 3^{1/2}(4) + 3^{1/2}(5) + (7) + (8) - 2(9) - (10) - (11) + 2(12)\}$
where		$(1) = \lvert\xi\bar{\xi}u\bar{u}\rangle$, $(2) = \lvert\eta\bar{\eta}u\bar{u}\rangle$, $(3) = \lvert\zeta\bar{\zeta}u\bar{u}\rangle$, $(4) = \lvert\xi\bar{\xi}v\bar{v}\rangle$, $(5) = \lvert\eta\bar{\eta}v\bar{v}\rangle$, $(6) = \lvert\zeta\bar{\zeta}v\bar{v}\rangle$, $(7) = \lvert\xi\bar{\xi}u\bar{v}\rangle$, $(8) = \lvert\eta\bar{\eta}u\bar{v}\rangle$, $(9) = \lvert\zeta\bar{\zeta}u\bar{v}\rangle$, $(10) = \lvert\xi\bar{\xi}\bar{u}v\rangle$, $(11) = \lvert\eta\bar{\eta}\bar{u}v\rangle$, $(12) = \lvert\zeta\bar{\zeta}\bar{u}v\rangle$.
$t_2^2(^1T_2)e^2(^1E)$	$^1T_1 z$	$\left(\frac{1}{2}\right)(\lvert\xi\bar{\eta}u\bar{v}\rangle - \lvert\bar{\xi}\eta u\bar{v}\rangle - \lvert\xi\bar{\eta}\bar{u}v\rangle + \lvert\bar{\xi}\eta\bar{u}v\rangle)$
$(^3T_1)e^2(^3A_2)$	$^1T_2\,\zeta$	$\left(\frac{1}{12}\right)^{1/2}(2\lvert\bar{\xi}\bar{\eta}uv\rangle + 2\lvert\xi\eta\bar{u}\bar{v}\rangle - \lvert\xi\bar{\eta}u\bar{v}\rangle - \lvert\bar{\xi}\eta u\bar{v}\rangle - \lvert\xi\bar{\eta}\bar{u}v\rangle - \lvert\bar{\xi}\eta\bar{u}v\rangle)$
$(^1T_2)e^2(^1A_1)$	$^1T_2\,\zeta$	$\left(\frac{1}{2}\right)(\lvert\xi\bar{\eta}u\bar{u}\rangle - \lvert\bar{\xi}\eta u\bar{u}\rangle + \lvert\xi\bar{\eta}v\bar{v}\rangle - \lvert\bar{\xi}\eta v\bar{v}\rangle)$
$(^1T_2)e^2(^1E)$	$^1T_2\,\zeta$	$\left(\frac{1}{2}\right)(- \lvert\xi\bar{\eta}u\bar{u}\rangle + \lvert\bar{\xi}\eta u\bar{u}\rangle + \lvert\xi\bar{\eta}v\bar{v}\rangle - \lvert\bar{\xi}\eta v\bar{v}\rangle)$
t_2e^3	$^3T_1\ z\ 1$	$\lvert\zeta u\bar{u}v\rangle$
	$^3T_2\ \zeta\ 1$	$\lvert\zeta uv\bar{v}\rangle$
	$^1T_1\ z$	$\left(\frac{1}{2}\right)(\lvert\zeta u\bar{u}\bar{v}\rangle - \lvert\bar{\zeta}u\bar{u}v\rangle)$
	$^1T_2\ \zeta$	$\left(\frac{1}{2}\right)^{1/2}(\lvert\zeta\bar{u}v\bar{v}\rangle - \lvert\bar{\zeta}uv\bar{v}\rangle)$
e^4	$^1A_1$	$\lvert u\bar{u}v\bar{v}\rangle$
t_2^5	$^2T_2\ \zeta\ \frac{1}{2}$	$\lvert\xi\bar{\xi}\eta\bar{\eta}\zeta\rangle$
$t_2^4(^3T_1)e$	$^4T_1\ z\ \frac{3}{2}$	$\lvert\xi\eta\zeta\bar{\zeta}u\rangle$
	$^4T_2\ \zeta\ \frac{3}{2}$	$\lvert\xi\eta\zeta\bar{\zeta}v\rangle$
	$^2T_1\ z\ \frac{1}{2}$	$\left(\frac{1}{6}\right)^{1/2}(\lvert\xi\bar{\eta}\zeta\bar{\zeta}u\rangle + \lvert\bar{\xi}\eta\zeta\bar{\zeta}u\rangle - 2\lvert\xi\eta\zeta\bar{\zeta}u\rangle)$
$(^3T_1)e$	$^2T_2\ \zeta\ \frac{1}{2}$	$\left(\frac{1}{6}\right)^{1/2}(\lvert\xi\bar{\eta}\zeta\bar{\zeta}v\rangle + \lvert\bar{\xi}\eta\zeta\bar{\zeta}v\rangle - 2\lvert\xi\eta\zeta\bar{\zeta}\bar{v}\rangle)$
$(^1T_2)$	$^2T_1\ z\ \frac{1}{2}$	$\left(\frac{1}{2}\right)^{1/2}(\lvert\xi\bar{\eta}\zeta\bar{\zeta}v\rangle - \lvert\bar{\xi}\eta\zeta\bar{\zeta}v\rangle)$
(^1E)	$^2A_1\ \frac{1}{2}$	$\left(\frac{1}{12}\right)^{1/2}\{2(1) - (2) - (3) + 3^{1/2}(5) - 3^{1/2}(6)\}$
	$^2A_2\ \frac{1}{2}$	$\left(\frac{1}{12}\right)^{1/2}\{3^{1/2}(2) - 3^{1/2}(3) - 2(4) + (5) + (6)\}$
	$^2E\ u\ \frac{1}{2}$	$\left(\frac{1}{12}\right)^{1/2}\{2(1) - (2) - (3) - 3^{1/2}(5) + 3^{1/2}(6)\}$
	$v\ \frac{1}{2}$	$\left(\frac{1}{12}\right)^{1/2}\{- 3^{1/2}(2) + 3^{1/2}(3) - 2(4) + (5) + (6)\}$
$(^1A_1)$	$^2E\ u\ \frac{1}{2}$	$\left(\frac{1}{3}\right)^{1/2}\{(1) + (2) + (3)\}$
	$v\ \frac{1}{2}$	$\left(\frac{1}{3}\right)^{1/2}\{(4) + (5) + (6)\}$

Configuration	Crystal term	Statevector
when		$(1) = \vert\xi\bar{\xi}\eta\bar{\eta}u\rangle$, $(2) = \vert\eta\bar{\eta}\zeta\bar{\zeta}u\rangle$, $(3) = \vert\xi\bar{\xi}\zeta\bar{\zeta}u\rangle$, $(4) = \vert\xi\bar{\xi}\eta\bar{\eta}v\rangle$, $(5) = \vert\eta\bar{\eta}\zeta\bar{\zeta}v\rangle$, $(6) = \vert\xi\bar{\xi}\zeta\bar{\zeta}v\rangle$.
$t_2^3({}^4A_2)e^2({}^3A_2)$	${}^6A_1\ \frac{5}{2}$	$\vert\xi\eta\zeta uv\rangle$
	${}^4A_1\ \frac{3}{2}$	$\left(\frac{1}{30}\right)^{1/2}\{-3(3) - 3(4) + 2(5) + 2(6) + 2(7)\}$
$e^2({}^1A_1)$	${}^4A_2\ \frac{3}{2}$	$\left(\frac{1}{2}\right)^{1/2}\{(1) + (2)\}$
$e^2({}^1E)$	${}^4E\ u\frac{3}{2}$	$\left(\frac{1}{2}\right)^{1/2}\{(3) - (4)\}$
	$v\frac{3}{2}$	$\left(\frac{1}{2}\right)^{1/2}\{(1) - (2)\}$
$t_2^3({}^2E)e^2({}^3A_2)$	${}^4E\ u\frac{3}{2}$	$\left(\frac{1}{6}\right)^{1/2}\{2(5) - (6) - (7)\}$
	$v\frac{3}{2}$	$\left(\frac{1}{2}\right)^{1/2}\{-(6) + (7)\}$
where		$(1) = \vert\xi\eta\zeta u\bar{u}\rangle$, $(2) = \vert\xi\eta\zeta v\bar{v}\rangle$, $(3) = \vert\xi\eta\zeta u\bar{v}\rangle$, $(4) = \vert\xi\eta\zeta\bar{u}v\rangle$, $(5) = \vert\xi\eta\bar{\zeta}uv\rangle$, $(6) = \vert\xi\bar{\eta}\zeta uv\rangle$, $(7) = \vert\bar{\xi}\eta\zeta uv\rangle$.
$t_2^3({}^2T_2)e^2({}^3A_2)$	${}^4T_1\ z\frac{3}{2}$	$\left(\frac{1}{2}\right)^{1/2}(\vert\xi\bar{\xi}\zeta uv\rangle + \vert\eta\bar{\eta}\zeta uv\rangle)$
$({}^2T_1)\ ({}^3A_2)$	${}^4T_2\ \zeta\frac{3}{2}$	$\left(\frac{1}{2}\right)^{1/2}(\vert\xi\bar{\xi}\zeta uv\rangle - \vert\eta\bar{\eta}\zeta uv\rangle)$
$({}^4A_2)\ ({}^3A_2)$	${}^2A_1\ \frac{1}{2}$	$\left(\frac{1}{18}\right)^{1/2}\{3\vert\xi\eta\zeta\bar{u}\bar{v}\rangle$
		$+ (1) + (2) + (3) - (4) - (5) - (6) - (7) - (8) - (9)\}$
$({}^2E)\ ({}^1\mathrm{E})$	${}^2A_1\ \frac{1}{2}$	$\left(\frac{1}{24}\right)^{1/2}\{2(4) - (5) - (6) - 2(7) + (8) + (9)$
		$- 3^{1/2}(11) + 3^{1/2}(12) + 3^{1/2}(14) - 3^{1/2}(15)\}$
	${}^2A_2\ \frac{1}{2}$	$\left(\frac{1}{24}\right)^{1/2}\{3^{1/2}(5) - 3^{1/2}(6) - 3^{1/2}(8) + 3^{1/2}(9) + 2(10)$
		$- (11) - (12) - 2(13) + (14) + (15)\}$
	${}^2E\ u\frac{1}{2}$	$\left(\frac{1}{24}\right)^{1/2}\{2(4) - (5) - (6) - 2(7) + (8) + (9)$
		$+ 3^{1/2}(11) - 3^{1/2}(12) - 3^{1/2}(14) + 3^{1/3}(15)\}$
	$v\frac{1}{2}$	$\left(\frac{1}{24}\right)^{1/2}\{3^{1/2}(5) - 3^{1/2}(6) - 3^{1/2}(8) + 3^{1/2}(9)$
		$- 2(10) + (11) + (12) + 2(13) - (14) - (15)\}$
$({}^2E)\ ({}^1A_1)$	${}^2E\ u\frac{1}{2}$	$\left(\frac{1}{2}\right)\{(11) - (12) + (14) - (15)\}$
	$v\frac{1}{2}$	$\left(\frac{1}{12}\right)^{1/2}\{2(10) - (11) - (12) + 2(13) - (14) - (15)\}$
$({}^2E)e^2({}^3A_2)$	${}^2E\ u\frac{1}{2}$	$\left(\frac{1}{6}\right)\{2(1) + 2(2) - 4(3) - 2(4) + (5) + (6) - 2(7)$
		$+ (8) + (9)\}$
	$v\frac{1}{2}$	$\left(\frac{1}{12}\right)^{1/2}\{-2(1) + 2(2) + (5) - (6) + (8) - (9)\}$
where		$(1) = \vert\xi\bar{\eta}\bar{\zeta}uv\rangle$, $(2) = \vert\bar{\xi}\eta\bar{\zeta}uv\rangle$, $(3) = \vert\bar{\xi}\bar{\eta}\zeta uv\rangle$, $(4) = \vert\xi\eta\bar{\zeta}u\bar{v}\rangle$, $(5) = \vert\xi\bar{\eta}\zeta u\bar{v}\rangle$, $(6) = \vert\bar{\xi}\eta\zeta u\bar{v}\rangle$,

Configuration	Crystal term	Statevector
		$(7) = \lvert\xi\eta\bar{\zeta}\bar{u}v\rangle$, $(8) = \lvert\xi\bar{\eta}\zeta\bar{u}v\rangle$, $(9) = \lvert\bar{\xi}\eta\zeta\bar{u}v\rangle$,
		$(10) = \lvert\xi\eta\bar{\zeta}u\bar{u}\rangle$, $(11) = \lvert\xi\bar{\eta}\zeta u\bar{u}\rangle$, $(12) = \lvert\bar{\xi}\eta\zeta u\bar{u}\rangle$,
		$(13) = \lvert\xi\eta\bar{\zeta}v\bar{v}\rangle$, $(14) = \lvert\xi\bar{\eta}\zeta v\bar{v}\rangle$, $(15) = \lvert\bar{\xi}\eta\zeta v\bar{v}\rangle$.
$t_2^3({}^2T_1)e^2({}^1A_1)$	${}^2T_1\ z\ \frac{1}{2}$	$\left(\frac{1}{2}\right)(\lvert\xi\bar{\xi}\zeta u\bar{u}\rangle - \lvert\eta\bar{\eta}\zeta u\bar{u}\rangle + \lvert\xi\bar{\xi}\zeta v\bar{v}\rangle - \lvert\eta\bar{\eta}\zeta v\bar{v}\rangle)$
$({}^1E)$	${}^2T_1\ z\ \frac{1}{2}$	$\frac{1}{2}\ (-\lvert\xi\bar{\xi}\zeta u\bar{u}\rangle + \lvert\eta\bar{\eta}\zeta u\bar{u}\rangle + \lvert\xi\bar{\xi}\zeta v\bar{v}\rangle - \lvert\eta\bar{\eta}\zeta v\bar{v}\rangle)$
$({}^2T_2)\ ({}^1A_1)$	${}^2T_2\ \zeta\ \frac{1}{2}$	$\left(\frac{1}{2}\right)(\lvert\xi\bar{\xi}\zeta u\bar{u}\rangle + \lvert\eta\bar{\eta}\zeta u\bar{u}\rangle + \lvert\xi\bar{\xi}\zeta v\bar{v}\rangle + \lvert\eta\bar{\eta}\zeta v\bar{v}\rangle)$
$({}^1E)$	${}^2T_2\ \zeta\ \frac{1}{2}$	$\left(\frac{1}{2}\right)(-\lvert\xi\bar{\xi}\zeta uu\rangle - \lvert\eta\bar{\eta}\zeta u\bar{u}\rangle + \lvert\xi\bar{\xi}\zeta v\bar{v}\rangle + \lvert\eta\bar{\eta}\zeta v\bar{v}\rangle)$
$({}^1E)$	${}^2T_1\ z\ \frac{1}{2}$	$\left(\frac{1}{2}\right)(\lvert\xi\bar{\xi}\zeta u\bar{v}\rangle + \lvert\eta\bar{\eta}\zeta u\bar{v}\rangle - \lvert\xi\bar{\xi}\zeta\bar{u}v\rangle - \lvert\eta\bar{\eta}\zeta\bar{u}v\rangle)$
$t_2^3({}^2T_2)e^2({}^3A_2)$	${}^2T_1\ z\ \frac{1}{2}$	$\left(\frac{1}{12}\right)^{1/2}(-\lvert\xi\bar{\xi}\zeta u\bar{v}\rangle - \lvert\eta\bar{\eta}\zeta u\bar{v}\rangle - \lvert\xi\bar{\xi}\zeta\bar{u}v\rangle - \lvert\eta\bar{\eta}\zeta\bar{u}v\rangle + 2\lvert\xi\bar{\xi}\bar{\zeta}uv\rangle$ $+ 2\lvert\eta\bar{\eta}\bar{\zeta}uv\rangle)$
$({}^2T_1)\ ({}^1E)$	${}^2T_2\ \zeta\ \frac{1}{2}$	$\left(\frac{1}{2}\right)(\lvert\xi\bar{\xi}\zeta u\bar{v}\rangle - \lvert\eta\bar{\eta}\zeta u\bar{v}\rangle - \lvert\xi\bar{\xi}\zeta\bar{u}v\rangle + \lvert\eta\bar{\eta}\zeta\bar{u}v\rangle)$
$({}^3A_2)$	${}^2T_2\ \zeta\ \frac{1}{2}$	$\left(\frac{1}{12}\right)^{1/2}(-\lvert\xi\bar{\xi}\zeta u\bar{v}\rangle + \lvert\eta\bar{\eta}\zeta u\bar{v}\rangle - \lvert\xi\bar{\xi}\zeta\bar{u}v\rangle + \lvert\eta\bar{\eta}\zeta\bar{u}v\rangle$ $+ 2\lvert\xi\bar{\xi}\bar{\zeta}uv\rangle - 2\lvert\eta\bar{\eta}\bar{\zeta}uv\rangle)$
$t_2^2({}^3T_1)e^3$	${}^4T_1\ z\ \frac{3}{2}$	$\lvert\xi\eta uv\bar{v}\rangle$
	${}^4T_2\ \zeta\ \frac{3}{2}$	$\lvert\xi\eta u\bar{u}v\rangle$
$({}^1E)$	${}^2A_1\ \frac{1}{2}$	$\left(\frac{1}{12}\right)^{1/2}\{(1) + (2) - 2(3) - 3^{1/2}(4) + 3^{1/2}(5)\}$
	${}^2A_2\ \frac{1}{2}$	$\left(\frac{1}{12}\right)^{1/2}\{3^{1/2}(1) - 3^{1/2}(2) + (4) + (5) - 2(6)\}$
	${}^2E\ u\ \frac{1}{2}$	$\left(\frac{1}{12}\right)^{1/2}\{-(1) - (2) + 2(3) - 3^{1/2}(4) + 3^{1/2}(5)\}$
	$v\ \frac{1}{2}$	$\left(\frac{1}{12}\right)^{1/2}\{-3^{1/2}(1) + 3^{1/2}(2) + (4) + (5) - 2(6)\}$
$({}^1A_1)$	${}^2E\ u\ \frac{1}{2}$	$\left(\frac{1}{3}\right)^{1/2}\{(1) + (2) + (3)\}$
	$v\ \frac{1}{2}$	$\left(\frac{1}{3}\right)^{1/2}\{(4) + (5) + (6)\}$
where		$(1) = \lvert\xi\bar{\xi}uv\bar{v}\rangle$, $(2) = \lvert\eta\bar{\eta}uv\bar{v}\rangle$, $(3) = \lvert\zeta\bar{\zeta}\mathrm{u}v\bar{v}\rangle$,
		$(4) = \lvert\xi\bar{\xi}u\bar{u}v\rangle$, $(5) = \lvert\eta\bar{\eta}u\bar{u}v\rangle$, $(6) = \lvert\zeta\bar{\zeta}u\bar{u}v\rangle$.
$t_2^2({}^3T_1)e^3$	${}^2T_1\ z\ \frac{1}{6}$	$\left(\frac{1}{6}\right)^{1/2}(2\lvert\xi\eta\bar{u}v\bar{v}\rangle - \lvert\xi\bar{\eta}uv\bar{v}\rangle - \lvert\bar{\xi}\eta uv\bar{v}\rangle)$
$({}^1T_2)$	${}^2T_2\ \zeta\ \frac{1}{2}$	$\left(\frac{1}{2}\right)^{1/2}(\lvert\xi\bar{\eta}uv\bar{v}\rangle - \lvert\bar{\xi}\eta uv\bar{v}\rangle)$
	${}^2T_1\ z\ \frac{1}{2}$	$\left(\frac{1}{2}\right)^{1/2}(\lvert\xi\bar{\eta}u\bar{u}v\rangle - \lvert\bar{\xi}\eta u\bar{u}v\rangle)$
$({}^3T_1)$	${}^2T_2\ \zeta\ \frac{1}{2}$	$\left(\frac{1}{6}\right)^{1/2}(2\lvert\xi\eta u\bar{u}\bar{v}\rangle - \lvert\xi\bar{\eta}u\bar{u}v\rangle - \lvert\bar{\xi}\eta u\bar{u}v\rangle)$
t_2e^4	${}^2T_2\ \zeta\ \frac{1}{2}$	$\lvert\zeta u\bar{u}v\bar{v}\rangle$

Appendix 4.4

SYMMETRY-CLASSIFIED LIGAND ORBITALS FOR OCTAHEDRAL, TETRAHEDRAL, AND CUBE COORDINATIONS†

1. OCTAHEDRAL COORDINATION

(a) s orbital:

$$a_{1g} = (\tfrac{1}{6})^{1/2}(s_1 + s_2 + s_3 + s_4 + s_5 + s_6),$$

$$e_g u = (\tfrac{1}{12})^{1/2}(-s_1 - s_2 - s_4 - s_5 + 2s_3 + 2s_6),$$

$$e_g v = \tfrac{1}{2}(s_1 - s_2 + s_4 - s_5),$$

$$t_{1u}x = (\tfrac{1}{2})^{1/2}(s_1 - s_4),$$

$$t_{1u}y = (\tfrac{1}{2})^{1/2}(s_2 - s_5),$$

$$t_{1u}z = (\tfrac{1}{2})^{1/2}(s_3 - s_6).$$

†Notation p is omitted

(b) π orbital:

$$
\begin{aligned}
t_{1g}x &= \tfrac{1}{2}\{(2z) - (3y) - (5z) + (6y)\},\\
y &= \tfrac{1}{2}\{-(1z) + (3x) + (4z) - (6x)\},\\
z &= \tfrac{1}{2}\{(1y) - (2x) - (4y) + (5x)\},\\
t_{1u}x &= \tfrac{1}{2}\{(2x) + (3x) + (5x) + (6x)\},\\
y &= \tfrac{1}{2}\{(1y) + (3y) + (4y) + (6y)\},\\
z &= \tfrac{1}{2}\{(1z) + (2z) + (4z) + (5z)\},\\
t_{2g}\xi &= \tfrac{1}{2}\{(2z) + (3y) - (5z) - (6y)\},\\
\eta &= \tfrac{1}{2}\{(1z) + (3x) - (4z) - (6x)\},\\
\zeta &= \tfrac{1}{2}\{(1y) + (2x) - (4y) - (5x)\},\\
t_{2u}\xi &= \tfrac{1}{2}\{(2x) - (3x) + (5x) - (6x)\},\\
\eta &= \tfrac{1}{2}\{-(1y) + (3y) - (4y) + (6y)\},\\
\zeta &= \tfrac{1}{2}\{(1z) - (2z) + (4z) - (5z)\}.
\end{aligned}
$$

2. TETRAHEDRAL COORDINATION

We choose a geometrical configuration of p orbitals on the four vertices, as shown in Fig. A–2. The direction cosines with respect to [100], [010], and [001] are

$1x$	$(\frac{1}{2})^{1/2}$	$-(\frac{1}{2})^{1/2}$	0
$1y$	$-(\frac{1}{6})^{1/2}$	$-(\frac{1}{6})^{1/2}$	$2(\frac{1}{6})^{1/2}$
$1z$	$-(\frac{1}{3})^{1/2}$	$-(\frac{1}{3})^{1/2}$	$-(\frac{1}{3})^{1/2}$
$2x$	$-(\frac{1}{2})^{1/2}$	$-(\frac{1}{2})^{1/2}$	0
$2y$	$(\frac{1}{6})^{1/2}$	$-(\frac{1}{6})^{1/2}$	$-2(\frac{1}{6})^{1/2}$
$2z$	$(\frac{1}{3})^{1/2}$	$-(\frac{1}{3})^{1/2}$	$(\frac{1}{3})^{1/2}$
$3x$	$(\frac{1}{2})^{1/2}$	$(\frac{1}{2})^{1/2}$	0
$3y$	$-(\frac{1}{6})^{1/2}$	$(\frac{1}{6})^{1/2}$	$-2(\frac{1}{6})^{1/2}$
$3z$	$-(\frac{1}{3})^{1/2}$	$(\frac{1}{3})^{1/2}$	$(\frac{1}{3})^{1/2}$
$4x$	$-(\frac{1}{2})^{1/2}$	$(\frac{1}{2})^{1/2}$	0
$4y$	$(\frac{1}{6})^{1/2}$	$(\frac{1}{6})^{1/2}$	$2(\frac{1}{6})^{1/2}$
$4z$	$(\frac{1}{3})^{1/2}$	$(\frac{1}{3})^{1/2}$	$-(\frac{1}{3})^{1/2}$

The z orbitals are σ orbital; x and y orbitals are π orbital in the configuration.

(a) σ orbital:

$$a_1 = \tfrac{1}{2}\{(1z) + (2z) + (3z) + (4z)\},$$
$$t_2\xi = \tfrac{1}{2}\{(1z) - (2z) + (3z) - (4z)\},$$
$$\eta = \tfrac{1}{2}\{(1z) + (2z) - (3z) - (4z)\},$$
$$\zeta = \tfrac{1}{2}\{(1z) - (2z) - (3z) + (4z)\}.$$

(b) π orbital:

$$eu = \tfrac{1}{2}\{(1y) + (2y) + (3y) + (4y)\},$$
$$v = \tfrac{1}{2}\{(1x) + (2x) + (3x) + (4x)\},$$
$$t_1x = \tfrac{1}{4}[-(1x) + (2x) - (3x) + (4x) + 3^{1/2}\{-(1y) + (2y) - (3y) + (4y)\}],$$
$$y = \tfrac{1}{4}[-(1x) - (2x) + (3x) + (4x) + 3^{1/2}\{(1y) + (2y) - (3y) - (4y)\}],$$
$$z = \tfrac{1}{2}\{(1x) - (2x) - (3x) + (4x)\},$$
$$t_2\xi = \tfrac{1}{4}[3^{1/2}\{-(1x) + (2x) - (3x) + (4x)\} + (1y) - (2y) + (3y) - (4y)],$$
$$\eta = \tfrac{1}{4}[3^{1/2}\{(1x) + (2x) - (3x) - (4x)\} + (1y) + (2y) - (3y) - (4y)],$$
$$\zeta = \tfrac{1}{2}\{-(1y) + (2y) + (3y) - (4y)\}.$$

3. CUBE COORDINATION†

(a) σ orbital

$$a_{1g} = (\tfrac{1}{8})^{1/2}\{(1z) + (2z) + (3z) + (4z) + (5z) + (6z) + (7z) + (8z)\},$$
$$a_{2u} = (\tfrac{1}{8})^{1/2}\{(1z) + (2z) + (3z) + (4z) - (5z) - (6z) - (7z) - (8z)\},$$
$$t_{1u}x = (\tfrac{1}{8})^{1/2}\{(1z) - (2z) + (3z) - (4z) - (5z) + (6z) - (7z) + (8z)\},$$
$$y = (\tfrac{1}{8})^{1/2}\{(1z) + (2z) - (3z) - (4z) - (5z) - (6z) + (7z) + (8z)\},$$
$$z = (\tfrac{1}{8})^{1/2}\{(1z) - (2z) - (3z) + (4z) - (5z) + (6z) + (7z) - (8z)\},$$
$$t_{2g}\xi = (\tfrac{1}{8})^{1/2}\{(1z) - (2z) + (3z) - (4z) + (5z) - (6z) + (7z) - (8z)\},$$
$$\eta = (\tfrac{1}{8})^{1/2}\{(1z) + (2z) - (3z) - (4z) + (5z) + (6z) - (7z) - (8z)\},$$
$$\zeta = (\tfrac{1}{8})^{1/2}\{(1z) - (2z) - (3z) + (4z) + (5z) - (6z) - (7z) + (8z)\}.$$

(b) π orbital:

†Orbitals 5 and 8 are to be obtained by rotating orbitals 1 and 4 by π around [110] in Fig. A-2; orbitals 6 and 7 by rotating 2 and 3 by π around [110].

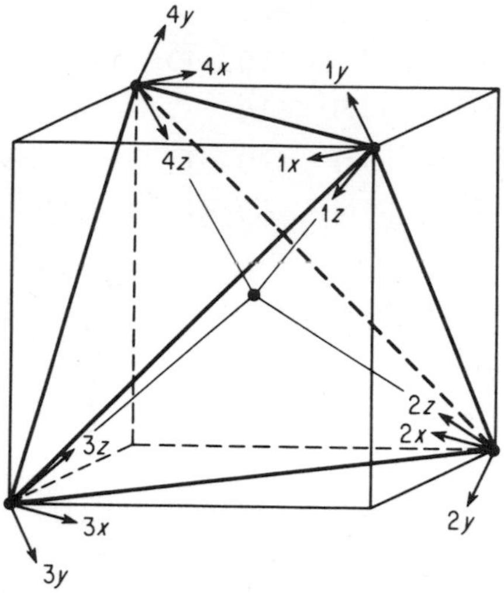

Figure A.2

$$e_g u = (\tfrac{1}{8})^{1/2}\{(1y) + (2y) + (3y) + (4y) + (5y) + (6y) + (7y) + (8y)\},$$
$$v = (\tfrac{1}{8})^{1/2}\{(1x) + (2x) + (3x) + (4x) - (5x) - (6x) - (7x) - (8x)\},$$
$$e_u u = (\tfrac{1}{8})^{1/2}\{(1x) + (2x) + (3x) + (4x) + (5x) + (6x) + (7x) + (8x)\},$$
$$v = (\tfrac{1}{8})^{1/2}\{-(1y) - (2y) - (3y) - (4y) + (5y) + (6y) + (7y) + (8y)\},$$
$$t_{1g}x = (\tfrac{1}{32})^{1/2}[-(1x) + (2x) - (3x) + (4x) + (5x) - (6x) + (7x) - (8x) + 3^{1/2}\{-(1y) + (2y) - (3y) + (4y) - (5y) + (6y) - (7y) + (8y)\}],$$
$$y = (\tfrac{1}{32})^{1/2}[-(1x) - (2x) + (3x) + (4x) + (5x) + (6x) - (7x) - (8x) + 3^{1/2}\{(1y) + (2y) - (3y) - (4y) + (5y) + (6y) - (7y) - (8y)\}],$$
$$z = (\tfrac{1}{8})^{1/2}\{(1x) - (2x) - (3x) + (4x) - (5x) + (6x) + (7x) - (8x)\},$$
$$t_{1u}x = (\tfrac{1}{32})^{1/2}[3^{1/2}\{(1x) - (2x) + (3x) - (4x) + (5x) - (6x) + (7x) - (8x)\} - (1y) + (2y) - (3y) + (4y) + (5y) - (6y) + (7y) - (8y)],$$
$$y = (\tfrac{1}{32})^{1/2}[3^{1/2}\{-(1x) - (2x) + (3x) + (4x) - (5x) - (6x) + (7x) + (8x)\} - (1y) - (2y) + (3y) + (4y) + (5y) + (6y) - (7y) - (8y)],$$
$$z = (\tfrac{1}{8})^{1/2}\{(1y) - (2y) - (3y) + (4y) - (5y) + (6y) + (7y) - (8y)\},$$
$$t_{2g}\xi = (\tfrac{1}{32})^{1/2}[3^{1/2}\{(1x) - (2x) + (3x) - (4x) - (5x) + (6x) - (7x) + (8x)\} - (1y) + (2y) - (3y) + (4y) - (5y) + (6y) - (7y) + (8y)],$$
$$\eta = (\tfrac{1}{32})^{1/2}[3^{1/2}\{-(1x) - (2x) + (3x) + (4x) + (5x) + (6x) - (7x) - (8x)\} - (1y) - (2y) + (3y) + (4y) - (5y) - (6y) + (7y) + (8y)],$$
$$\zeta = (\tfrac{1}{8})^{1/2}\{(1y) - (2y) - (3y) + (4y) + (5y) - (6y) - (7y) + (8y)\},$$

$$t_{2u}\xi = (\tfrac{1}{32})^{1/2}\,[-(1x) + (2x) - (3x) + (4x) - (5x) + (6x) - (7x) + (8x)$$
$$+ 3^{1/2}\,\{-(1y) + (2y) - (3y) + (4y) + (5y) - (6y) + (7y) - (8y)\}],$$
$$\eta = (\tfrac{1}{32})^{1/2}\,[-(1x) - (2x) + (3x) + (4x) - (5x) - (6x) + (7x) + (8x)$$
$$+ 3^{1/2}\,\{(1y) + (2y) - (3y) - (4y) - (5y) - (6y) + (7y) + (8y)\}],$$
$$\zeta = (\tfrac{1}{8})^{1/2}\,\{(1x) - (2x) - (3x) + (4x) + (5x) - (6x) - (7x) + (8x)\}.$$

Appendix 5

ENERGY CONVERSION TABLE

	erg	ev	cm^{-1}	°K	gauss	Mc/sec
1erg	1	$6.242(10^{11})$	$5.0347(10^{15})$	$7.244(10^{15})$	$1.0784(10^{20})$	$1.5094(10^{20})$
1ev	$1.6021(10^{-12})$	1	$8.066\ (10^{3})$	$1.1606(10^{4})$	$1.7276(10^{8})$	$2.4181(10^{8})$
$1cm^{-1}$	$1.9862(10^{-16})$	$1.2398(10^{-4})$	1	1.4388	$2.1419(10^{4})$	$2.9979(10^{4})$
1°K	$1.3804(10^{-16})$	$8.616\ (10^{-5})$	$6.950\ (10^{-1})$	1	$1.4886(10^{4})$	$2.0836(10^{4})$
1gauss	$0.9273(10^{-20})$	$5.7883(10^{-9})$	$4.6688(10^{-5})$	$6.719\ (10^{-5})$	1	1.3997
1Mc/sec	$6.6252(10^{-21})$	$4.1354(10^{-9})$	$3.3356(10^{-5})$	$4.7994(10^{-5})$	$7.144\ (10^{-1})$	1

Energy is measured by the electron volt (ev) in the units of the electronic charge; by the wave number (cm^{-1}) in the units of Planck's constant multiplied by the light velocity (*hc*); by the absolute temperature (°K) in the units of Boltzmann's constants; by the magnetic field (gauss) in the units of the Bohr magneton; and by the megacycles per second (Mc/sec) in the units of Planck's constant.

BIBLIOGRAPHY

Quantum Mechanics and Angular Momentum

1. Brink, D. M., and G. R. Satchler, *Angular Momentum*. Oxford: Clarendon Press, 1962.
2. Condon, E. U., and G. H. Shortley, *The Theory of Atomic Spectra*, 2d ed. London: Cambridge University Press, 1953.
3. Edmonds, A. R., *Angular Momentum in Quantum Mechanics*. Princeton, N. J.: Princeton University Press, 1957.
4. Rose, M. E., *Elementary Theory of Angular Momentum*. New York: John Wiley & Sons, Inc., 1957.

Quantum Mechanics and Group Theory

1. Cotton, E. A., *Chemical Applications of Group Theory*. New York: Interscience, Inc., 1963.
2. Eyring, H., J. Walter, and G. F. Kimbal, *Quantum Chemistry*. New York: John Wiley & Sons, Inc., 1944.
3. Hamermesh, M., *Group Theory*. Reading, Mass.: Addison-Wesley Publishing Co., Inc., 1962.
4. Heine, V., *Group Theory in Quantum Mechanics*. London: Pergamon Press, 1960.
5. Landau, L., and E. M. Lifshitz, trans., *Quantum Mechanics*. New York: Pergamon Press Inc., 1958.
6. Mariot, L., trans., *Group Theory and Solid State Physics*. Englewood Cliffs, N. J.: Prentice-Hall, Inc., 1962.
7. Tinkham, M. *Group Theory and Quantum Mechanics*. New York: McGraw-Hill Book Company, 1964.

8. Wigner, E. P., *Group Theory*. New York: Academic Press, Inc., 1959.

Ions in Complexes and Crystalline Solids

1. Ballhausen, C. J., *Introduction to Ligand Field Theory*. New York: McGraw-Hill Book Company, 1962.
2. Bleaney, B., and K. W. H. Stevens, *Repts. Progr. Phys.* **16**, 108 (1953).
3. Dunn, T. M., *Modern Coordination Chemistry*. New York: Interscience, Inc., 1960, pp. 229–300.
4. Fick, E., and G. Joos, *Handbuch der Physik*, Vol. 28. Berlin: Springer, 1957, p. 205.
5. Griffith, J. S., *The Theory of Transition Metal Ions*. London: Cambridge University Press, 1961. *The Irreducible Tensor Methods for Molecular Symmetry Groups*. Englewood Cliffs, N. J.: Prentice-Hall, Inc., 1962.
6. Herzfeld, C. M., and P. H. E. Meijer, *Solid State Physics*, vol. 12. New York: Academic Press, Inc., 1961, pp. 1–91.
7. Jørgensen, C. K., *Solid State Physics*, vol. 13. New York: Academic Press, Inc., 1962, p. 375. *Orbitals in Atoms and Molecules*. New York: Academic Press, Inc., 1962. *Absorption Spectra and Chemical Bonding in Complexes*. London: Pergamon Press, 1962.
8. McClure, D. S., *Solid State Physics*, vol. 9. New York: Academic Press, 1959, pp. 399–525.
9. Moffit, W., and C. J. Ballhausen, *Ann. Rev. Phys. Chem.* **7**, 107 (1956).
10. Orgel, L. E., *An Introduction to Transition Metal Chemistry*. New York: John Wiley & Sons, Inc., 1960.
11. Sugano, S., *Progr. Theoret. Phys. Supplement*, no. 14, 66 (1960).
12. Tanabe, Y., *Progr. Theoret. Phys. Supplement*, no. 14, 17 (1960).

For calculations from first principles, refer to the following articles.

1. Kleiner, W. H., *J. Chem. Phys.* **20**, 1784 (1952).
2. Tanabe, Y., and S. Sugano, *J. Phys. Soc. (Japan)* **11**, 864 (1956).
3. Phillips, J. C., *J. Phys. Chem. Solids* **11**, 26 (1959).
4. Freeman, A. J., and R. E. Watson, *Phys. Rev.* **120**, 1254 (1960).
5. Sugano, S., and R. G. Shulman, *Phys. Rev.* **130**, 517 (1913).
6. Watson, R. E., and A. J. Freeman, *Phys. Rev.* **134**, A1521 (1964).

INDEX